Fiber Reinforced Concrete
Developments and Innovations

James I. Daniel
Surendra P. Shah
Editors

SP-142

DISCUSSION of individual papers in this symposium may be submitted in accordance with general requirements of the ACI Publication Policy to ACI headquarters at the address given below. Closing date for submission of discussion is September 1, 1994. All discussion approved by the Technical Activities Committee along with closing remarks by the authors will be published in the March/April 1995 issue of either ACI Structural Journal or ACI Materials Journal depending on the subject emphasis of the individual paper.

The papers in this volume have been reviewed under Institute publication procedures by individuals expert in the subject areas of the papers.

AMERICAN CONCRETE INSTITUTE
P.O. Box 19150, Redford Station
Detroit, Michigan 48219

Printed in the United States of America

Editorial production Victoria Wieczorek

Library of Congress catalog card number 93-73071

PREFACE

These proceedings are a result of the collective efforts of Committee 544 on Fiber Reinforced Concrete and Committee 549 on Ferrocement and Other Thin Reinforced Products. By ACI Committee 544 definition, fiber reinforced concrete is concrete made primarily of hydraulic cements, aggregates, and discrete reinforcing fibers. This definition does not include a provision for concretes reinforced with continuous meshes, woven fabrics, or continuous fiber networks.

Therefore, to address all potential types of fiber reinforced concrete, both ACI Committees 544 and 549 cosponsored a technical symposium. Original papers for this symposium were presented at the ACI Conventions in Boston, March 1991, and in Dallas, November 1991. The papers were reviewed by members of both ACI committees as well as members of the international community of experts on fiber reinforced concrete. These original, reviewed, and revised papers constitute this ACI Special Publication.

The editors gratefully acknowledge ACI Committees 544 and 549, the reviewers, the authors, Dr. Gordon B. Batson (symposium co-chairman and then Chairman of ACI Committee 549), and the staff of ACI who have made this volume a timely contribution to the awareness and growth of fiber reinforced concrete.

James I. Daniel
Co-editor and Chairman ACI Committee 544

Surendra P. Shah
Co-editor and Past-Chairman ACI Committee 544

ACI Committee 544
FIBER REINFORCED CONCRETE

James I. Daniel
Chairman

Vellore S. Gopalaratnam
Secretary

Melvyn A. Galinat
Membership Secretary

Shuaib H. Ahmad
M. Arockiasamy
P.N. Balaguru
Hiram P. Ball, Jr.
Nemkumar Banthia
Gordon B. Batson
M. Ziad Bayasi
Marvin E. Criswell
Daniel P. Dorfmueller
Marsha Feldstein
Antonio V. Fernandez
Sidney Freedman
David M. Gale
Antonio Jose Guerra
Lloyd E. Hackman
C. Geoffrey Hampson
M. Nadim Hassoun
Carol D. Hays
George C. Hoff
Roop L. Jindal
Colin D. Johnston
Mark A. Leppert
Clifford N. MacDonald
Pritpal S. Mangat
Henry N. Marsh, Jr.
Nicholas C. Mitchell
Henry J. Molloy
D.R. Morgan
Antoine E. Naaman
Antonio Nanni
Seth L. Pearlman
Max L. Porter
V. Ramakrishnan
Ken Rear
D.V. Reddy
E.K. Schrader
Morris Schupack
Surendra P. Shah
George D. Smith
Philip A. Smith
Parvis Soroushian
J.D. Speakman
David J. Stevens
R.N. Swamy
Peter C. Tatnall
Ben L. Tilsen
George J. Venta
Gary L. Vondran
Methi Wecharatana
Gilbert R. Williamson
Spencer T. Wu
Robert C. Zellers
Ronald F. Zollo

Consulting Members

Claire G. Ball
Craig A. Ballinger
Arnon Bentur
Andrzej M. Brandt
Zhi-Yuan Chen
Graham T. Gilbert
Charles H. Henager, Sr.
David R. Lankard
A.J. Majumdar
Roman Malinowski
Winston A. Marsden
Yoshihiko Ohama
Stanley L. Paul
C.D. Pomeroy
Ake Skarendahl
Junji Takagi
George Y. Wu

ACI Committee 549
FERROCEMENT AND OTHER THIN REINFORCED PRODUCTS

P.N. Balaguru
Chairman

Parvis Soroushian
Secretary

Shuaib H. Ahmad
M. Arockiasamy
Nemkumar Banthia
Gordon B. Batson
Jose O. Castro
James I. Daniel
David M. Gale
Antonio J. Guerra
Lloyd E. Hackman
Martin E. Iorns
Colin D. Johnston
Mohammed A. Mansur
James R. McConaghy
Barzin Mobasher
Henry J. Molloy
John L. Mulder
Antoine E. Naaman
Antonio Nanni
P. Paramasivam
D.V. Reddy
James P. Romualdi
Surendra P. Shah
R.N. Swamy
Ben L. Tilsen
Methi Wacharatana
Robert B. Williamson
Robert C. Zellers
Ronald F. Zollo
Rogerio C. Zubieta

CONTENTS

SP 142-1

Comparison of Shrinkage Cracking Performance of Different Types of Fibers and Wiremesh

by S.P. Shah, M. Sarigaphuti, and M.E. Karaguler

Synopsis: Concrete structures shrink when they are subjected to a drying environment. If this shrinkage is restrained, then tensile stresses develop and concrete may crack. One of the methods to reduce the adverse effects of shrinkage cracking is to reinforce concrete with short randomly distributed fibers. Another possibility is the use of wiremesh. The efficiencies of fibers and wiremesh to arrest cracks in cementitious composites were studied. Different types of fiber (steel, polypropylene, and cellulose) with fiber content of 0.25% and 0.5% by volume of concrete were examined. Ring-type specimens were used for restrained shrinkage cracking test. These fibers and wiremesh show significant reduction in crack width. Steel fiber reinforced concrete (0.5% addition) showed 80% reduction in maximum crack width and up to 90% reduction in average crack width. Concrete reinforced with 0.5% polypropylene or cellulose fibers was as effective as 0.25% steel fibers or wiremesh reinforced concrete (about 70% reduction in maximum and average crack width). Other properties such as free (unrestrained) shrinkage and compressive strength were also investigated.

Keywords: Compressive strength; cracking (fracturing); drying shrinkage; fiber reinforced concretes; fibers; shrinkage; tensile stress; welded wire fabric

Surendra P. Shah is a Walter P. Murphy Professor of Civil Engineering and Director of the National Science Foundation Center for Science and Technology of Advanced Cement-Based Materials, Northwestern University, Evanston, Illinois

M. Sarigaphuti is a member of the Research and Development Center, The Siam Cement Company, Bangkok, Thailand

M.E. Karaguler is an Associate Professor, Architectural Department at the Technical University of Istanbul, Turkey

INTRODUCTION

One of the disadvantages of concrete is that it tends to shrink and crack if the shrinkage is restrained. This shrinkage cracking is a major concern for concrete structures especially for walls, slabs, and pavements. The possibility of shrinkage cracking for a given environment may depend on the properties of concrete such as free (unrestrained) shrinkage, creep, the tensile strength, and the degree of restraint.

One way to reduce the adverse effects of shrinkage cracking is to reinforce concrete with short, randomly distributed fiber. This will not change the properties of concrete mentioned above but it will prevent cracks form widening. Uniformly dispersed fibers can prevent microcracks from opening further and becoming macrocracks [1,2]. It is known that the addition of fiber will considerably reduce the crack width resulting from restrained shrinkage [1,3,4,5]. To evaluate the efficiency of different types and amounts of fibers in controlling shrinkage cracking, tests were conducted using a ring-type specimen. Three different types of fiber (steel, polypropylene, and cellulose) were studied. In addition, for cellulose fiber, three different types were investigated. The results of different fibers were compared with the conventional mesh reinforced concrete (wiremesh). The effect on other properties such as free shrinkage and compressive strength were also examined.

RESEARCH SIGNIFICANCE

It is shown that a relatively small content of cellulose fibers, polypropylene fibers, and steel fibers can significantly reduce crack widths resulting from restrained shrinkage. Specimens reinforced by steel fibers with a volume fraction of 0.25% showed a comparable reduction in crack widths as that shown by 6 x 6 inch welded wire mesh fabric, as well as cellulose and polypropylene fibers with a volume fraction of 0.5%. Since slabs and pavements in practice are considerably thicker than the ring specimens used in the laboratory, a single wire mesh layer is likely to be considerably less effective in the field than was observed for the ring specimens.

TEST SPECIMENS

There is no standard test method available to evaluate shrinkage cracking potential of concrete. The free shrinkage test as recommended by ASTM C157 does indicate the potential shrinkage of a given concrete. However, the possibility of cracking depends on other factors in addition to the free shrinkage characteristics of concrete. One possibility of simulating shrinkage cracking of slabs is to cast slab-type specimens and subject them to a controlled drying environment. Such a specimen will be subjected to a biaxial state of stress. The extent of biaxiality will depend on the dimensions of the slab. The number of cracks and crack width will also be a function of the size of the test specimen. A better specimen to evaluate shrinkage cracking would be a long specimen with cross-sectional dimensions such that the drying shrinkage is essentially one-dimensional and the uniaxial tensile stresses are produced as a result of restraint. Such uniaxial tests are difficult to perform. In this study, an axisymmetric ring-type of test specimen was used which is relatively easy to conduct and which approximates the desirable uniaxial condition. Because of the axial symmetry, the specimen can be considered very long and the cracking response may be regarded as size independent. A detailed analysis of the stresses in the ring test as well as a theoretical model developed to predict restrained cracking from the knowledge of free shrinkage, creep, and other material properties is described in Reference 2. Using this theoretical model and the data from the ring specimen, accurate predictions of the cracking response of slab-type specimens can be made [2].

The dimensions of the ring specimen are given in Fig. 1. The concrete annulus was cast around the steel ring. As a result of drying, the concrete ring would want to shrink but will be prevented by the steel ring. This would create an internal uniform pressure: hoop tensile stress and radial compressive stress. The calculation based on the theory of elasticity shows that the difference between the hoop tensile stress on the outer and the inner surface is 10%. In addition to hoop stress, the concrete ring is also subjected to radial compressive stresses. However, the maximum value of the radial stress is only 20% of the hoop stress. Thus, one can assume that the concrete is subjected to essentially uniform, uniaxial tensile stress when it is internally restrained by the steel ring, provided the effects of non-uniform drying are negligible.

Drying was only allowed from the outer, circumferential surface of the concrete specimen. Furthermore, since the width of the specimen (140 mm) (5.5") is greater than the thickness (35 mm) (1.38") of the specimen, uniform shrinkage along the width of the specimen can be assumed.

The free shrinkage specimen was 285 mm (11 1/4") long and had a 100 mm (4") square cross-section. This prismatic specimen is recommend by ASTM C157. It is assumed that if the length of the specimen is greater than the cross-sectional dimensions, the shrinkage takes place only in the length direction. The measurement of change in the length with time can then provide a measure of one-dimensional shrinkage of concrete.

TEST PROGRAM

For every batch of concrete the following tests were conducted: 1) restrained shrinkage cracking, 2) free shrinkage and weight loss, and 3) seven and twenty-eight days compressive strengths. For polypropylene fiber reinforced concretes, the results of restrained shrinkage and free shrinkage are taken from the study done earlier by Grzybowski and Shah [1,2]. They used the identical ring-type specimen and free shrinkage prism with similar curing conditions. Each test series was accompanied by a control specimen (unreinforced concrete with the same water:cement ratio).

DETAILS OF COMPOSITION AND FABRICATION

Matrix

The mix-proportions by weight for the matrix were 1:2:2:0.5 or 1:2:2:0.55 (cement:coarse aggregate:sand:water). Maximum aggregate size of 9 mm was used. The sand was dried natural river sand of a maximum grain size of 3mm. Type I portland cement was used in all batches.

The w/c (water:cement) ratio of 0.5 was used for concrete reinforced with steel, polypropylene fiber, or wiremesh. For cellulose fiber reinforced concrete, the w/c was 0.55 in order to obtain a comparable workability without using any admixture.

Steel and Polypropylene Fibers

The fiber content of steel and polypropylene fibers varied from 0.25% to 0.5% by volume of concrete. Hooked-end steel fibers with 30 mm (1.2") long and diameter of 0.5 mm (0.02") were tested. The aspect ratio of steel fibers was 60. The polypropylene fibers used were collated, fibrillated fibers which were 19 mm (3/4") long. The density of steel fiber was approximately 7800 kg/m^3, and it was 908 kg/m^3 for polypropylene fibers.

Cellulose Fibers

The cellulose fiber content was 0.5% by volume or about 1% by weight of cement. Three different cellulose fibers were tested: type 1, type 2, and type 3 respectively. The fibers contained varying amounts of hardwood, softwood springwood, and softwood summerwood fibers. Depending on the species, softwood pulps have varying amounts of springwood and summerwood fibers. Springwood enriched pulps offer high unrefined strength and low porosity. Summerwood enriched pulps offer bulk and high tear strength. All of the cellulose fibers were provided by the Procter & Gamble Cellulose Company. The fibers were supplied in a dry fluffed form.

Conventional Mesh Reinforcement (Wiremesh)

Welded wiremesh fabric is often used to control cracking due to the shrinkage and temperature induced strain. The dimension of the commonly used wiremesh are: 150 mm x 150 mm (6"x6") with its diameter of 4.76 mm (3/16"). Welded wiremesh with the same dimensions were used in this study. In addition, 75 mm x 150 mm (3"x6") wiremesh was also used to examine whether a decrease in spacing would have any beneficial effect. It should be noted that since the thickness of the specimen used in this study was considerably less than the slabs, walls, and pavements used in the field, the results overestimate the efficiency of the welded wiremesh fabric.

Mixing Procedure

Every concrete batch was mixed in a regular vertical mixer. First, coarse aggregate and sand were mixed with half of the total amount of water for one minute. Then cement was added to the mixture and mixed for another minute. Finally, the rest of the water with or without fibers was added and mixed for another four minutes. All specimens were also subjected to vibration for two minutes.

MEASUREMENT

Specimens were subjected to a drying environment after 4 hours of moist curing. This relatively short curing time was selected to increase the potential of shrinkage cracking. Cracking in restrained specimens was investigated between four hours and forty-two days. To measure crack width, a special microscope set-up was designed (Fig. 2). The microscope was fixed to an adjustable and scaled locator which is connected to the round steel plate installed on the top of the specimen. The ball-bearing on the top of the plate enabled the microscope to move around the specimen, whereas the locator, which is connected to a horizontal bar, permitted up-and-down movement so that the whole circumferential surface of the specimen could be observed with the microscope. The crack width reported here is an average of three measurements: one at the center of the ring and the other two at the centers of the top and bottom half of the ring (Fig. 2). The surface of the specimens was examined for new crack and the measurements of the widths of already existing cracks every 24 hours during the first few days after cracking, and then every 48 hours.

Free shrinkage measurements were performed with a dial-gage extensometer. Values of the free shrinkage were recorded every 24 hours. At the same time using the same specimens, weight loss measurements were also conducted.

Specimens both for restrained shrinkage ring and free shrinkage prism were cured for four hours at 20°C (68°F), 100% RH, then after demolding exposed to drying in the humidity room at 20°C (68°F), 40% RH for 42 days.

In addition, the 3"x6" cylindrical specimens were tested for compressive strength. The specimens were cured in water for 7 days then subjected to a drying environment at 20°C, 40% RH.

RESULTS AND DISCUSSION

In order to see the effectiveness of reinforcement, all results of reinforced specimens are compared with the control specimen (plain concrete) of the same w/c ratio. The following results will be discussed: restrained shrinkage cracking, free shrinkage, and compressive strength.

Restrained Shrinkage Cracking

The development of restrained shrinkage cracking for different specimens is shown in Figs. 3-13. The effectiveness of different types and amount of fibers and wiremesh in controlling shrinkage cracking can also be seen in Table 1. Addition of all type of fibers shows significant reduction in crack width. The higher the amount of fiber (steel/polypropylene) added, the lower in maximum and average crack width.

For comparison, the weight of reinforcement for specimen reinforced with wiremesh 1 (6"x6") and 0.25% steel fiber were almost identical (275 grams and 245 grams respectively). These two sets of specimens showed a similarity in maximum crack width (about 70% reduction). However, if only one mesh is used in the field, then its effectiveness will be considerably less in the field than that observed in this study.

In the case of wiremesh 2, one additional vertical reinforcement (3"x6") did not reduce either the maximum or the average crack width as compared to that of wiremesh 1.

The results of 0.5% cellulose fiber reinforced concretes were also very satisfactory. Type 1 cellulose fiber gave results comparable to 0.25% steel fiber, wiremesh, and 0.5% polypropylene fiber (approximately 70% reduction in maximum and average crack width). Types 2 and 3 cellulose fibers were also very effective. The maximum crack width was reduced by 55%, and the average crack width was reduced by 60%.

When subjected to drying, the concrete ring will shrink and tensile stress will develop if its shrinkage is restrained (in this case by the steel ring). If the cumulative value of this tensile stress reaches the tensile strength of the concrete, crack will occur. After cracking, the uncracked portion of the concrete will continue to shrink and the crack will widen. In the case of reinforced concrete, the widening of a crack is prevented due to the fiber bridging at the crack surface. The tensile stress will transfer through the uncracked matrix by shear deformation at the fiber-matrix interface. If these development stresses exceed the tensile strength, then another crack may form. Conventionally reinforced concrete (wiremesh) also acts in a very similar way. The ability of the reinforcement to control shrinkage cracking may depend on the distribution as well as on its properties such as strength, length, aspect ratio, density, and fiber-matrix bond.

Furthermore, the value of the crack widths on the outer surface, exposed to drying, and on the inner surface sealed off by the steel ring, were found to be very close. This proves the assumption of uniform stresses in the cross-section of the concrete ring.

Free Shrinkage

Results of free shrinkage of steel and cellulose fiber reinforced concretes can be seen in Figs. 14-15. The addition of steel or cellulose fibers does not substantially alter the drying free shrinkage. For steel fiber reinforced concrete, this confirmed other test data [1,6,11]. The work by Grzybowski and Shah [1,2] also reported that polypropylene fiber reinforcement has no significant effect on the free shrinkage behavior of concrete.

Weight Loss

Table 2 shows the percentage weight loss of different concrete at 42 days. The measurement is on the free shrinkage specimen. The weight loss of specimen is due to loss of water as the specimen is dried. Addition of steel fiber has little effect on the water loss of concrete. Since cellulose fiber has the ability to retain water, weight loss of this specimen was somewhat lower than that of the plain concrete specimen.

Compressive Strength

Table 3 shows the results of 1 day, 7 days, and 28 days compressive strength of different specimens. There is no influence on strength caused by an addition of 0.25% steel fibers. However, there is a 16% increase in 28 days compressive strength for 0.5% steel fiber reinforced concrete. In contrast, there is a reduction in strength due to an addition of cellulose fibers. This reduction is relatively small (approximately 10% for 7 days and 1-8% for 28 days compressive strength). A small reduction in compressive strength for cellulose fiber reinforced concrete is also reported by Soroushian and Marikunte [7]. The reason why strength decreases is still unclear, but may be related to the increasing amount of entrapped air voids due to the fiber addition.

It should be noted that, many references [8,9,10] also report a strength reduction for polypropylene fiber reinforced concrete. The reduction varied between 5% and 30%, depending primary on the length and amount of polypropylene used.

Heat of Hydration

In order to find out the possible effects of thermal expansion, the temperature in the middle of the free shrinkage specimen was recorded using K-type thermocouple, digital thermometer and chart recorder. The temperature was recorded immediately after casting up to 24 hours while specimens were kept at 20°C and 50% relative humidity. Maximum temperature increases of 1°C was observed. This result shows that temperature rise due to heat of hydration was not a factor in this type of experimental set-up.

CONCLUSION

The ring test seems to be an appropriate test to measure the influence of fibers on cracking of concrete due to restrained shrinkage. The addition of fibers does not alter the free shrinkage behavior of concrete. Thus, the ability of fibers to control cracks depends on how well they prevent crack from widening. Wiremesh also acts in the same manner. Small amounts of fiber (steel, polypropylene, and cellulose) show the ability to reduce crack width significantly. For comparison purposes, concrete reinforced with 0.25% steel fiber, 0.5% polypropylene fiber, 0.5% cellulose fiber (type 1), or wiremesh show equally good performance (about 70% reduction in maximum crack width). The influence on compressive strength of fiber addition is minimal. It should be mentioned that the current study overestimates the effectiveness of the wiremesh since the thickness of the specimen used was considerably less than that used in the field.

ACKNOWLEDGMENT

The support of Procter & Gamble Cellulose Company and the National Science for Advanced Cement-Based Materials (ACBM) at Northwestern University is gratefully appreciated. The useful comments of Ken Vinson and Wendy Arbuckle of Proctor & Gamble Company are gratefully acknowledged.

REFERENCES

1. Grzybowski, M. and Shah, S.P., "Shrinkage Cracking of Fiber Reinforced Concrete," Journal of American Concrete Institute, March-April 1990.

2. Grzybowski, M. and Shah, S.P., "Model to Predict Cracking in Fiber Reinforced Concrete Due to Restrained Shrinkage," Magazine of Concretes Research, 1989, NO. 148, September, 125-135.

3. Krenchel, H., and Shah, S.P., "Restrained Shrinkage Test with PP-Fiber Reinforced Concrete, " SP-105 ACI-Fiber Reinforced Concrete Properties and Application," 1987, pp. 211-223.

4. Malmberg, B., Skarendahl A., "Method of Studying the Cracking of Fiber Concrete under Restrained Shrinkage," RILEM Symposium 1978, Testing and Test Method of Fiber Cement Composites, pp. 211-223.

5. Swamy, R. N. and Stavrides, H., "Influence of Fiber Reinforcement on Restrained Shrinkage and Cracking," ACI Journal, v76, No.3, March 1979, pp.443-460.

6. Balaguru, P., and Ramakrishnan, V., "Properties of Fiber Reinforced Concrete: Workability Behavior Under Long Term Loading and Air-Void Characteristics," ACI Material Journal, Vol. 85, No. 3, May-June 1988, pp.189-196.

7. Soroushian, P. and Marikunte, S. "Reinforcement of Cement-Based Materials With Cellulose Fibers," pp.22-23.

8. Dardare J., "Contribution a l' Etude du Comportement Mecanique des Betons Renforces avec des fibres de Polypropylene," RILEM Sympos. on Fiber-Reinforced Cement and Concrete, London pp. 227-235 (1975)

9. Hughes, B.P. and Fattuhi N.I., "Stress-Strain Curves for Fiber Reinforced Concrete in Compression," Cem. Conc. Res., 7(2), pp.173-184 (1977)

10. Zollo, R.F. and Hays, C.D., "Practical Aspects of the Use of Synthetic Fiber Reinforced Concrete in Florida," ACI 1988 Annual Convention, Orlando, Fl

11. Karaguler M.E. and Shah S.P., "A Test Method to Evaluate Shrinkage Cracking of Concrete," ASCE Materials Engineering Congress, Denver, Colorado (1990)

12. Coutts R.S.P., "Air-Cured Woodpulp, Fibre/Cement Mortars," Composites, v.18, No.4, September 1987

13. Beaudoin, J.J., "Handbook of Fiber-Reinforced Concrete: Principles, Properties, Developments and Applications," Noyes Publications, New Jersey, 1990.

TABLE 1 — THE RESULTS OF RESTRAINED SHRINKAGE CRACKING AT 42 DAYS

Concrete Code	First Visible Crack (days after casting)	Number of Cracks	Maximum Crack Width (mm)	Average Crack Width (mm)
Plain (w/c=0.5)	6-7	1	0.72 (1.00)	0.72 (1.00)
S0.25*	7	2	0.24 (0.33)***	0.23 (0.32)
S0.5	14	4	0.12 (0.17)	0.08 (0.11)
P0.25*	6	1	0.48 (0.67)	0.48 (0.67)
P0.5	17	1	0.23 (0.32)	0.23 (0.32)
Wiremesh1**	9	3	0.22 (0.30)	0.174 (0.21)
Wiremesh2	6	3	0.22 (0.30)	0.176 (0.24)
Plain (w/c=0.55)	8	1	0.90 (1.00)	0.90 (1.00)
C1-0.5*	9	2	0.32 (0.35)***	0.284 (0.32)
C2-0.5	9	2	0.48 (0.53)	0.395 (0.44)
C3-0.5	8	2	0.53 (0.59)	0.383 (0.42)

*S0.25 and S0.5 refer to concretes reinforced with 0.25 and 0.5% by volume of steel fibers.

*P0.25 and P0.5 refer to concretes reinforced with 0.25 and 0.5% by volume of polypropylene fibers.

*C1-0.5, C2-0.5, and C3-0.5 refer to concretes reinforced with 0.5% by volume of type 1, type 2, and type 3 respectively of cellulose fibers.

**Wiremesh1 is 6"x6" reinforcement.
Wiremesh2 is 3"x6" reinforcement.

***The values in parenthesis show the relative values comparatively to plain concrete of the same w/c ratio.

TABLE 2 — WEIGHT LOSS OF DIFFERENT CONCRETES AT 42 DAYS

Concrete Code	Weight Loss (%)	Relative Weight Loss (%)
Plain (w/c=0.5)	3.20	100
S0.25	3.15	100
S0.5	3.46	108
Plain (w/c=0.55)	4.57	100
C1-0.5	4.07	89
C2-0.5	3.93	86
C3-0.5	4.33	95

TABLE 3 — COMPRESSIVE STRENGTH OF DIFFERENT CONCRETES

Concrete Code	1-day Comp. Strength (psi)	7-days Comp. Strength (psi)	28-days Comp. Strength (psi)
Plain (w/c=0.5)	754 (1.00)	3271 (1.00)	5157 (1.00)
S0.25	790 (1.05)	3385 (1.03)*	5404 (1.04)
S0.5	-	-	5500 (1.06)
Plain (w/c= 0.55)	580 (1.00)	3062 (1.00)	4795 (1.00)
C1-0.5	-	2760 (0.90)*	4950 (1.03)
C2-0.5	555 (0.96)	2803 (0.92)	4624 (0.96)
C3-0.5	-	2883 (0.94)	4702 (0.98)

* The values in parenthesis show the relative values comparatively to plain concrete of the same w/c ratio.

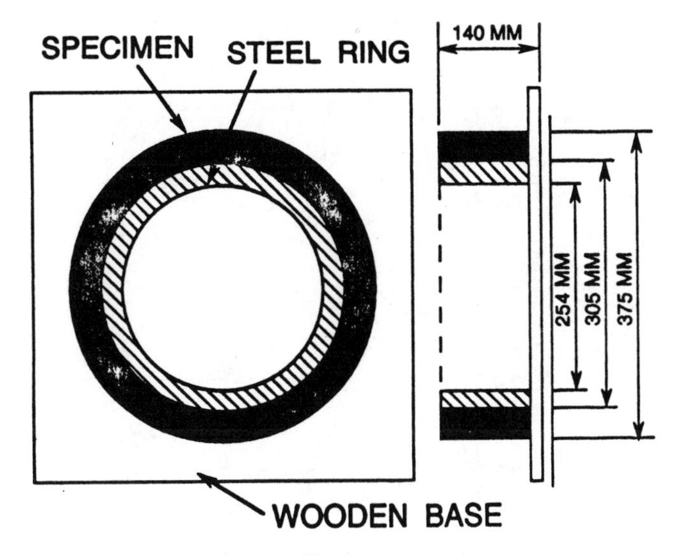

Fig. 1—Dimension of the test specimen

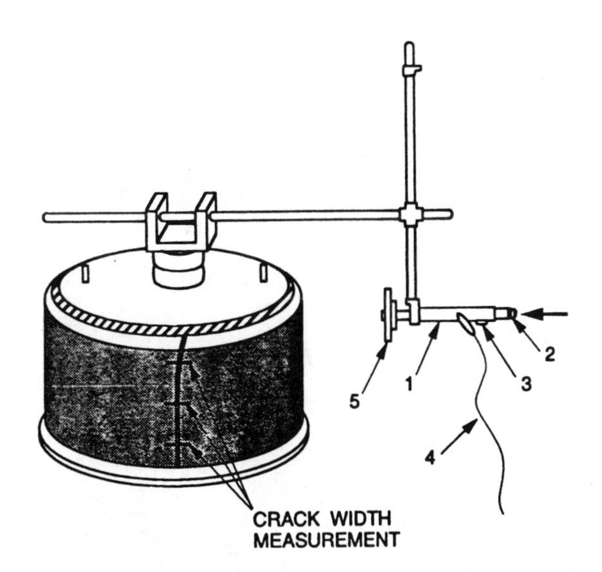

Fig. 2—Test set-up to measure crack width with a microscope

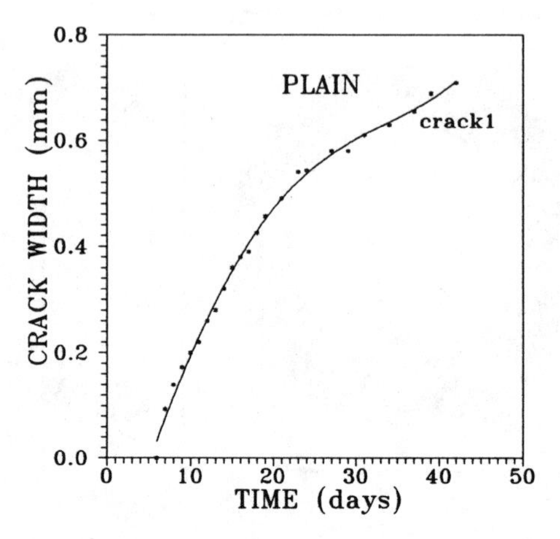

Fig. 3—Crack width measurements of plain concrete (w/c = 0.5)

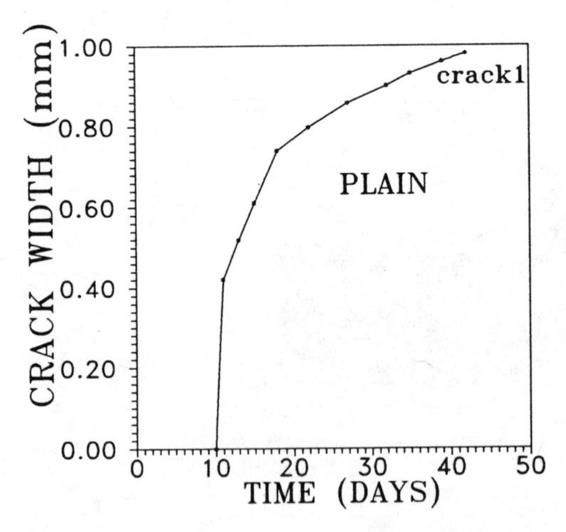

Fig. 4—Crack width measurements of plain concrete (w/c = 0.55)

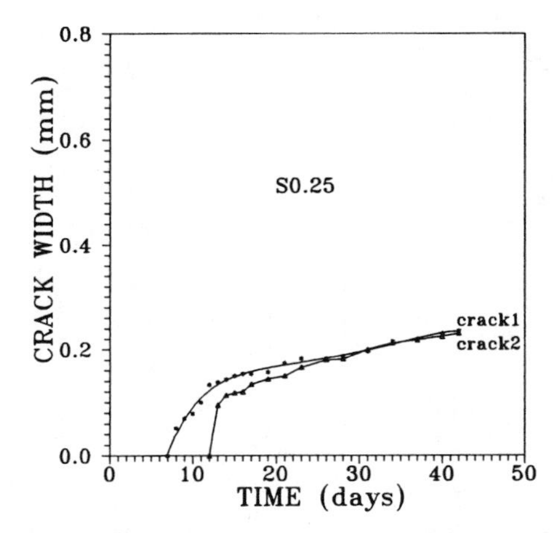

Fig. 5—Crack width measurements of 0.25 percent steel fiber reinforced concrete (w/c = 0.5)

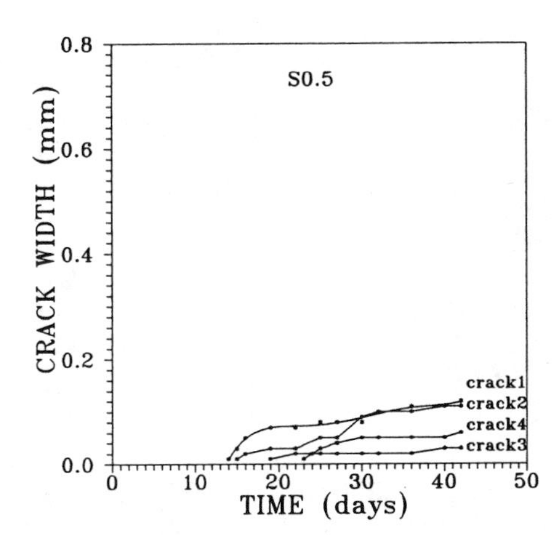

Fig. 6—Crack width measurements of 0.5 percent steel fiber reinforced concrete (w/c = 0.5)

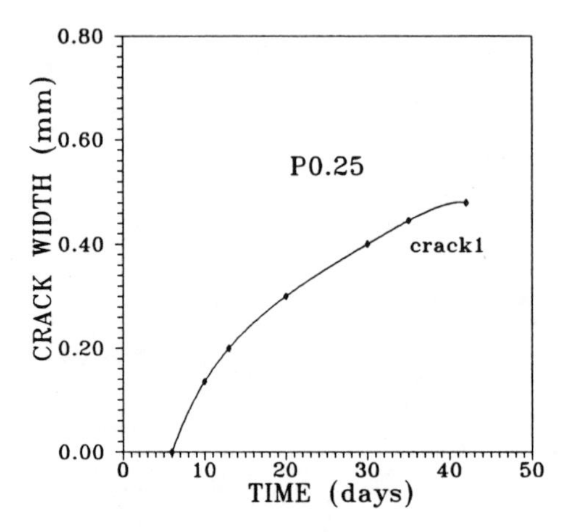

Fig. 7—Crack width measurements of 0.25 percent polypropylene fiber reinforced concrete (w/c = 0.5)

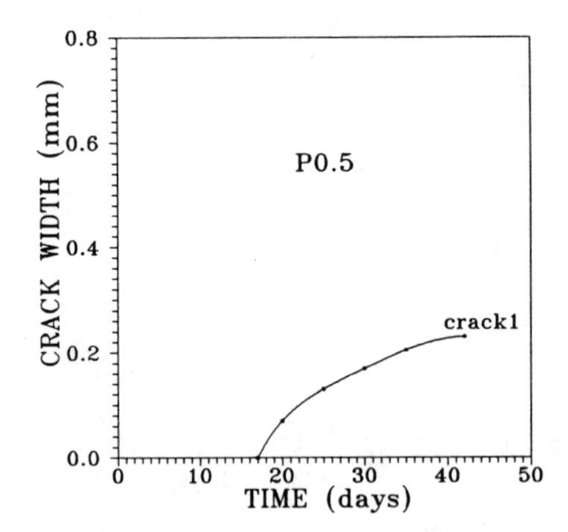

Fig. 8—Crack width measurements of 0.5 percent polypropylene fiber reinforced concrete (w/c = 0.5)

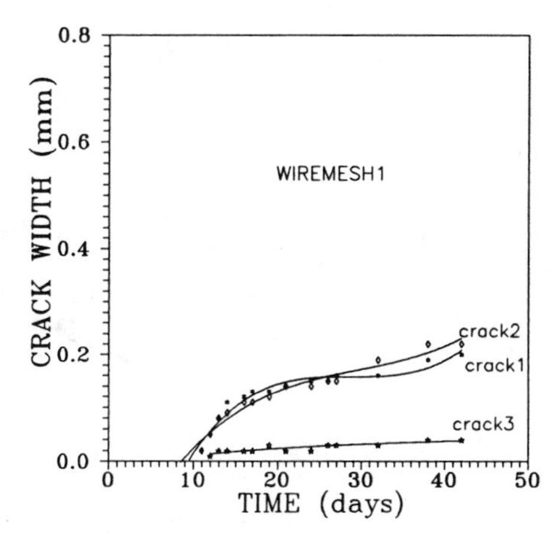

Fig. 9—Crack width measurements of wiremesh (6 in. x 6 in.) reinforced concrete (w/c = 0.5)

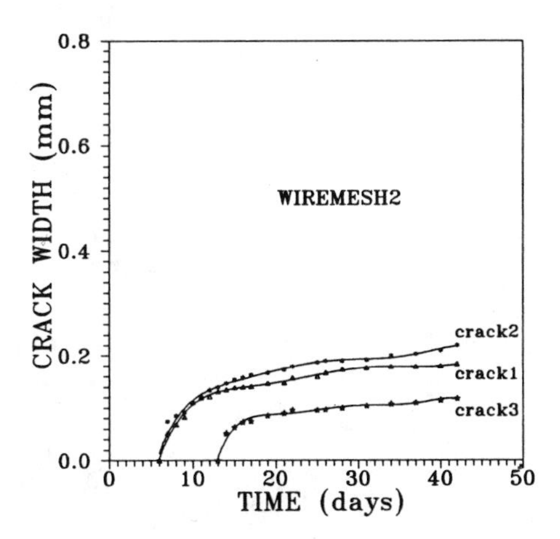

Fig. 10—Crack width measurements of wiremesh (3 in. x 6 in.) reinforced concrete (w/c = 0.5)

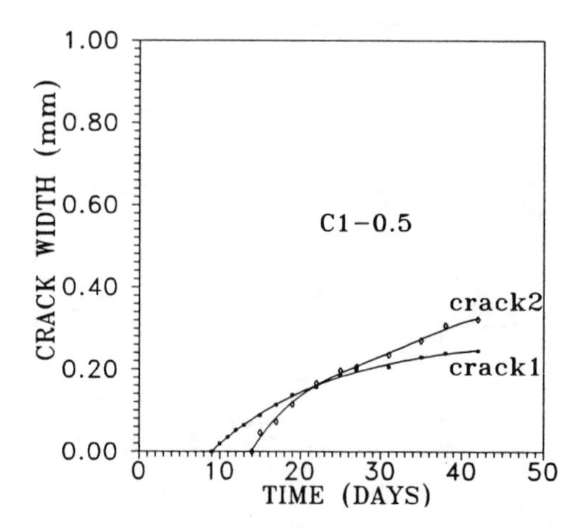

Fig. 11—Crack width measurements of 0.5 percent type 1 cellulose fiber reinforced concrete (w/c = 0.55)

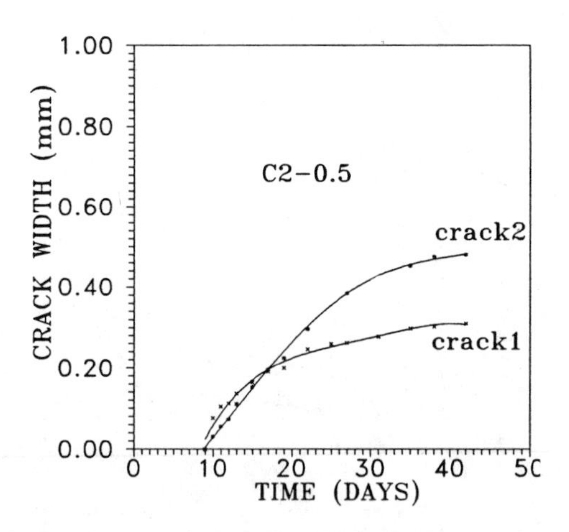

Fig. 12—Crack width measurements of 0.5 percent type 2 cellulose fiber reinforced concrete (w/c = 0.55)

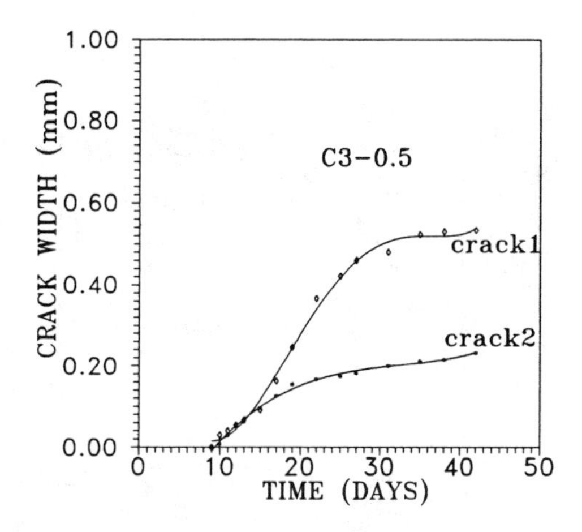

Fig. 13—Crack width measurements of 0.5 percent type 3 cellulose fiber reinforced concrete (w/c = 0.55)

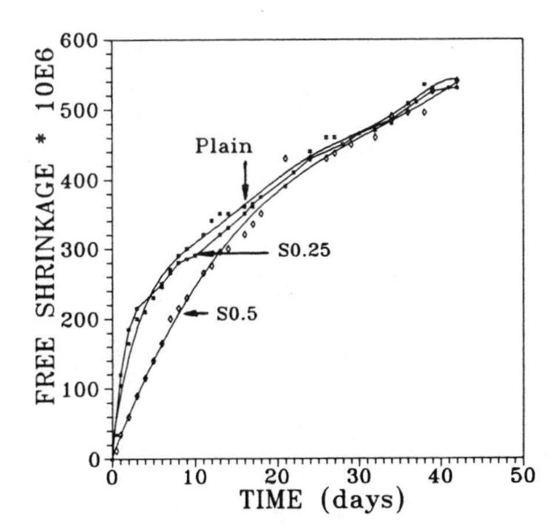

Fig. 14—Free shrinkage test results of 0.25 percent and 0.5 percent steel fiber reinforced concrete and plain (w/c = 0.5)

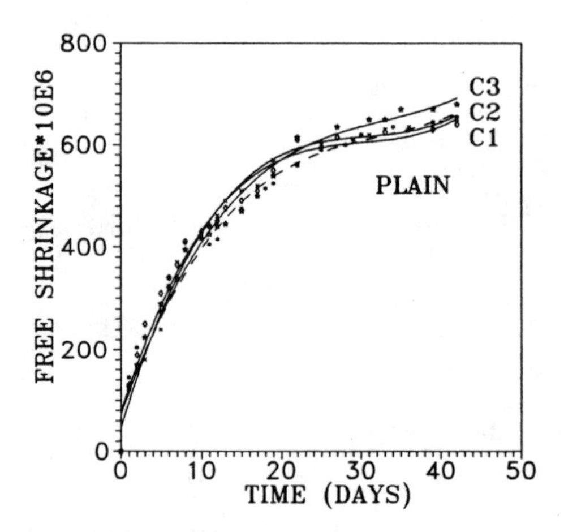

Fig. 15—Free shrinkage of different type of cellulose fiber reinforced concretes (w/c = 0.55, fiber content = 0.5 percent volume) and plain concrete (w/c = 0.55)

SP 142-2

The Effect of Low Addition Rates of Polypropylene Fibers on Plastic Shrinkage Cracking and Mechanical Properties of Concrete

by N.S. Berke and M.P. Dallaire

Synopsis: The results of a study of the effects of low addition rates of polypropylene fibers on plastic shrinkage cracking and mechanical properties of concrete are discussed. Addition rates of 0.75 lb/cubic yard, 1.5 lb/cubic yard, and 3.0 lb/cubic yard (0.05 to 0.2 volume percent) were used, with fiber lengths that varied between 0.5 inches and 2 inches. Relatively low addition rates are shown to significantly reduce plastic shrinkage cracking. Freezing and thawing durability was not affected by the addition of fibers. Modulus of elasticity, flexural strength, and compressive strength were not changed by the addition rates of polypropylene fibers studied. At the addition rates of polypropylene fibers studied, ASTM Method C1116 Level II I_5 toughness index values were satisfied. The drop weight hammer test as described in ACI Committee 544's report, "ACI 544.2R-89, Measurement of Properties of Fiber Reinforced Concrete" was utilized for determining the impact resistance of fiber reinforced concrete. Drop weight hammer impact results for fiber reinforced concrete at the fiber addition rate of 3.0 lb/cubic yard demonstrated a significant improvement.

Keywords: Compressive strength; cracking (fracturing); fiber reinforced concretes; flexural strength; freeze thaw durability; impact strength; mechanical properties; modulus of elasticity; polypropylene fibers; shrinkage

ACI member Neal S. Berke is a Research Manager in Grace Construction Products, W.R. Grace & Co, Conn. He is a member of ASTM Committee C09.42 - Fiber Reinforced Concrete. He has a PhD in Metallurgical Engineering from the University of Illinois at Urbana-Champaign.

Michael P. Dallaire received his B.S. and M. S. in Civil Engineering from the University of New Hampshire. He is currently a Senior Research Engineer in the Cement and Concrete Products Research section of Grace Construction Products.

INTRODUCTION

A wide range of tests were performed to investigate the properties of concrete having polypropylene fibers at low addition rates (up to 0.2 volume percent). Low addition rates of fibers have been utilized for some time by the industry to reduce plastic shrinkage cracking of concrete. One purpose of the paper was to document the effectiveness of fibers in reducing plastic shrinkage cracking and to develop a test method to illustrate this. Additionally, there is little published data showing the effect of low addition rates of polypropylene fibers on mechanical properties. The purpose of the mechanical testing was to show the effects and the benefits of low fiber addition rates on specific mechanical properties of concrete. The results of this diverse testing program are presented.

EXPERIMENTAL PROGRAM

Materials, Specimen Fabrication and Test Procedures

The coarse aggregate utilized for the study met ASTM Method C33 specifications. A rounded gravel meeting ASTM Method C33 size 67 was used for the majority of the testing. A crushed quartz diorite was utilized for the remainder of the testing, with three sizes 3/4 inch, 1/2 inch and 3/8 inch blended to meet size 67 specifications. An expanded shale coarse aggregate was used for lightweight coarse aggregate-normal weight fine aggregate concrete. A fine aggregate meeting ASTM

Method C33 specifications and a Type I cement were utilized throughout the program. Specimens were fabricated according to ASTM Method C192. The admixtures used were an air entraining agent, a water reducing agent, a high range water reducing agent, and a retarder. Material properties are found in Table 1.

Plastic Shrinkage

A series of tests were performed to ascertain the influence of collated, fibrillated polypropylene fibers in reducing plastic shrinkage of concrete. Several fiber addition rates and fiber lengths were studied. Fiber loading rates ranged from 0.75 pcy to 3.0 pcy. Fiber length ranged from 1/2 inch to 2 inches. The cement factor for the study was 517 pcy with a w/c ratio of 0.48. Standard doses of retarding admixture and air entraining agent was utilized. The mix design used for the study along with a summary of fiber addition rates, type, and length can be found in Table 2. Concrete was mixed according to ASTM Method C192, with the fibers being added 1 minute after the addition of the cement. Standard ASTM test methods for slump, unit weight, air content by the pressure method, and compressive strength were measured. Plastic shrinkage specimens were fabricated using a plyform mold with a surface area to volume ratio of 3:1. Specimen dimensions were 14.5 inches in width x 22 inches in length x 4 inches in depth. A metal insert in the bottom of the mold was oiled to allow for debonding of the plastic concrete. End restraint was provided by risers at each end of the mold. A center stress riser promoted the formation of cracks. A schematic drawing of the mold can be found in Figure 1.

Specimens were vibrated for a total of 15 seconds. The shrinkage slabs were moved to the environmental room and maintained at an average temperature of 95 ^{o}F and 40 % relative humidity. The specimens were then placed on a fan table to increase the severity of the test. A schematic drawing of the fan table is found in Figure 2. After placing the specimen on the fan table, the specimen was floated with a magnesium float for a total of 20 passes. The drying fans were turned on and the air velocity was measured with a hand held anemometer. The average wind velocity over the specimens was 17 mph.

After a period of 24 hours, the specimens were removed from the environmental room. The specimens were carefully gridded into 2 inch x 2 inch squares and the surface was inspected for cracks. Any crack found was marked by tracing along the length of the crack. A crack comparitor with a minimum crack width of 0.002 inch was used to measure average crack width at 1/2 inch intervals. The length of cracks and the average width for each grid square was recorded. These values were then summed up to obtain the total crack length and total crack area of the specimen. The crack areas of concrete specimens with fiber additions were compared to crack area of the control concrete specimen(s) fabricated the same day. The reduction of crack area of the fiber addition concretes was expressed as:

$$\text{PERCENT OF CONTROL CRACK AREA} = \frac{\text{Crack Area of Fiber Concrete}}{\text{Crack Area of Control Concrete}} \times 100\%$$

Freezing and Thawing Durability

he performance of polypropylene fiber reinforced concrete in freezing and thawing durability tests was investigated. Normal weight concrete was tested with 1.5 pcy of fibrillated fiber. Two fiber lengths of 1/2 inch and 3/4 inch were investigated. The cement factor for the study was 517 pcy, with a w/c ratio of 0.55. Concrete mix design data can be found in Table 3. Testing for slump, unit weight, air content by the pressure method, and compressive strength were measured Specimens were cured and removed from curing according to ASTM Method C666.

The freezing and thawing specimens were run according to ASTM Method C666, Procedure A. Initial dynamic modulus readings and beam weights were recorded after curing 14 days in limewater. Dynamic modulus readings were then taken according to ASTM Method specifications throughout the duration of the test. For each reading, Relative Dynamic Modulus (RDME) was calculated and the specimen weight recorded. Scaling of the specimens was also evaluated qualitatively and mass loss of the specimens was calculated.

Flexural Strength

oncrete having addition rates of 0.75 pcy and 1.5 pcy of fibrillated fiber were tested. Fiber lengths of 1/2 inch and 3/4 inch were investigated for normal weight concrete and lightweight coarse aggregate-normal weight fine aggregate concrete. The cement factor for both normal weight concrete and coarse aggregate lightweight concrete was 517 pcy. W/c ratio for the normal weight concrete was 0.62 and 0.51 for lightweight coarse aggregate-normal weight fine aggregate concrete. Specimen dimensions were 3 inches in width x 4 inches in depth x 16 inches in length. Slump, unit weight, air content by the pressure method, and compressive strength were also performed for normal weight concrete. Air content for sand- lightweight concrete was determined by the volumetric method as specified by ASTM Method C173. Concrete mix data can be found in Table 4.

The flexural strength of the concrete was determined by ASTM Method C78, Flexural Strength of Concrete by the Third Point Method. The apparent ductility of the specimen (ie did the specimen remain in one piece after ultimate load) at failure was noted.

Modulus of Elasticity

Concretes made with addition rates of 0.75 pcy, 1.5 pcy, and 3.0 pcy of 3/4 inch fibrillated fiber were tested. The cement factor was 500 pcy, identical to the concrete utilized for plastic shrinkage cracking. Slump, unit weight, and air content by the pressure method were measured and compressive strength cylinders were also made and tested. Concrete mix design data can be found in Table 5.

The Modulus of Elasticity of the concrete was determined according to ASTM Method C469, Static Modulus of Elasticity and Poisson's Ratio of Concrete in Compression. Deflection of the specimens during compression was recorded using a comparitor equipped with an LVDT. The output from the LVDT was directly tied to an X-Y plotter. Load was also recorded on the X-Y plotter.

Toughness

The addition rates studied for the determination of toughness by ASTM Method C1018 were a control mix, and mixes with 0.75 pcy, 1.5 pcy, and 3.0 pcy addition rates of polypropylene fibers. Fiber lengths investigated were 1/2 inch and 3/4 inch length. The cement factor was 517, with a w/c ratio of 0.62 . Mix design data can be found in Table 6. Specimen dimensions were 3 inches in width x 4 inches in depth x 16 inches in length. Slump, unit weight, air content by the pressure method were measured, and compressive strength cylinders were also made and tested.

The toughness of the concrete was determined according to ASTM Method C1018. An MTS position control hydraulic testing machine was used to provide the 0.003 in/min deflection rate. The system was a closed loop system with deflection rate control feedback provided by an LVDT. The LVDT was positioned at the mid-span and mid-with of the of the specimen to calculate nonminal mid-span deflections. An X-Y plotter plotted the toughness curve. A typical load deflection curve is presented in Figure 3. The area under the curve was determined by the use of a planimeter.

Drop Weight Hammer Impact

The drop weight hammer test as described in ACI Committee 544's report, "ACI 544.2R-89, Measurement of Properties of Fiber Reinforced Concrete" was utilized for determining the impact resistance of fiber reinforced concrete. An illustration of the test apparatus can be found in Figure 4. The test apparatus was anchored to a concrete base with a mass of 100 lbs to eliminate rebounding of the test apparatus. Cement factors in the concrete tested were 400 pcy and 517 pcy. Mix design data can be found in Table 7. Specimens were fabricated as a 6 inch diameter x 12 inch cylinder in accordance to ASTM Method C192. The cylinders were then cut into the appropriate thickness, 2 1/2 inches thick, for the test method.

Foam shims were placed between the four supports and the specimens. The number of blows to the first visible crack was recorded. The shims were then removed and the number of blows required for the specimen to come in contact with three of the four supports was recorded.

Compressive Strength

Compressive strength data was generated as part of the testing for flexural strength, freezing and thawing, toughness, and Modulus of Elasticity. Since a wide range of data was generated from various portions of the research, compressive strength data from the plastic shrinkage study is analyzed. The plastic shrinkage study encompassed a broad cross section of fiber lengths and addition rates. Mix design data is shown in Table 8. The specimen size chosen for the study was 4 inch diameter x 8 inch cylinders. Specimens were tested according to ASTM Method C39 specifications.

Specimens were tested according to ASTM Method C39, Compressive Strength of Cylindrical Concrete Specimens. Specimens were cured in a fog room, sulphur capped the day of testing and kept moist until tested.

RESULTS AND DISCUSSION

Plastic Shrinkage

Results of plastic shrinkage cracking are presented in Figure 5. All fiber addition rates and fiber lengths tested resulted in significant reductions in plastic shrinkage cracking. Similar reduction in plastic shrinkage cracking was noted by Vondron. **(1)** At a fiber addition rate of 1.5 pcy, the Percent of Control Crack Area of the combined average of the three fiber lengths was reduced to under 40 percent. An increase of the fiber addition rate to 3.0 pcy reduced the combined average of the Percent of Control Crack Area to under 20 percent. The increase in length from 1/2 inch to 3/4 inch shows a marked decrease in crack area at low addition rates due to the increase in efficiency of the fibrillation. There is little difference between the performance of the 3/4 inch length fiber and the 2 inch length fiber.

Freezing and Thawing

Results of testing are found in Table 9. RDME values are close to or exceed 100%. RDME values indicate that the addition of fibers at the rates utilized in this study does not affect the freezing and thawing durability of properly air entrained concrete. The weight loss of the specimens was minimal. These results agree with work presented by Vondron.(1)

Flexural Strength

Results of flexural strength testing are found in Table 10. At 95% confidence, the control concrete and the fiber reinforced concrete at the low fiber volume percents studied had the same flexural strengths. Results are similar to those reported by Romauldi.(2)

Modulus of Elasticity

Results of Modulus of Elasticity testing are found in Table 11. Results at the various ages and mix designs indicate that there was little difference in the Modulus of Elasticity of the control concrete and the fiber reinforced concrete.

Toughness

Results of Toughness testing are found in Table 12. All mixes including the control mix achieved toughness values greater than 4.0. All concrete mixes meet ASTM Method C1116 specifications for Level II performance at I_5 toughness levels. The average toughness values were slightly larger for specimens containing fibers, but the 95% confidence intervals indicated that the results were not significantly different.

Drop Hammer Impact

Results of Drop Hammer Impact testing are found in Table 13. The test results indicate that good repeatability is achievable utilizing this test method based on pooled standard deviations and 95% confidence intervals.

Results from both mix designs indicate that there is a definite improvement at the fiber loading rate of three pounds per cubic yard. The data indicate that the fiber loading rate of 1.5 pounds per cubic yard does not provide an increase in impact resistance.

Compressive Strength

Results of Compressive strength testing are found in Table 14. Overall, pooled standard deviation of the data set was 143 psi. Average Coefficient of Variation was 2.4%. Compressive strength at 28 days averaged 5,290 psi. Average air content of the concrete was 5.3%. Table 14 gives the 95% confidence intervals for the compressive strengths. Since these tests were performed over a long period of time, a comparison of mixes performed on the same day is a good indicator of how fibers affect the compressive strength of concrete. The confidence interval values have been normalized by dividing the average compressive strength of the control mix for a given mix day into the 95% upper confidence intervals, 95% lower confidence intervals, and averages of the fiber mixes tested the same day.

To summarize the results of the compressive strength testing, a graph which averages the normalized confidence intervals is presented in Figure 6. The average normalized values for each fiber length and addition rate is plotted against the average of the control mixes for each fiber length and addition rate. The results indicate that there is no significant difference between the control mixes and the fiber addition mixes. ACI 544.1R reports similar findings. (3)

CONCLUSIONS

Plastic shrinkage cracking is significantly reduced with the addition of low volume percentages of fiber.

Mechanical properties of compressive strength, flexural strength, and Modulus of Elasticity are not affected by the low volume addition rate of fibers in this study.

Freezing and thawing durability of concrete is not affected by the low volume addition rate of fibers in this study. This confirms work by Vondron.

ASTM Method C1116 Level II Toughness for I_5 is met by the low volume percent fiber addition rates in this study, but it is not clear that fiber concrete is different from the reference.

Impact resistance as measured by the drop weight hammer test method of ACI Committee 544's report "ACI 544.2R-89, Measurement of Properties of Fiber Reinforced Concrete" is significantly improved at 0.2% volume percent (3 lbs/yd^3) fiber addition rate.

1. Vondron, G. , "Making More Durable Concrete with Polymeric Fibers", ACI SP-100, Concrete Durability, Katherine and Bryant Mather International Conference, 1987, pp 377-396.

2. Romauldi, J. P., "The Effect of Polypropylene Fibers in the Early Curing Stages of Concrete", Department of Civil Engineering, Carnegie Mellon University, October 1988.

3. ACI 544.1R, "State-of-the Art Report on Fiber Reinforced Concrete", ACI Manual of Concrete Practice, Vol. 5, 1990.

TABLE 1 — FIBER REINFORCED CONCRETE STUDY MATERIAL PROPERTIES

Material	Specific Gravity	Percent Absorption
Lab Fine Aggregate	2.62	0.9
Lab Gravel	2.63	0.9
Lab Trap Rock	2.95	0.5
Lightweight CA	1.25	14% for 24 hours of soaking
Air Entraining Agent	1.05	---
Retarder (ASTM C494 Type D)	1.21	---
Water Reducer (ASTM C494 Type A)	1.22	---

TABLE 2 — PLASTIC SHRINKAGE CRACKING MIX DESIGN DATA

Cement Factor	500 pcy	
Coarse Aggregate	1750 pcy	Gravel
Fine Aggregate	1370 pcy	
Unit Weight	143 pcy	
W/C Ratio	0.48	
Air Content	6-8%	

0.75 oz/cwt AEA
4 oz/cwt Retarder

Fiber Length and Addition Rate Data

Fiber Length (Inches)	Fiber Addition (pcy)
0.5	0.75
0.5	1.5
0.5	3
0.75	0.75
0.75	1.5
0.75	3
2	0.75
2	1.5
2	3

TABLE 3 — FREEZE THAW MIX DESIGN DATA

Normal Weight Concrete

Cement Factor	517 pcy	
Coarse Aggregate	1800 pcy	
Fine Aggregate	1180 pcy	
Unit Weight	140 pcf	
W/C Ratio	0.55	
Air Content	5.5-7%	

Fiber Length (Inches)	Fiber Addition (PCY)
0.5	1.5
0.75	1.5

Lightweight Concrete

Cement Factor	517 pcy	
Coarse Aggregate	750 pcy	Expanded Shale Lightweight
Fine Aggregate	1400 pcy	
Unit Weight	116 pcf	
W/C Ratio	0.55	
Air Content	5.1 - 6.6%	

Fiber Length (Inches)	Fiber Addition (pcy)
0.5	0.75
0.75	0.75
0.5	1.5
0.75	1.5

TABLE 4 — FLEXURAL STRENGTH MIX DESIGN DATA

Normal Weight Concrete

Cement Factor	517 pcy	
Coarse Aggregate	1700 pcy	Trap Rock
Fine Aggregate	1180 pcy	
Unit Weight	140 pcf	
W/C Ratio	0.62	
Air Content	2-3%	

Fiber Length (Inches)	Fiber Addition (pcy)
0.5	0.75
0.75	0.75
0.5	1.5
0.75	1.5
0.75	3

Lightweight Concrete

Cement Factor	517 pcy	
Coarse Aggregate	750 pcy	Expanded Shale Lightweight
Fine Aggregate	1400 pcy	
Design W/c	0.55	
Actual W/c	0.51	
Air Content	6-7%	
Unit Weight	113 pcf	

Fiber Length (Inches)	Fiber Addition (PCY)
0.5	0.75
0.5	1.5
0.75	1.5

TABLE 5 — MODULUS OF ELASTICITY MIX DESIGN DATA

Cement Factor	500 pcy	650 pcy	
Coarse Aggregate	1750pcy Gravel	1750 pcy	Trap Rock
Fine Aggregate	1370 pcy	1370 pcy	
Unit Weight	143 pcf	150 pcf	
W/C Ratio	0.48	0.48	
Air Content	3-6%	3-6%	
4 oz/cwt Retarder			
0.75 oz/cwt AEA			

Fiber Length (Inches)	Fiber Addition (PCY)
0.75	0.75
0.75	1.5
0.5	3

TABLE 6 — TOUGHNESS MIX DESIGN DATA

Normal Weight Concrete		
Cement Factor	517 pcy	
Coarse Aggregate	1700 pcy	Trap Rock
Fine Aggregate	1580 pcy	
Unit Weight	151 pcf	
W/C Ratio	0.62	
Air Content	2-3%	

Fiber Length (Inches)	Fiber Addition (PCY)
0.5	0.75
0.75	0.75
0.5	1.5
0.75	1.5
0.75	3

TABLE 7 — DROP WEIGHT HAMMER IMPACT MIX DESIGN DATA

Normal Weight Concrete		
Cement Factors	400 - 517 pcy	
Coarse Aggregate	1750	Gravel
Coarse Aggregate	1700	Trap Rock
Fine Aggregate	1650-1380 pcy	
Unit Weight	141-150 pcf	
W/C Ratio	0.56- 0.78	
Air Content	2-3%	

Fiber Length (Inches)	Fiber Addition (PCY)
0.75	0.75
0.75	1.5
0.75	2.25
0.75	3
0.75	4.5
2	0.75
2	1.5

TABLE 8 — COMPRESSIVE STRENGTH MIX DESIGN DATA

Normal Weight Concrete	
Cement Factor	500 pcy
Coarse Aggregate	1750 pcy
Fine Aggregate	1370 pcy
Unit Weight	143 pcf
W/C Ratio	0.48
Air Content	6-8%

Fiber Length (Inches)	Fiber Addition (PCY)
0.5	0.75
0.5	1.5
0.5	3
0.75	0.75
0.75	1.5
0.75	3
2	0.75
2	1.5
2	3

Lightweight Concrete	
Cement Factor	517 pcy
Coarse Aggregate	750 pcy
Fine Aggregate	1400 pcy
Unit Weight	116 pcf
W/C Ratio	0.55
Air Content	5.1 - 6.6%

Fiber Length (Inches)	Fiber Addition (PCY)
0.5	0.75
0.75	0.75
0.5	1.5
0.75	1.5

TABLE 9 — FREEZING AND THAWING DURABILITY DATA

Normal Weight Concrete

Cement Factor (PCY)	W/C	Air Content %	Fiber Length (IN)	Fiber Addition (PCY)	RDME Value '@ 302 Cycles	% Weight Loss
517	0.55	6.8	0	0	100	1.4
517	0.55	6.2	0.5	1.5	103	0.6
517	0.55	6.8	0.75	1.5	105	0.9
517	0.55	7	0.75	1.5	104	0.8
517	0.55	6.75	0.75	1.5	102	1

RDME 95% Confidence Interval= ± 5
Weight Loss 95% Confidence Interval= ± 1%

Lightweight Concrete

Cement Factor (PCY)	W/C	Air Content %	Fiber Length (IN)	Fiber Addition (PCY)	RDME Value '@ 311 Cycles	% Weight Loss
517	0.51	6	0	0	96	0.1
517	0.51	6.6	0.75	1.5	90	0.2
517	0.51	6.4	0.5	1.5	99	0
517	0.51	5.1	0.75	0.75	98	0
517	0.51	6.1	0.5	0.75	100	0

RDME 95% Confidence Interval= ± 4

TABLE 10 — FLEXURAL STRENGTH DATA – NORMAL WEIGHT CONCRETE

Normal Weight Concrete

Cement Factor (pcy)	W/C	Fiber Length (in)	Fiber Addition (pcy)	Flexural Strength 7 Day (psi)	Flexural Strength 28 DAY (psi)
517	0.62	0	0	615	760
517	0.62	0.5	0.75	570	690
517	0.62	0.75	0.75	585	710
517	0.62	0.5	1.5	540	705
517	0.62	0.75	1.5	590	780
517	0.62	0.75	3	600	750

7 Day 95% Confidence Interval= ± 44 psi
28 Day 95% Confidence Interval= ± 100 psi

Lightweight Concrete

Cement Factor (pcy)	W/C	Fiber Length (in)	Fiber Addition (pcy)	Flexural Strength 7 Day (psi)	Flexural Strength 28 DAY (psi)
517	0.51	0	0	590	670
517	0.51	0.75	1.5	520	680
517	0.51	0.5	1.5	585	645
517	0.51	0.75	0.75	580	675

7 Day 95% Confidence Interval= ± 106 psi
28 Day 95% Confidence Interval= ± 30 psi

TABLE 11 — MODULUS OF ELASTICITY DATA FOR FIBER CONCRETE

Mix #	Cement Factor (pcy)	Micro-Silica (pcy)	Fiber Length (in)	Fiber Addition (pcy)	w/c ratio	Slump (in)	Air Content%	Compressive Strength 28 Day (psi)
1	500	0	0.00	0.00	0.47	5.75	6.1	4900
2	500	0	0.75	0.75	0.47	5.75	5.4	5455
3	500	0	0.75	1.50	0.47	4.75	3.8	5470
4	500	0	0.75	3.00	0.47	4.00	3.2	5533
5	650	65	0.00	0.00	0.40	5.50	5.0	9570
6	650	65	0.75	3.00	0.40	5.00	5.3	9720
7	517	0	0.00	0.00	0.58	6.25	7.6	4460
8	517	0	0.75	3.00	0.58	3	6.2	4040

Table 11 Continued
Modulus of Elasticity Data
(x 10^6 psi)
(Average)

Mix #	1 Day	7 Day	14 DAy	28 Day	9 Months
1	2.09		2.52		3.50
2	2.22		3.12		3.60
3	2.11		2.95		4.01
4	1.97		2.89		4.19
5	3.97	4.90		5.57	
6	3.40	4.95		5.55	
7	1.96	3.55		4.45	
8	1.97	3.65		4.05	

TABLE 12 — ASTM METHOD C 1018 TOUGHNESS DATA

Cement Factor (pcy)	Fiber Length (in)	Fiber Addition (pcy)	W/C	I_5 Toughness Values
517	0.00	0.00	0.62	4.031
517	0.50	1.50	0.62	4.407
517	0.50	0.75	0.62	4.694
517	0.75	0.75	0.62	4.444
517	0.75	1.50	0.62	4.256
517	0.75	3.00	0.62	4.425

95% Confidence Interval= ± 0.52

TABLE 13 — DROP WEIGHT HAMMER IMPACT DATA

Cement Factor (pcy)	Fiber Length (in)	Fiber Addition (pcy)	W/C	Average Number of Drops To Test Comple- tion	Statist- cally Signif- icant Difference
400	0.00	0.00	0.76	3.8	not applicable
400	0.75	0.75	0.76	6.8	no
400	0.75	1.50	0.76	6.2	no
400	0.75	2.25	0.76	7.7	yes
400	0.75	3.00	0.76	8.8	yes
400	0.75	4.50	0.76	8.4	yes
	95% Confidence Interval= ±1.8				
400	0.00	0.00	0.78	4.40	not applicable
400	0.75	0.75	0.78	5.20	no
400	0.75	1.50	0.78	6.20	no
400	0.75	3.00	0.78	9.00	yes
	95% Confidence Interval= ±1.7				
517	0.00	0.00	0.56	3.8	not applicable
517	2	0.75	0.56	3.2	no
517	2	1.5	0.56	3.4	no
517	2	3.00	0.56	13.20	yes
517	0.75	0.75	0.56	3.20	no
517	0.75	1.50	0.56	3.20	no
517	0.75	3.00	0.56	12.60	yes
	95% Confidence Interval= ±2.8				

TABLE 14 — FIBER CONCRETE COMPRESSIVE STRENGTH SUMMARY

MIX DAY	Fiber Additior (pcy)	Fiber Length (in.)	Air Contei %	Compressive Strength Avg. (psi)	Compressive Strength Standard Deviatior (psi)	Compressive Strength 95 % Confidence Intervals UPPER CONFIDENCE INTERVAL	Avg.	LOWER CONFIDENCE INTERVAL	Normalized Strength Fiber Avg ------' x 100% Control Avg. UPPER CONFIDENCE NTERVAl	Avg	LOWER CONFIDENCE NTERVAL
1	0.00	0.00	6.40	4435	80	4599	4435	4271	103.5	100.0	96.2
1	0.75	0.50	6.40	4260	65	4424	4260	4096	99.9	96.1	92.3
1	0.75	0.75	5.80	4687	170	4851	4687	4523	109.5	105.7	101.9
1	0.75	0.75	6.20	4811	50	4975	4811	4647	112.3	108.5	104.7
2	0.00	0.00	6.00	4825	295	4989	4825	4661	103.3	100.0	96.5
2	0.75	0.75	6.60	4662	122	4826	4662	4498	100.1	96.6	93.0
3	0.00	0.00	6.10	4746	94	4910	4746	4582	103.3	100.0	96.4
3	0.75	0.50	6.40	4600	228	4764	4600	4436	100.5	96.9	93.3
3	0.75	0.75	6.60	4374	120	4538	4374	4210	95.9	92.3	88.7
4	0.00	0.00	7.10	4342	38	4809	4645	4481	103.9	100.0	96.1
4	0.75	0.75	8.00	4226	116	4506	4342	4178	101.2	97.3	93.4
5	0.75	0.50	6.90	5381	86	5545	5381	5217	103.0	94.7	91.7
5	0.00	0.00	6.60	5683	73	5847	5683	5519	103.0	100.0	97.0
5	0.75	0.75	6.60	5443	40	5607	5443	5279	98.8	95.8	93.8
6	0.00	0.00	3.40	6005	141	6169	6005	5841	102.8	100.0	97.2
6	0.75	2.00	3.50	5993	48	6157	5993	5829	102.6	99.8	97.0
6	1.50	2.00	4.00	5573	105	5737	5573	5409	95.6	92.8	90.0
7	0.00	0.00	5.90	5159	120	5323	5159	4995	103.3	100.0	96.7
7	0.75	0.75	6.00	5232	208	5433	5232	5031	104.7	101.4	98.1
7	1.50	0.75	6.20	5468	98	5632	5468	5304	109.3	106.0	102.7
8	0.00	0.00	4.30	5972	37	6136	5972	5808	102.8	100.0	97.2
8	1.50	2.00	3.50	6480	221	6644	6480	6316	111.3	108.5	105.7
9	0.00	0.00	1.80	5392	58	5593	5392	5191	103.1	100.0	96.9
9	0.75	2.00	2.10	6215	124	6416	6215	6014	118.3	115.2	112.1
9	1.50	2.00	2.20	5956	294	6157	5956	5755	113.5	110.4	107.3
9	3.00	2.00	2.20	5686	31	5887	5686	5485	108.6	105.5	102.4
10	0.00	0.00	7.60	5211	224	5375	5211	5047	103.2	100.0	96.8
10	0.75	2.00	7.10	5741	98	5905	5741	5577	113.4	110.2	107.0
11	0.00	0.00	4.30	5210	224	5374	5210	5046	103.2	100.0	96.8
11	1.50	2.00	4.80	5739	98	5903	5739	5575	116.9	113.7	110.5
11	3.00	2.00	5.00	6210	20	6374	6210	6046	122.4	119.2	116.0
12	0.00	0.00	3.60	4973	188	5137	4973	4809	103.4	100.0	96.6
12	3.00	2.00	4.30	5385	90	5549	5385	5221	111.5	108.3	105.1
12	3.00	2.00	4.60	5182	163	5346	5182	5018	107.6	104.2	100.8
13	0.00	0.00	3.70	5440	79	5604	5440	5276	103.1	100.0	96.9
13	1.50	0.50	3.80	5517	49	5681	5517	5353	104.4	101.4	98.3
13	1.50	0.50	3.90	5014	53	5178	5014	4850	95.3	92.2	89.1
14	0.00	0.00	3.40	5517	60	5681	5517	5353	103.0	100.0	97.0
14	1.50	0.50	3.90	5446	115	5610	5446	5282	101.7	98.7	95.7
15	0.00	0.00	2.80	5820	80	5984	5820	5656	102.9	100.0	97.1
15	1.50	0.50	3.00	5647	43	5811	5647	5483	99.9	97.0	95.1
15	3.00	0.50	3.00	5483	53	5683	5483	5282	97.1	94.2	91.3
16	0.00	0.00	7.90	4095	242	4259	4095	3931	104.1	100.0	95.9
16	1.50	0.75	7.40	4105	233	4269	4105	3941	104.3	100.2	96.1
17	0.00	0.00	9.80	4258	161	4422	4258	4094	104.0	100.0	96.0
17	1.50	0.50	9.00	4144	29	4308	4144	3980	101.3	97.3	94.3
18	0.00	0.00	6.50	5022	85	5186	5022	4858	103.4	100.0	96.6
18	1.50	0.75	6.00	5262	121	5426	5262	5098	108.2	104.8	101.4
19	0.00	0.00	4.90	5202	130	5366	5202	5038	103.2	100.0	96.8
19	3.00	0.75	5.40	5368	145	5568	5368	5167	106.4	103.2	100.0

Pooled Standard Deviation= 143 psi

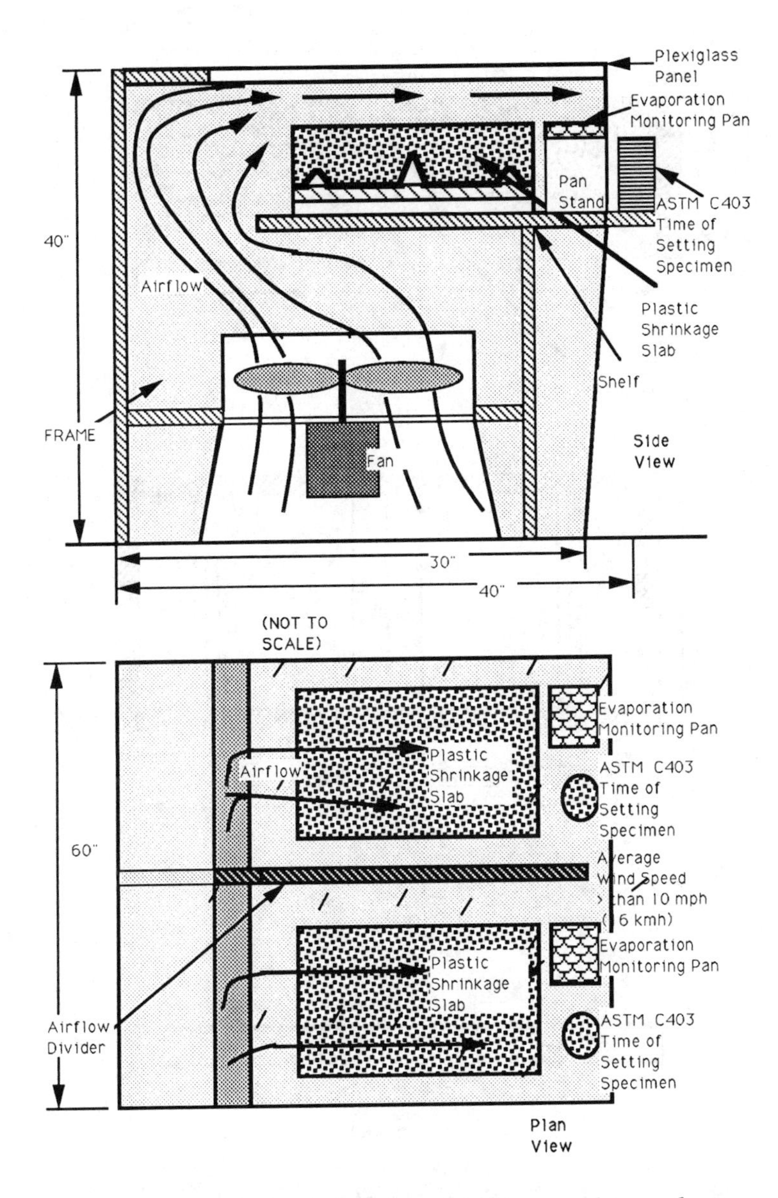

Fig. 1—Schematic drawing of fan box used to evaluate plastic shrinkage cracking

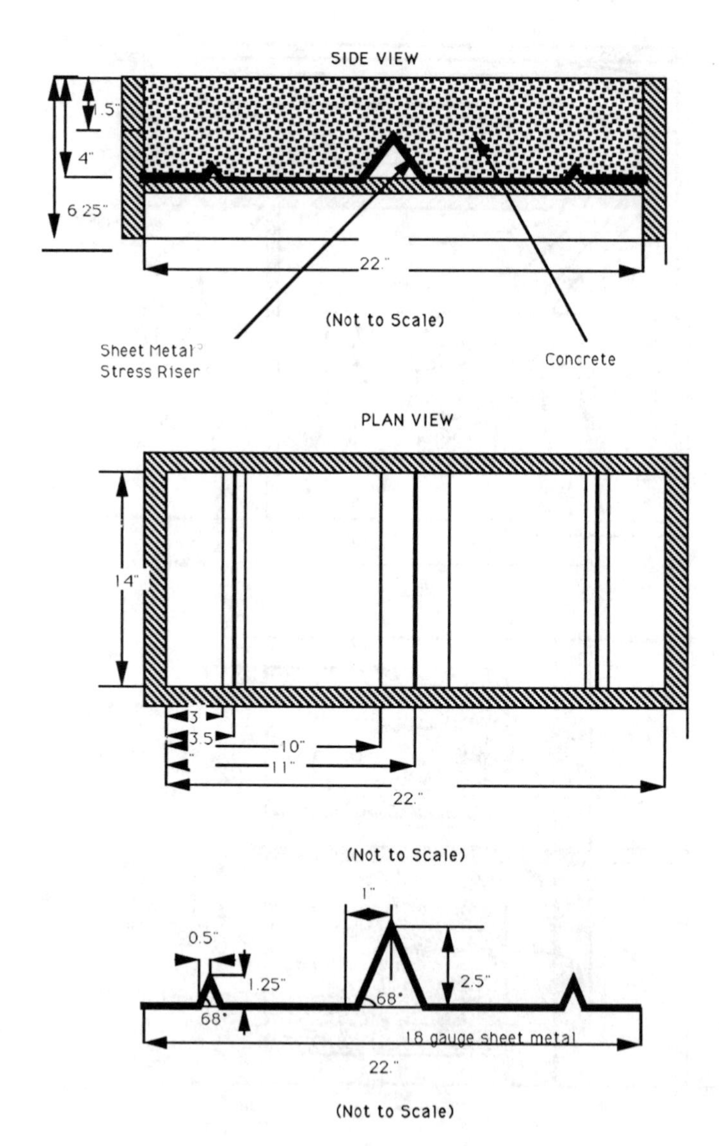

Fig. 2—Schematic of mold

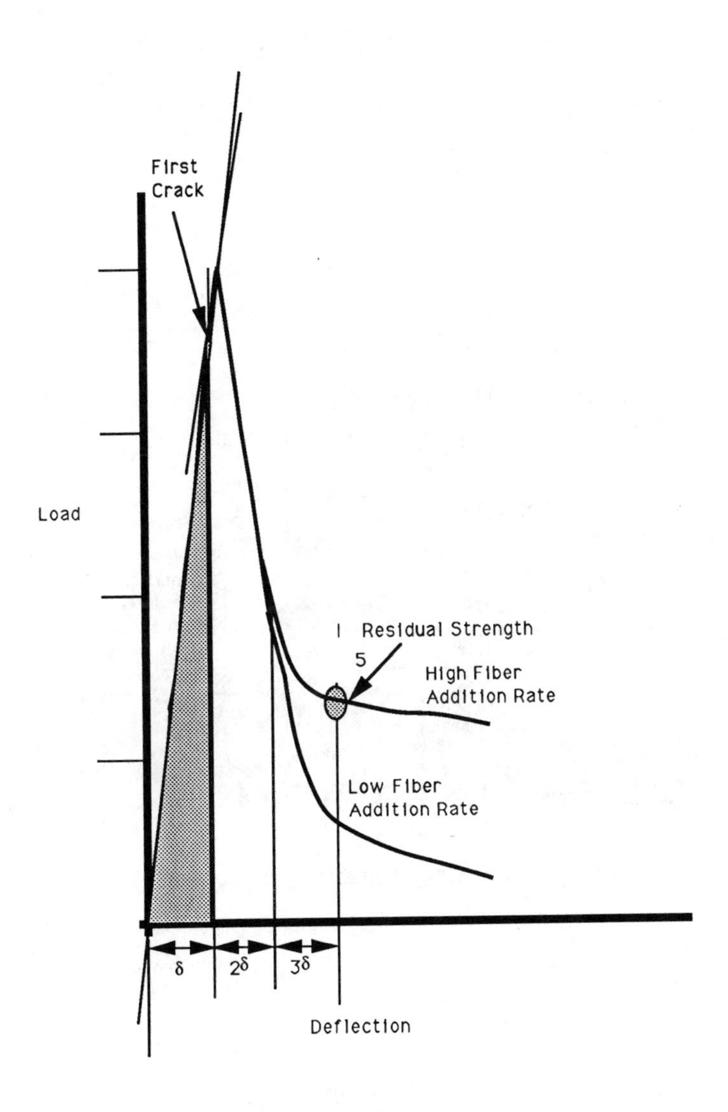

Fig. 3—I_5 toughness curve

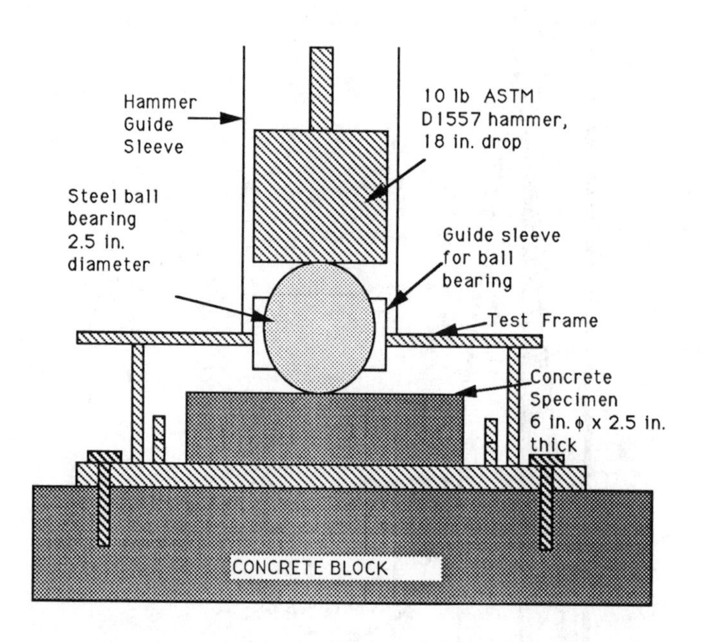

Fig. 4—Drop weight hammer impact test

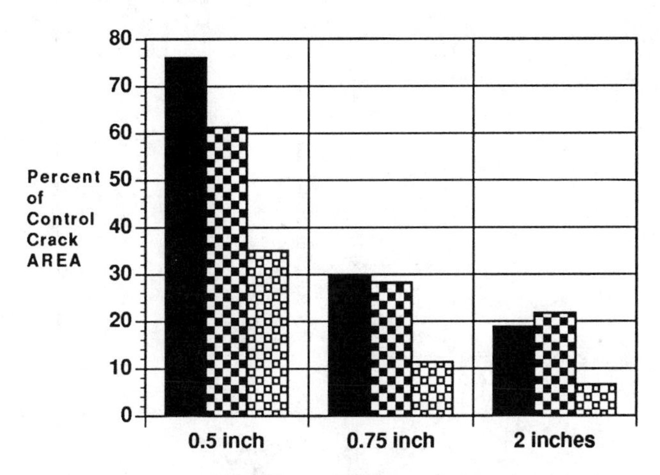

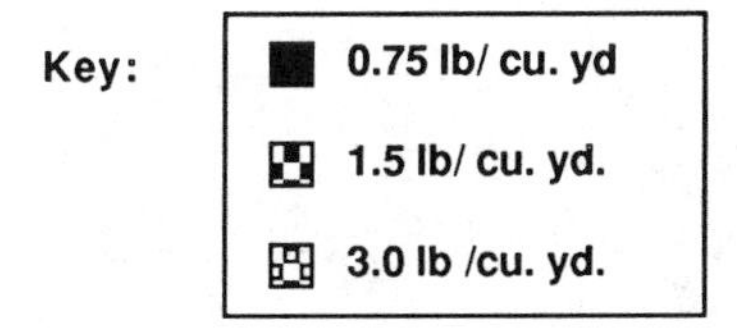

Fig. 5—Summary of crack reduction properties fiber lengths and loading

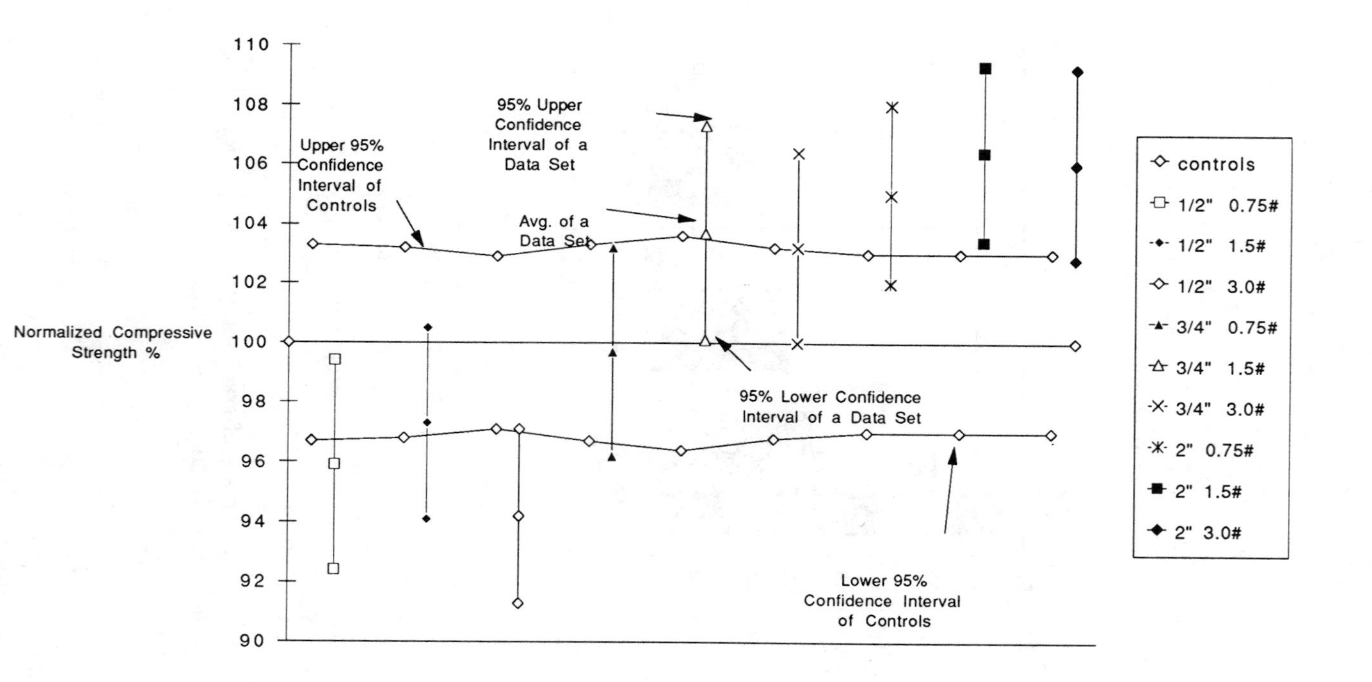

Fig. 6—Normalized compressive strength data

SP 142-3

Toughness of Slurry Infiltrated Fibrous Concrete (SIFCON)

by V.S. Parameswaran, K. Balasubramanian, V. Ramakrishnan, and T.S. Krishnamoorthy

Synopsis: It is well recognised that steel fibre reinforced concrete composites exhibit improved resistance to fracture and impact loads. Both fracture and impact resistance are primarily governed by the toughness characteristics of the material defined by its energy-absorption capacity.

Toughness can be measured by carrying out tests involving direct tension, compression or flexure. However, flexural tests are mostly favoured for measurement of toughness because of their simplicity and also their close representation of the stress conditions under field conditions. The test procedures for the measurement of toughness indices given in codes of practice such as, ASTM C-1018, JCI-SF4, JSCE-SF4, and ACI 544 help one to obtain information on the qualitative performance of different materials and mix designs.

Little information has been reported on the toughness characteristics of slurry-infiltrated fibrous concrete (SIFCON) which is basically a material formed by infiltrating a preplaced 'fibre stack' with a cement slurry. The paper describes the details of toughness tests carried out on SIFCON at the Structural Engineering Research Centre, Madras, India, and summarizes the results of the investigations.

Keywords: Cracking (fracturing); ductility; energy absorption; fiber reinforced concretes; flexural strength; load-deflection curve; metal fibers; slurries; standards; tests; toughness

Dr. V.S.Parameswaran is the Deputy Director and Head of the Concrete Composites Laboratory at the Structural Engineering Research Centre, Madras, India. His research interests include reinforced and prestressed concrete and special concrete composites. Currently he is the President of the Indian Concrete Institute and also the Chief Executive of Information Centre for Fibre Reinforced Concrete Composites, Madras.

Dr. V.Ramakrishnan is the Professor of Civil Engineering at the South Dakota School of Mines and Technology, Rapid City, SD. He has authored two books and has over 100 publications in the field of concrete structures and concrete technology. He received the Presidential Award as Outstanding Professor 1980 from SDSM&T for excellence in teaching, research, and community service.

K.Balasubramanian is a Scientist at the Structural Engineering Research Centre, Madras. He got his B.E. and M.E. degrees from the College of Engineering, Guindy, Madras, India.

T.S.Krishnamoorthy is a Scientist at the Structural Engineering Research Centre, Madras. He got his B.E. degree from the Annamalai University, Madras and M.E. degree from the Anna University, Madras, India.

INTRODUCTION

Slurry infiltrated fibrous concrete (SIFCON) is a relatively new construction material. The technique of producing SIFCON basically involves the random placement of steel fibres in a mould or form by hand to form a "fibre bed". A cement slurry or a rich flowing mortar is then poured onto the fibre bed and vibrated so as to ensure complete infiltration of the slurry through the depth of the mould. The curing procedure for SIFCON is the same as for other Portland cement-based materials. The technique of infiltrating layers of steel fibres with Portland cement-based materials was first reported by Haynes [1] in 1968. Lankard and Newell [2] modified the method used by Haynes to produce SIFCON with high percentages of steel fibres. In practice, packed fibre beds upto 36 inches in thickness have been successfully infiltrated.

While the fibre volume content in normal fibre reinforced concrete generally varies from one to two per cent, it varies from 5 to 12 per cent in a typical SIFCON mix and, in some special situations, it goes even up to 20 per cent.

SIFCON has already been successfully used for the construction of structures subjected to impact, blast, and dynamic loading and also for refractory applications, overlays, and repair of structural components because of its high tensile strength and ductility. While several properties of SIFCON have already been evaluated and made use of in the construction of several types of structures, not much information is available at present on the toughness characteristics of the material, which should necessarily form the basis for the design of structures subjected to dynamic, impact, and abnormal loading.

MEASUREMENT OF TOUGHNESS

Toughness is one of the important mechanical performance parameters presently being used in construction specifications. While procedures for design of structural members based on strength have been fairly well established, this is not the case with design and construction practices that have to meet specified toughness requirements.

Toughness is generally defined as the energy absorption capacity of a composite. Failure in a typical SIFCON composite, like that in the unreinforced matrix, is initiated by the tensile fracture of the matrix. Depending upon the reinforcing parameters, subsequent failure is largely due to pull-out of fibres. In some instances, fracture of the fibres may also accompany fibre pull-out. A great deal of debate is still going on as to how toughness should be measured, interpreted, and used in the design of composites.

The available test standards such as ASTM C-1018-85, [3], JCI SF4 [4], JSCE SF4 [5], and guidelines of ACI Committee 544 [6] for the measurement of toughness indices are useful in comparing the relative performances of different mix designs and in providing information on strength as well as toughness for the particular parameters as defined for the tests. However, definite recommendations on how one goes about using the results of these tests for designing and specifying different fibre composites for particular applications are still to be formulated.

Most of the tests for toughness measurements mentioned earlier [3-6] use a static third-point bending configuration. Besides being a relatively simple test to conduct, this configuration closely represents the stress conditions that the composite is most likely to experience in many practical applications. Fig. 1 shows a schematic representation of the methods proposed for toughness measurement. In all these methods, the energy absorbed by the specimen is computed from the area under the load-deflection response.

The ASTM C-1018 [3] procedure involves determining the amount of energy required to deflect the beam to a specified multiple of the first-crack deflection, with this multiple based on functional (e.g., serviceability) considerations. The toughness indices I_5, I_{10} and I_{30} are calculated as ratios of the area of the load-deflection curve up to deflections of 3, 5.5, and 15.5 times the first-crack deflection divided by the area of the load-deflection curve up to the first-crack deflection (first-crack toughness), respectively (Fig. 1c). These indices provide an indication of the relative toughness at these deflections and give information on the approximate shape of the post-cracking load-deflection response. These indices (I_5, I_{10}, and I_{30}) have a minimum value of unity (elastic-brittle behavior) and values of 5, 10, and 30, respectively, for ideal elastic-plastic behaviour. The specification requires that the first-crack strength and the corresponding deflection and toughness be reported in addition to the toughness indices. ASTM C-1018 allows an extension of the toughness index rationale to greater indices, such as I_{50} and I_{100}. In the JCI method, toughness is defined in absolute terms as the energy required to deflect an FRC beam to a mid-point deflection of 1/150 of its span.

DETAILS OF EXPERIMENTAL INVESTIGATION

(a) Test Specimens

Altogether 16 series of SIFCON specimens, each series comprising three identically cast specimens, were tested in flexure to compare their relative toughness characteristics. The specimens in each series were flexural beams of size 100 mm x 100 mm x 500 mm. Companion plain mortar specimens of size 100 mm x 500 mm x 500 mm were also cast for comparison purposes. Details of the test specimens are given in Table 1.

(b) Materials

The materials used in casting the test specimens consisted of Portland cement, sand, flyash, straight steel fibres, water, and a high-range water-reducing admixture. The cement used conformed to IS 269-1976 [7]. The sand used was river sand sieved through a 1.18 mm sieve. The flyash used had a fineness of 2763 x 10^4 sq mm/N.

The steel fibres used were cold-drawn, high-tensile, plain wires having a tensile strength of 1000 MPa and a diameter of 0.4 mm. Prior to their actual use, the fibres were washed to remove the lubricants and dirt. Only straight steel fibres having an aspect ratio of 75 were used in the tests. The high-range, water-reducing admixture used was CONPLAST 430 marketed by a local company in collaboration with Fosroc International Limited, U.K.

(c) Mix proportions

Table 1 presents the details of the four different mix proportions used for casting the test specimens. A fibre volume of 8% and an aspect ratio of 75 were adopted in casting all the test specimens. The slurry used for infiltration essentially consisted of Portland cement and sand mixed in the proportion of either 1:1 or 1:1.5 by weight. In both the above mixes, flyash equal to 20% by weight of cement was used to study how its addition affected the fluidity (workability) of the mix. While the water-cement ratio was kept constant at 0.375, the quantity of CONPLAST-430 used in the test specimens varied from 1% to 3% by weight of cement.

(d) Preparation of the test specimens

The flexural test specimens were cast using steel moulds. Three techniques were employed for incorporating the steel fibres in the matrix. In the first case, the fibres were prepacked in the moulds and the cement slurry was allowed to infiltrate into the pack assisted by proper compaction by means of a table vibrator (single layer technique designated as SL series). The second technique comprised of placing the fibres in the mould only upto its one-third depth followed by infiltration of the slurry upto this level. The contents with the mould were then vibrated. The process was repeated till the entire mould was filled and compacted (three layer technique designated as TL series). The third technique consisted of filling the mould upto a certain height (preferably one-third depth) first by the slurry and then implanting the fibres into the slurry immediately thereafter (immersion technique designated as 'I' series - Fig.2). As mentioned earlier, table vibrator was used for compacting the test specimens.

In addition to the flexural test specimens, SIFCON cylinders of size 75 mm diameter and 150 mm height were also cast following the same casting technique as adopted for the test specimens to ascertain their compressive strength. Plain mortar cubes of size 70.7 mm x 70.7 mm x 70.7 mm were also cast in each series to determine the compressive strength of the mortar used.

The test specimens were demoulded after 24 hours. They were then cured for 14 days by immersing them in a curing tank, after which period, they were removed from the tank for testing.

(e) Testing

Static flexural tests were carried out on the test specimens using a universal testing machine of 400 kN capacity. A two-point loading system, as suggested in the ASTM and JCI test procedures, was adopted in which the specimen was simply-supported over a span of 300 mm. The loads were applied at a distance of 100 mm from each support. A dial gauge having a least count of 0.01 mm and mounted on a specially fabricated steel frame was used for accurate measurement of net deflection (Fig.3).

The testing machine was operated so that the deflection of the specimen at midspan increased at a rate of 0.05 to 0.10 mm/min as specified in reference 3. Deflection measurements were recorded at various stages of loading until the failure of the specimens.

The cylindrical SIFCON specimens and companion mortar cubes were also tested using the universal testing machine. Fig.4 shows one of the tested specimens after failure.

Cubes of size 100 mm x 100 mm x 100 mm were cut from the tested flexural test specimens with the help of a concrete cutting machine. These were tested for their compressive strength using a compression testing machine.

ANALYSIS OF TEST RESULTS

Results obtained from static flexural strength tests are tabulated in Table 2. The values given represent the average of three test results. The apparent flexural strength at failure f_r included in the table was calculated using the equation

$$f_r = \frac{Md}{2I}$$

where f_r = apparent flexural strength; I = moment of inertia of the uncracked test specimen; M = applied bending moment, and d = depth of the specimen.

It can be seen from Table 2 that the maximum flexural strength is registered by a slurry composition of 1:1 having a flyash content of 20% in the case of single layer and three layer series (SLC & TLC). In the case of the immersion series (ID), the maximum flexural strength occurs for a slurry composition of 1:1.5 with 20% flyash. The flexural strength of SIFCON specimens was 600% more than that of plain mortar specimens. The maximum flexural strength achieved was 46 N/sq mm in the case of TLC series.

Load-deflection relationships of SIFCON mixes were drawn using the data from the static flexural tests. These are shown in Figs.5-7. A significant difference in performance of concretes made out of SIFCON is observed in the load-deflection curves with regard to first crack strength and toughness indices. Unlike plain concrete, SIFCON does not fail in a brittle, catastrophic manner at the formation of the first crack under a clearly identifiable maximum load. Well before signs of significant material distress are visible, the load-deflection curve becomes non-linear. A comparison of the load-deflection curves also shows an improvement in the elasto-plastic behaviour of SIFCON. The SIFCON beams did not fail immediately after the appearance of the first crack as in the case of plain mortar specimens.

The values of the toughness indices I_5, I_{10}, and I_{30} calculated as per ASTM C1018-85 and the Japanese methods are tabulated in Table 3. As mentioned earlier, toughness index I_5 was calculated for a deflection of three times the first crack deflection. Likewise, I_{10} and I_{30} were indices corresponding to 5.5 and 15.5 times the first crack deflection, respectively.

The toughness index for plain concrete is equal to 1 because all plain concrete beams failed immediately after first crack. The SLC, TLC, and ID series gave higher toughness indices, as compared to counterpart specimens cast using the same technique of casting.

CONCLUSIONS

The following conclusions are drawn based on the results obtained from the present investigation.

1. In normal fibre reinforced concrete, there is always a possibility that the fibres may not be distributed evenly throughout the member and could as well be less concentrated at a few critical locations. However, in the case of SIFCON, the fibres are preplaced ensuring uniform distribution of fibres across the depth and this leads to significant contribution to the strength of the composite besides imparting high ductile behaviour. A strength improvement of as much as 600% (in flexure) as compared to plain mortar specimens was obtained during the tests.

2. The ductility of SIFCON specimens was found to be very high compared to companion mortar specimens as may be seen from Table 3.

3. The toughness index for SIFCON specimens was found to be significantly high as compared to plain mortar specimens (Table 3). The values of I_{30} obtained for SIFCON are 45 to 65 times more than those for plain mortar specimens. The toughness values computed for SIFCON specimens using the JCI procedure, however indicate an increase of about 125 to 175 times over companion plain mortar specimens. From a survey of earlier literature [8], it is seen that SIFCON specimens exhibits a much superior toughness characteristic as compared to normal fibre reinforced concrete.

4. The ratios I_{10}/I_5 and I_{30}/I_{10} shown in Table 3 indicate that the behaviour of SIFCON is akin to ideal elasto-plastic materials.

5. All the three techniques used during the investigations for incorporating the fibres in the mortar specimens proved effective. There was not much difference in the results obtained from the tests on specimens having the same mix proportions, but cast differently using any of the three techniques. However, the three-layer and immersion techniques were found to be easier and simpler in actual practice as compared to the single layer technique. The possibility of these two techniques resulting in 'cold-joints', however, needs further investigation, even though in the flexural strength tests reported in this paper, this phenomenon did not show up.

ACKNOWLEDGMENT

The authors wish to express their appreciation to the technical staff of the Concrete Composites Laboratory of SERC for the assistance and cooperation rendered by them in carrying out the tests. The paper is being published with the kind permission of the Director, Structural Engineering Research Centre, Madras, India.

REFERENCES

1. Haynes, H., "Investigation of Fiber Reinforcement Methods For Thin Shell Concrete," Naval Civil Engineering Laboratory, Port Hueneme, California, N-979, September 1968, pp.1-26.

2. Lankard, D.R. and Newell, J.K., "Preparation of Highly Reinforced Steel Fiber Reinforced Concrete Composites", Fiber Reinforced Concrete - International Symposium, SP-81, American Concrete Institute, Detroit, pp. 287-306, 1984.

3. American Society for Testing and Materials, "Standard Method of Test for Flexural Toughness of Fiber-Reinforced Concrete", ASTM Standards for Concrete and Mineral Aggregates, Vol. 04.02, Standard Number C 1018, August 1984, pp.637-644.

4. Japan Concrete Institute, "Method of Test for Flexural Strength and Flexural Toughness of Fiber Reinforced Concrete", Standard SF4, JCI Standards for Test Methods of Fiber Reinforced Concrete, 1983, pp. 45-51.

5. Japan Society of Civil Engineers, "Method of Tests for Steel Fiber Reinforced Concrete", Standard SF4 for Flexural Strength of SFRC and Standard SF5 for Compressive Strength and Compressive Toughness of SFRC, June 1984, pp.45-74.

6. American Concrete Institute Committee-544, "Measurement of Properties of Fiber Reinforced Concrete", ACI Journal Vol.75, No.7, July 1978, pp. 283-289.

7. IS 269-1976, "Ordinary and Low-Heat Portland Cement", Bureau of Indian Standards, New Delhi, India.

8. Ramakrishnan, V., George Y. Wu, and Girish Hosalli, "Flexural Behaviour and Toughness of Fiber Reinforced Concretes", International Symposium on Recent Development in Concrete Fibre Composites, Transportation Research Board, National Research Council, Washington D.C. 1989, pp. 69-77.

TABLE 1 — DETAILS OF TEST SPECIMENS

Sl.No.	Series	Mix-ratio Cement:Sand	Flyash (% by wt.of cement)	Super-plasticiser (% by wt.of cement)	Remarks
1	SLA	1:1	-	2	Single Layer
2	SLB	1:1.5	-	3	-do-
3	SLC	1:1	20	4	-do-
4	SLD	1:1.5	20	5	-do-
5	TLA	1:1	-	2	Three Layers
6	TLB	1:1.5	-	3	-do-
7	TLC	1:1	20	3	-do-
8	TLD	1:1.5	20	5	-do-
9	IA	1:1	-	1	Immersion
10	IB	1:1.5	-	2.5	-do-
11	IC	1:1	20	3	-do-
12	ID	1:1.5	20	5	-do-
13	PA	1:1	-	1	Plain
14	PB	1:1.5	-	3	-do-
15	PC	1:1	20	3	-do-
16	PD	1:1.5	20	5	-do-

Note: 1) Each series consisted of 3 specimens. Values shown here are the average of results obtained for these three numbers.

2) For all the test specimens, water-cement ratio was kept constant at 0.375 and the % by volume of fibres at 8%. The fibres had an aspect ratio of 75.

TABLE 2 — FLEXURAL STRENGTH TEST RESULTS

Specimen series	Average Cracking Stress N/sq mm	Average apparent flexural strength at failure(f_r) N/sq mm	Average strength of SIFCON cubes ** N/sq mm	Average strength of SIFCON cylinders N/sq mm	Average strength of plain mortar cubes N/sq mm
SLA	16.25	27.03	112.2	71.55	41.3
SLB	9.75	18.42	22.0	-	39.8
SLC	13.3	28.65	97.9	70.31	36.0
SLD	8.5	15.93	25.65	-	34.1
TLA	15.85	27.03	122.6	78.06	40.0
TLB	14.03	28.60	74.4	-	36.0
TLC	16.1	46.75	99.3	66.45	38.0
TLD	12.7	29.75	119.5	-	26.5
IA	12.75	22.4	80.8	88.36	42.6
IB	14.6	31.15	96.2	89.03	34.4
IC	12.9	25.2	93.3	97.6	43.4
ID	15.3	39.45	129.3	107.0	26.5
PA	3.9	3.9	65.0	29.1	35.8
PB	3.95	3.95	63.7	29.0	37.0
PC	3.0	3.0	59.2	26.6	29.2
PD	2.4	2.4	37.71	25.6	30.0

** Cubes cut from tested flexural beams

TABLE 3 — TOUGHNESS INDEX OF TESTED SIFCON SPECIMENS

Name of Specimen	Toughness Index as per ASTM Procedure					Toughness by JCI Method (N mm)
	I_5	I_{10}	I_{30}	I_{10}/I_5	I_{30}/I_{10}	
SLA	6.37	16.25	51.52	2.55	3.17	163540
SLB	6.43	14.8	45.68	2.3	3.09	100300
SLC	6.35	16.3	52.99	2.57	3.25	164150
SLD	6.28	15.13	48.17	2.41	3.18	91250
TLA	6.9	17.53	60.7	2.54	3.46	168090
TLB	6.65	16.22	53.32	2.44	3.29	166730
TLC	6.35	17.52	66.67	2.76	3.81	229600
TLD	6.98	17.83	66.36	2.55	3.72	180340
IA	5.89	14.19	46.53	2.41	3.28	134670
IB	6.55	16.08	54.09	2.45	3.36	177050
IC	5.86	14.32	47.16	2.44	3.29	144580
ID	6.78	17.4	65.92	2.57	3.78	227820

Note: 1. For plain mortar specimens tested as per ASTM procedure, the toughness index is unity, since the first crack strength and the failure strength are one and the same.

2. For plain mortar specimens tested as per JCI method, the average toughness measured from respective load-deflection graphs works out to 1330 N mm.

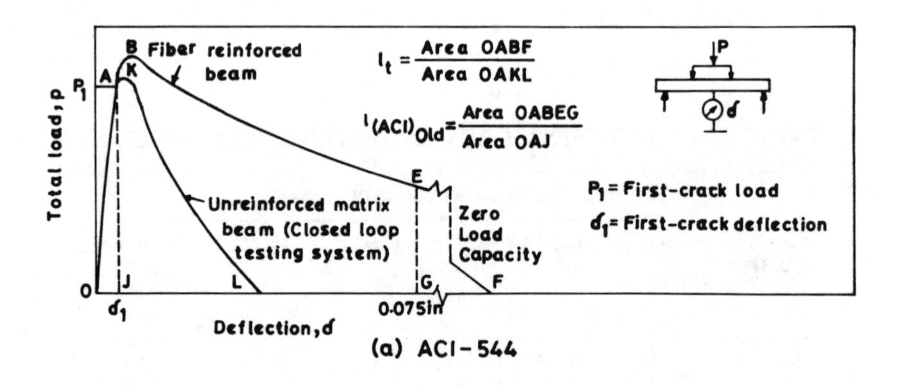

(a) ACI-544

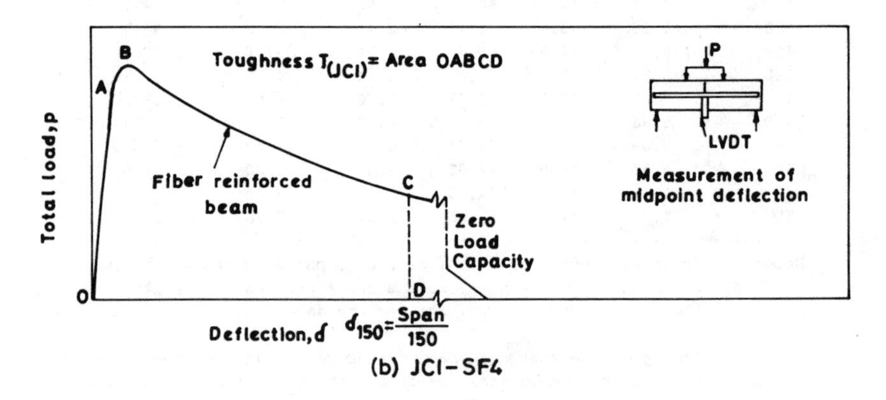

(b) JCI-SF4

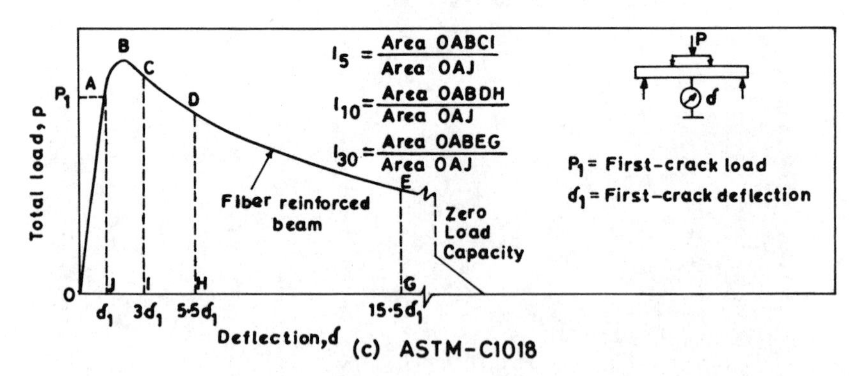

(c) ASTM-C1018

Fig. 1—Presently available measures of toughness and toughness index definitions

Fig. 2—Preparation of test specimens

Fig. 3—Test set-up

Fig. 4—Typical failure pattern of tested specimen

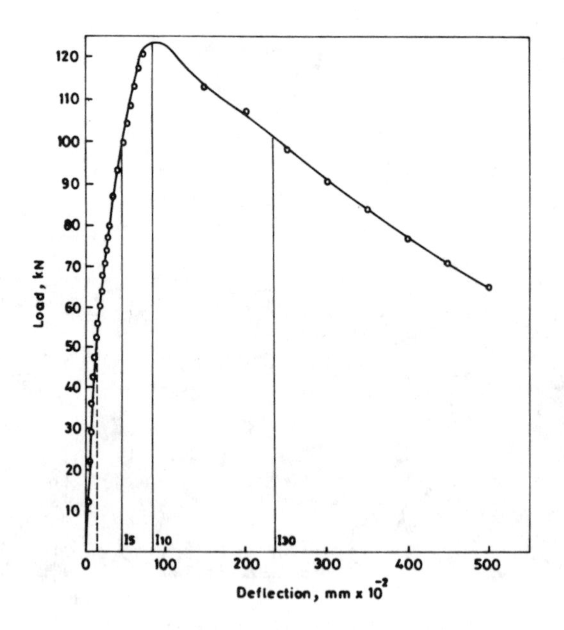

Fig. 5—Load-deflection behavior of specimen SLC/1

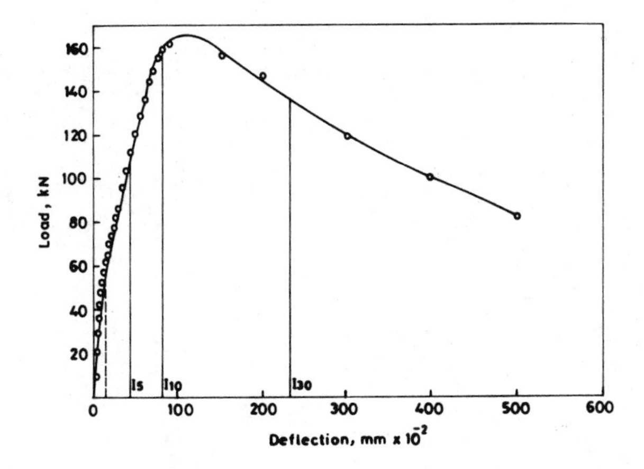

Fig. 6—Load-deflection behavior of specimen TLC/2

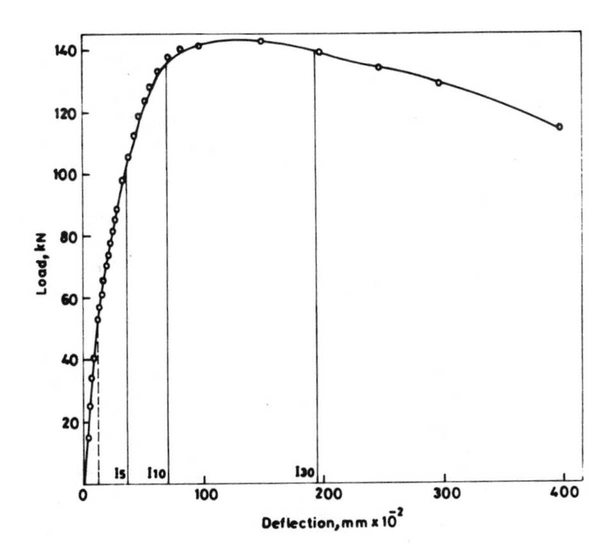

Fig. 7—Load-deflection behavior of specimen ID/2

SP 142-4

Tensile and Compressive Strengths of Polypropylene Fiber Reinforced Concrete

by M. Tavakoli

Synopsis: The experiments disucssed in the present paper, have been performed on concrete specimens reinforced randomly with polypropylene fibers. To obtain the true properties of the fibers, their tensile stress-strain diagram has been obtained through tests. The fibers used had a tensile strength of 2800 kgf/cm^2 (40000 psi), a failure Strain of about 11%, and a Young modulus of elasticity of 2.55×10^5 kgf/cm^2 (3642857 psi). Then, the 7 and 28 day polypropylene fiber reinforced concrete (PFRC) samples with 0, 0.5, 1.0, 1.5, 2.0, and 2.5 percent by volume of fibers have been tested in splitting tensile and compressive strength tests, and the tensile strength, max. tensile strain and compressive strength vs. percentage by volume of fibers diagrams have been plotted.

The results showed that the compressive strength did not change significantly, but the tensile strength had an increase of about 80%, and significant improvement in ductility was achieved. The tests also showed that the best improvement was obtained at an optimum percentage by volum of fibers of about 1.5%.

Keywords: Compressive strength; ductility; fiber reinforced concretes; modulus of elasticity; polypropylene fibers; strength; tensile strength; tests

Mostafa Tavakoli, ph.D., ACI member, is an assistant professor in the department of civil engineering at Sharif University of Technology. He has done considerable research on the behavior of concrete. Recent projects have included polypropylene fibers in conrete; the behavior and strengths.

INTRODUCTION

Low ductility and tensile strength are two poor characteristics of concrete. A progressive technique to improve these characteristics is to use fibers distributed randomly in concrete, with the final aim to improve ductility and crack resistance of steel bar reinforced concrete.

The random distribution of fibers has many advantages, some of which are: improving the ductility and crack resisting characteristics of concrete due to the distribution of fibers at all points and in all directions; and making the studies of the behavior of the homogeneous and isotropic composite easier.

Steel and glass fibers have extensively been studied and used in construction industries. Research has also been done on fibers produced from petrochemical materials, one of which is polypropylene fiber.

The main concern in using the fibers is their high cost. However, polypropylene fibers can be produced at more economical cost in oil producing countries, and those where there are advanced petro-chemical industries. Therefore, working on polypropylene fibers should be of interest in many countries.

The present experiments have been performed after the need for an alternative to steel bars to reinforce concrete has been felt. In the experiments, the tensile and compressive strengths of polypropylene fiber reinforced concrete (pfrc) samples have been studied. However, to achieve better test progam, steel and glass fiber reinforced concrete samples have also been tested.

MATERIALS AND TEST SETUP

Portland cement satisfying the requirements of ASTM-C109 and C 150; broken gravel with the maximum size of 1.3 mm($\frac{1}{2}$ inch); and river sand were used.

The aggregates were washed in the mixer, dried for a few days, and then used.

The water used was drinking water. Due to the large bond

area and for better bonding between fibers and concrete, the cement content was higher than in steel bar reinforced concrete.

The gravel to sand ratio was $\frac{4}{3}$ by volume. For 1 m^3(35.3 ft^3) concrete, 570 liters (20.1 ft^3) of gravel and 430 liters(15.2 ft^3) of sand were used.

The relative aggregate moisture, washed and then dried in the oven for a week, was about five percent. With this moisture and a water cement ratio of about 0.5, the concrete showed a slump of about 6 cm (2.36 in). But in the case of frc, the slump was different depending upon the type of fibers. For glass frc, the water cement ratio was higher than steel frc for the same slump. However, in the experiments discussed in this paper, a constant w/c ratio of 0.5 was used for all fibers, disregarding variation in slump.

TEST SPECIMENS

Cylindrical samples 30 cm (11.81 in) in hight and 15 cm (5.91 in) in cross-sectional diameter were subjected to splitting tensile test. The percentage of fibers by volume and the fiber density were used to compute the weight of the fibers required in the mix. The mix was poured in the molds and vibrated on a vibrating table, refilled after a few cycles, and vibrated faster in the second set of vibrating cycles. The samples were taken out of the molds after 24 hours, transfered to the curing room, and cured under curing blanket wetted every day for a week at 80-90 percent moisture. Then they were placed freely in the lab conditions until the test time.

TEST RESULTS

Steel Fibers

γ_f = 7800 kgf/m^3(490.83 pcf)
l = 32 mm (1.26 in)
d = 0.5 mm (0.20 in)
$\frac{l}{d}$ = 64
σ_{fu} = 3700 kgf/cm^2(52857 psi)

$\frac{w}{c}$ = 0.5
room temperature = 20-25°C
cement content = 300 kgf/m^3 (18.88 pcf)
v_f = 0, 0.5, 1.0, 2.0
ratio of coarse to fine aggregates = $\frac{4}{3}$

Tables 1 and 2 show the results of the tests, and compare them with those obtained by others.

Glass Fibers

γ =2500 kgf/m^3(157.32 pcf)
1 =5 cm (1.97 in)
$\frac{1}{d}$ =65
$\frac{w}{c}$ =0.5
room teperature = 20–25°C
cement content = 300 kgf/m^3 (18.88 pcf)
v_f= 0, 0.5, 1.0, 1.5
ratio of coarse to fine aggregates= $\frac{4}{3}$

To prevent breaking of fibers, first, concrete materials were mixed, then the fibers were poured in the mixer by hand rapidly (in a 1–2 minute period) which was followed by molding.

Table 3 shows the test results and their comparison with those indicated by others.

Polypopylene Fibers

The main purpose of the study presented herein was to investigate the behavior of pfrc. The fibers are ductile and do not have the breaking problem of glass fibers. All materials including the fibers were mixed in the mixer for about 6 minutes. To prevent porosity, vibrating table was used for vibration. The length of the fibers was equal to 7 cm (2.76 in). The fiber stress-strain curve was obtained from experimental work (Fig. 1). From Fig. 1 an ultimate tensile strength (σ_{fu}) of about 2800 Kgf/cm^2 (40000 psi), and a modulus of elasticity of about 2.55 X 10^5 kgf/cm^2 (3642857 psi), based on the initial linear stage can be found. Fig. 2 shows the almost linear variation fo slump vs. volumetric percentage of fibers.

From Fig. 3, the specific gravity, (ρ_o) of pfrc can be obtained. It can be seen that ρ_o decreases with increasing fiber ratio.
1 = 7 cm(2.76 in)
$\frac{1}{d}$ = 50
$\frac{w}{c}$ = 0.5
room temperature = 20–25°C
cement content = 300 Kgf/m^3 (18.88 pcf)
rotio of coarse to fine aggregates = $\frac{4}{3}$

Table 4 shows the results obtained. Note that the tensile strength, $_{t-max}$, was obtained using the relationship $_t = \frac{2p}{1D}$; where P is the applied load at failure, and D and 1 are the diameter and length of the specimen, respectively.(4)

THE BEHAVIOR OF PFRC UNDER SPLLITTING TEST

In steel bar reinforced concrete, prediction of failure model is possible by studying the craze cracks formed under the loading, but in pfrc, the craze cracks do not appear until the ultimate loading is achieved. Therefore, the failure model of pfrc can be studied from the stress-srain($\sigma_t - \varepsilon$)curve, the typical of which are shown in Fig.4. As can be seen, the maximum tensile strength and strain both increase with increasing fiber ratio. That means, the strength and ductility both increase by addition of fibers. However, at a fiber ratio higher than 1.5%, the strength starts to decrease. The decrease can also be seen in Fig. 5 which shows the relationship between the tensile strength (σ_{t-max}) and the percetage by volume of fibers.

Fig. 6 shows the relationship between the maximum tensile strain (ε_{t-max}) and the volumetric percentage of fibers. It can be seen that the optimum fiber percentage for ductility consideration is also 1.5, % by Volume.

From Fig. 7 an insignificant reduction in compressive strength of pfrc with increasing fiber ratio is observed. The reduction is similar to that of the specific gravity. It seems that the increase in porosity of pfrc at higher fiber ratio affects both the specific gravity and the compressive strength.

Fig. 8 shows that the change in maximum compressive strain due to the addition of fibers is much less than that of tensile strain.

ANALYSIS OF THE RESULTS

Tensile strength increases almost linearly with increasing fiber volumetric percentage until a ratio of about 1.5%, and then decreases. The strain and ductility of pfrc also increase until a fiber ratio of 1.5%. The seven day strength starts decreasing at a fiber ratio less than that at which the 28 day tensile strength starts to decrease. In fact, the fibers act effectively when adequate bonding is developed between fibers and concrete. The tests show that this level of bonding is reached in a longer time period with increasing fiber ratio, and the corresponding time is longer than seven days. Therefore, the seven day strengths at high fiber ratios are not reliable.

CONCLUSIONS

1. Adding about 1.5% by volume of polypropylene fibers increases the tensile strength of composite by about 80%.
2. Increasing the polypropylene fiber ratio (up to about 1.5% by

volume) increases the strain at maximum tensile stress (ε_{t-max}) and the length of the non-linear portion of the $\sigma - \varepsilon$ curve; hence increasing the ductility of pfrc.
3. Increasing the polypropylene fiber ratio results in a slight reduction of specific gravity and compressive strength.

NOTATIONS

D = fiber cross-sectional diameter
E_f = modulus of elasticity of fibers
l = length of fibers
$\frac{l}{d}$ = fiber aspect ratio
v_f = percentage by volume of fibers in frc
$\frac{w}{c}$ = water-cement ratio
σ_c = Compressive strength of pfrc
σ_{fu} = ultimate tensile stress of fibers
σ_{t-max} = maximum tensile stress of pfrc
ε_{t-max} = strain corresponding to $_{t-max}$
ρ_0 = specific gravity of pfrc
γ = specific gravity of fibers

REFERENCES

1. Abrishami, Homayoun, "Steel Fiber Reniforced Concrete"; M. Sc. Thesis, Sharif University of Technology; Tehran; Iran; 1987.

2. Chen, W; Carson, J.L.; "Stress-Strain Properties of Random Wire Reinforced Concrete"; ACI Journal, Proceedings Vol. 68 No. 12, Dec-1971, pp. 936-9.

3. An International Symposium; "Fiber Reinforced Concrete"; Publication SP-44, ACI, 1974.

4. O, Driscoll, K. F. ; "The Nature of Chemistry of High Polymers"; Reinhold Publishing Corporation; NY; 1964.

TABLE 1 — TENSILE AND COMPRESSIVE STRENGTHS OF STEEL FRC

% of Fibers by Volum	Tensile strength Kgf/cm² (psi)		Comp. Strength Kgf/cm²(psi)
	7 day	28 day	28 day
0	15(214.3)	25(357.1)	280(4000)
0.5	17(242.9)	38(542.9)	300(4285.7)
1.0	12.5(178.6)	45(642.9)	305(4357.1)
1.5	12(171.4)	46(657.1)	307(4385.7)
2.0	10.0(142.9)	43(614.3)	310(4428.6)

TABLE 2 — COMPARISON OF TEST RESULTS FOR STEEL FRC

	Present Study	Ref.1	Ref.2
Max. Increase In Tensile Strength	85%	80%	70%

TABLE 3 — TENSILE STRENGTH OF GLASS FRC

% of Fibers by Volume	Tensile Strength Kgf/cm² (psi)		
	Present Study		Ref.3 28 day
	7 day	28 day	
0	14.4(205.7)	24(342.9)	20.2(288.6)
0.5	21(300)	30(428.6)	31.5(450)
1.0	23(328.6)	35(500)	30.3(432.9)
1.5	22.3(318.6)	37.1(530)	-

TABLE 4 — TENSILE AND COMPRESSIVE STRENGTHS OF PFRC

% of Fibers by Volume	Tensile Strength Kgf/cm² (psi)		Comp. Strength Kgf/cm² 28 day
	7 day	28 day	
0	15(214.3)	23(328.6)	282(4028.6)
0.5	19(271.4)	29(414.3)	280(4000)
1.0	20.4(291.4)	36(514.3)	278(3971.4)
1.5	18.5(264.3)	40(571.4)	275(3928.6)
2.0	14.5(267.1)	35(500)	270(3857.1)
2.5	10(142.9)	32(457.1)	265(3785.7)

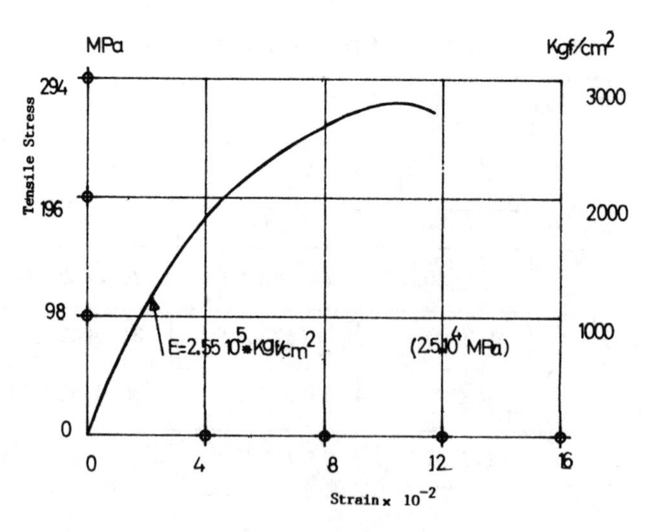

Fig. 1—Polypropylene fiber stress-strain curve

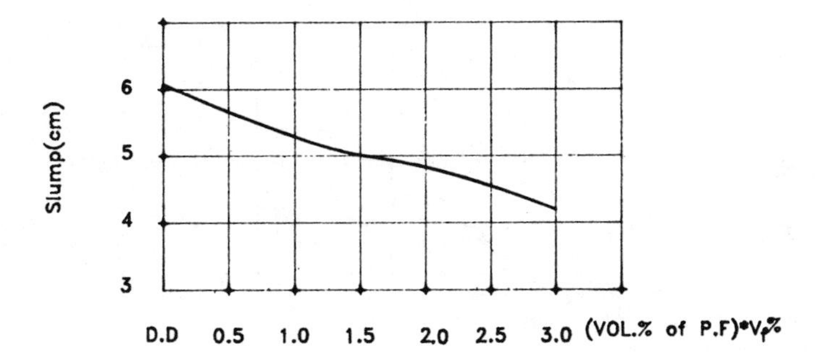

Fig. 2—Slump versus volumetric percent of PF

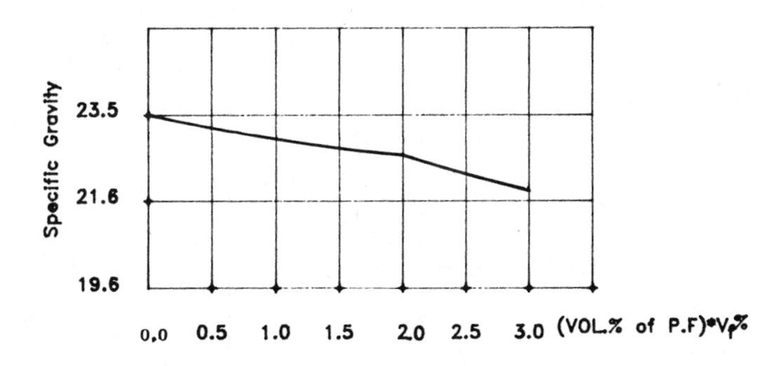

Fig. 3—Specific gravity versus volumetric percent of PF

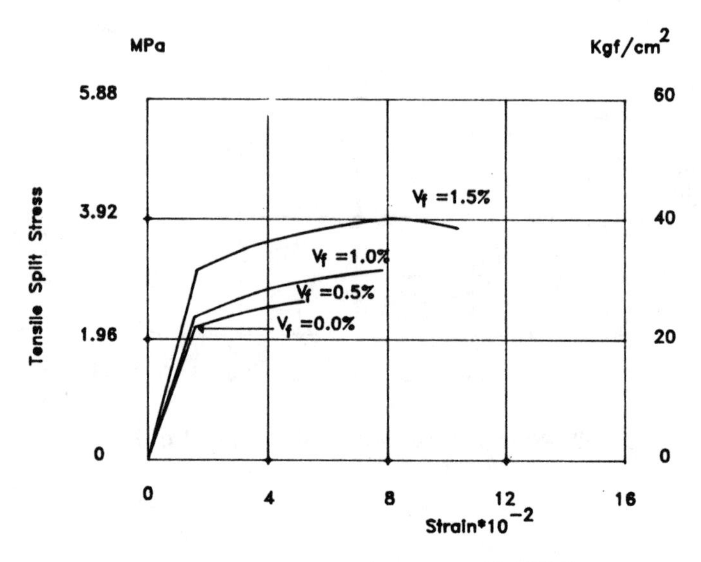

Fig. 4—Stress-strain curves of PFRC

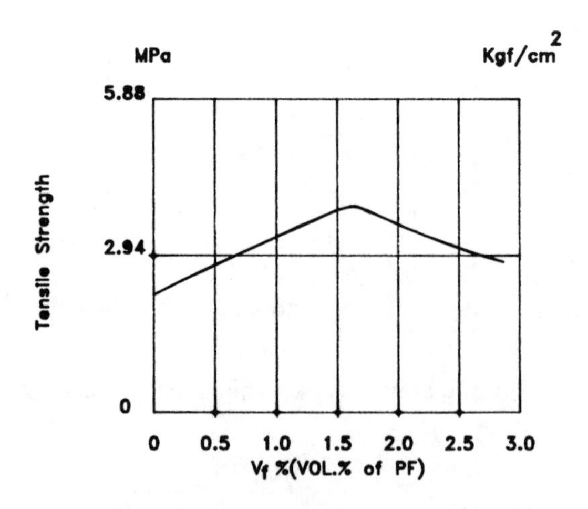

Fig. 5—Tensile strength versus volume percent of PF

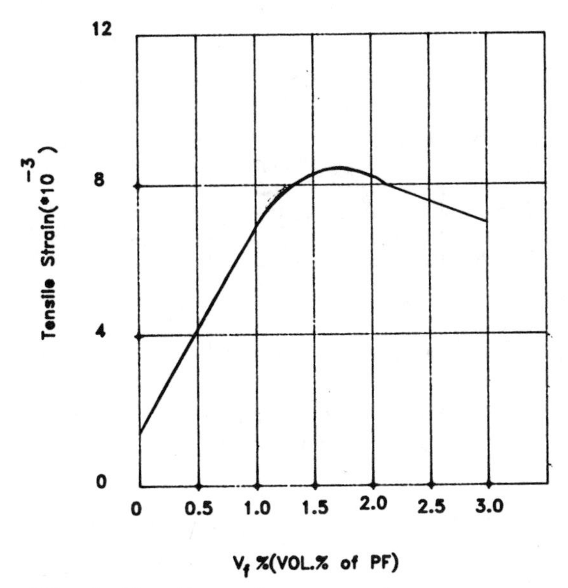

Fig. 6—Tensile strain versus volume percent of PF

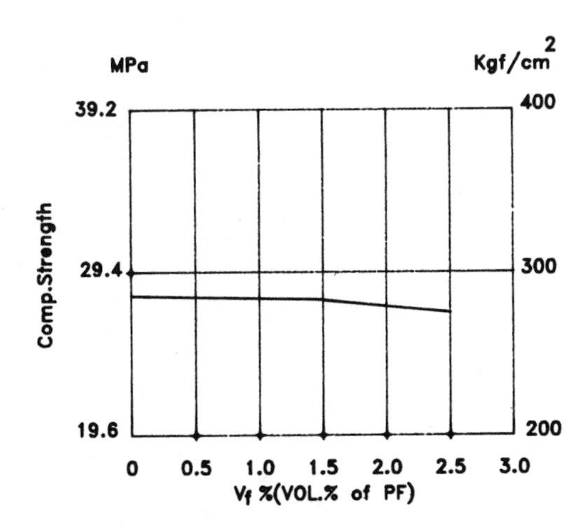

Fig. 7—Compressive strength versus volume percent of PF

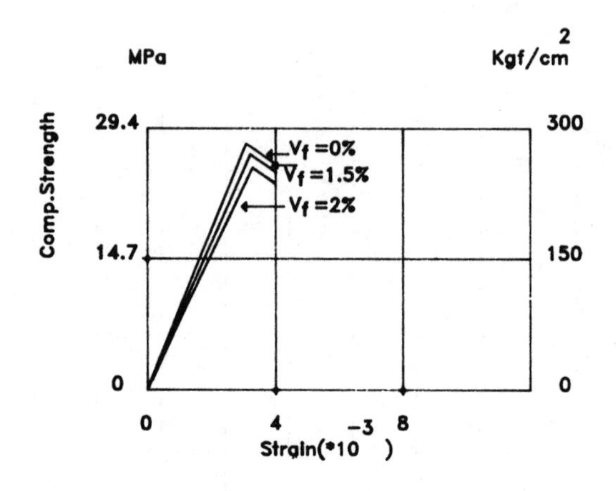

Fig. 8—Compressive strength versus strain

SP 142-5

Durability Characteristics of Cellulose Fiber Reinforced Cement Composites

by P. Soroushian and S. Marikunte

Synopsis: Relatively low-cost and energy efficient materials with desirable short-term mechanical properties can be constructed using cellulose fibers as cement reinforcement. There are, however, concerns regarding the long-term performance of cellulose fiber reinforced cement composites; some cellulose fibers tend to disintegrate in the alkaline environment of cement. The growth of cement hydration products within the hollow cellulose fibers may also lead to excessive fiber-to-matrix bonding and brittle failure after exposure to natural weathering. This paper presents the results of an experimental study concerned with the long-term performance of cellulose fiber reinforced cement composites. Cellulose fiber reinforced cement composites were investigated using accelerated weathering conditions representing repeated wetting and drying of materials in outside exposure conditions. The cement composites considered in this investigation incorporated 2% mass fractions of kraft pulp. Comprehensive replicated flexural test data was generated for various test ages at different wetting-drying cycles and was analyzed statistically. The analysis of variance and multiple comparison techniques were employed in order to derive reliable conclusions regarding the effect of accelerated wetting-drying cycles on the flexural strength and toughness characteristics of cellulose fiber reinforced cement composites. The results generated in this study showed, at 95% level of confidence, that accelerated ageing under repeated wetting-drying cycles had negligible effects on flexural strength, but led to reduced toughness and embrittlement of cellulose fiber reinforced cement composites.

Keywords: Cellulose fibers; cements; composite materials; durability; flexure; mechanical properties; reinforced concretes; strength; toughness; weathering; wetting and drying tests

Parviz Soroushian is an Associate Professor of Civil Engineering at Michigan State University. He received his Ph.D. in 1983 from Cornell University, and his specialty is in Concrete Materials and Technology. He has authored more than fifty papers in this area and serves on a number of ACI and TRB Technical Committees.

Shashidhara Marikunte is a Research Associate in the Department of Civil and Environmental Engineering at Michigan State University. He received his Ph.D. in 1992 from Michigan State University, and his research interest is in concrete materials, structures and structural mechanics.

INTRODUCTION

Cellulose fibers have been used for many years as processing fibers in the production of thin-sheet asbestos cement products. Recent studies have shown that the reinforcement action of cellulose fibers in cementitious matrices is quite good relative to other fibers such as glass [1].

Cellulose fibers derived from softwood and hardwood, being fairly strong and stiff as well as cheap and plentiful with relatively low energy demand are particularly suited for the reinforcement of thin-sheet cement products [2, 3]. Cellulose fibers are effective in increasing the fracture energy of cementitious matrices, and also in enhancing the tensile and flexural strength, toughness, and impact resistance of the material [1, 4, 5]. These improvements are achieved mainly through the stopping and deflection of micro-cracks by fibers, and also through the pull-out action of fibers at cracks.

Cellulose fiber reinforced cement composites have found commercial applications for the production of flat and corrugated sheets [2, 3]. These thin sheets are commonly used in the interior of buildings. They also have potentials for exterior applications once their durability characteristics in harsh environments is better understood.

OBJECTIVES

It is important to ensure that the improvements in material properties of cement achieved through cellulose fiber reinforcement would be retained over long time periods in actual exposure conditions. Much of the available test data on durability of cellulose fiber-cement composites deal with the use of natural fibers (e. g. sisal and coir) in cement-based materials [6]. The main thrust of this research is to assess the durability characteristics of cement composites reinforced with chemically processed cellulose fibers (kraft pulps).

BACKGROUND

A key concern with the use of cellulose fiber reinforced cement composites relates to the long-term durability of fibers in cement, particularly when the product is used in severe exposure conditions. Much of the available test data on durability of cellulose fiber-cement composites deals with the use of natural fibers (e. g. sisal and coir). Accelerated wetting-drying (rain-heat) test results on natural fiber reinforced concrete cause considerable drop in flexural strength and toughness with ageing (see Figure 1) [6]. This can be attributed mainly to the attack on the lignin content of natural fibers by the alkaline pore water of concrete. The alkaline pore water in concrete reacts with the lignin and hemicellulose existing in the middle lamellae of cellulose fibers, thus weakening the link between the individual fiber cells which constitute the natural fibers (Figure 2). Outside exposure conditions increase the moisture movements needed for alkaline pore water to reach and progressively decompose the natural fibers leading to the embrittlement of the composite material. Cycles of wetting-drying seem to provide a particularly aggressive environment for cellulose fiber reinforced cement composites, where rapid transport of alkaline pore water to the embedded fibers and the removal of the decomposition products from fibers are facilitated. Partial success in control of alkaline attack on cellulose fibers has been achieved through the reduction of the alkalinity of cement environment by the use of pozzolanic admixtures [6].

Cellulose fibers obtained by chemical pulping processes are the dominant types used for the production of thin-sheet cement products in developed countries. These cellulose fibers contain negligible amounts of lignin and are thus expected to better withstand alkaline attack in cement. There are, however, other ageing mechanisms which may lead to the embrittlement of cellulose fiber reinforced cement composites. In particular, in the presence of moisture, the gradual filling of the fiber cell cores with hydration products and the densification of matrix in the vicinity of fibers [7] may encourage brittle breakage of fibers under stress, leading to the embrittlement of cellulose fiber reinforced cement composites; a similar phenomenon is partly responsible for the embrittlement of glass fiber reinforced cement composites under long-term environmental effects. This phenomenon, in the case of chemical pulps with low lignin contents, can lead to increased flexural strength, modulus of elasticity and reduced flexural toughness of cellulose fiber-cement composites.[8]

EXPERIMENTAL PROGRAM

The cellulose fibers used in this investigation were Southern Softwood Kraft (SSK) [9]. Some key properties of this cellulose fiber are presented in Table 1. Canadian Standard Freeness (CSF) in this Table represents the level of refinement of fibers achieved through mechanical beating. The refined (beaten) fibers have exposed fibrils on their surfaces, which help in the development of mechanical bonding. A lower CSF is indicative of a higher refinement (beating) level. An important consideration in the refinement of cellulose fibers is to optimize the refinement level such that the fiber-to-matrix bond strength is increased to the point where flexural strength gain is not accompanied with substantial loss in the toughness characteristics of the composite materials [10, 11].

The fiber mass fraction and matrix mix proportions used in this study are presented in Table 2. The matrix contained equal amounts of cement and silica sand (particle size 0.15 to 0.6 mm, 0.006 to 0.024 in). The water and superplasticizer (only for fibrous mixture, superplasticizer/cement = 0.01) content were adjusted to achieve reasonable fresh mix workability characteristics represented by a flow (ASTM C-230) of 55% to 65% at 1 minute after mixing.

Thin-sheet cellulose fiber composites were cast in this study using a regular mortar mixer. The mixing procedure adopted is as follows: (1) add cement and 70 percent of water, and mix at low speed (140 RPM) for about 1 minute or until a uniform mixture is achieved; (2) gradually add the fibers and the remainder of water into the mixture as the mixer is running at low speed (over a period of 2-5 minutes depending on the fiber content), taking care that no fiber balls are formed; and (3) turn the mixer speed to medium (285 RPM) and mix for 1 minute, stop the mixer and wait for 1 minute, and then finalize the process by mixing at high speed (450 RPM) for another minute. This production process is suited for composites with relatively low fiber contents. In this study the mechanisms of ageing in cellulose fiber-cement composites are investigated using composites with a relatively low fiber mass fraction of 2%.

The fresh fibrous cement mixtures were tested for: (1) flow (ASTM C-230); (2) air content and unit weight (ASTM C-185); and (3) setting time by penetration resistance (ASTM C-403).

Panel specimens (280 mm x 400 mm x 10 mm,11 in. x 15.5 in. x 0.40 in.) were manufactured from each mix. All the specimens were compacted by external vibration and were kept inside molds underneath wet burlap covered with a plastic sheet for 24 hours. They were then demolded and moist cured for 5 days before being air cured in a regular laboratory environment of about 40 to 60% RH and 19 to 25 deg. C (66 to 77 deg. F) up to the age of 28 days, when the accelerated ageing tests were initiated.

An accelerated wetting-drying test procedure was developed in order to study the ageing behavior of cellulose fibers under the environmental effects stimulating the alkaline pore water attack on cellulose fibers (e. g. conditions involving repeated exposure to rain and sun shine). For this purpose an accelerated wetting-drying test chamber (Climate box) [6] was developed. The 10 mm (0.40 in.) thick panel specimens were subjected in the climate box to moisture by spraying for 1/2 hour until the capillary pores were filled with pore water; the panels were then heated to reach 82 deg. C (180 deg. F) and the temperature was maintained at this level for a sufficiently long period (5 1/2 hours) to dry out the capillary pore system. Under these conditions the fibers embedded in the specimens come in contact with the alkaline pore water of cement during the moistening phase, the decomposition products which are formed as a result of the reaction between the fiber components and the pore water, are transported away from the fiber during the drying phase.

Six panel specimens were subjected to this accelerated ageing test. After 0, 12, 24, 30, 60 and 120 cycles one panel specimen was taken out and minimum of ten flexural specimens (38.1 mm x 152.4 mm x 10 mm, 1.5 in. x 6 in. x 0.4 in.) were cut out using a diamond saw. Flexural tests were then performed according to Japanese specification JCI-SF [12]. The Japanese method of measuring flexural deflections (Figure 3) is particularly effective in reducing errors associated with rigid body movements of the specimen and local deformations at the supports and loading points.

An important consideration in flexural tests performed on fiber reinforced cement composites is the measurement of energy absorption capacity, defined as the area underneath the load-deflection curve. The Japanese fixtures which monitor flexural deflections during the test give accurate results for energy absorption calculations. According to the Japanese specification JCI-SF 4, flexural toughness is defined as the area underneath the flexural load-deflection curve up to a deflection equal to the span length divided by 150, which is 0.76 mm (.03 in.) in the flexural tests of this investigation.The unaged specimens (at 0 cycles of wetting-drying) were also subjected to the void content, specific gravity and water absorption tests (ASTM C-642).

TEST RESULTS AND DISCUSSIONS

The test results are presented in two parts. First the results regarding the effects of cellulose fiber on the water requirement, setting time, unit weight, air content, permeable void content, specific gravity and water absorption capacity of cement based materials are briefly reviewed. Then the experimentally observed effects of fiber content and accelerated ageing on the flexural behavior of cellulose fiber reinforced cement composites are discussed and the results of statistical analysis of accelerated wetting-drying test data are presented.

Table 2 presents water requirements (for achieving comparable levels of workability represented by flow, (ASTM C-230), and the average values and ranges (obtained in two replicated tests) for air content, water absorption, and setting time of plain and cellulose fiber reinforced cement composites. The water requirement was observed to increase from 0.3 for plain mortar to 0.43 for the mix containing 2% mass fraction of kraft fibers. Kraft fibers, being smaller in diameter, have relatively large surface areas and thus require more water to wet surfaces and achieve reasonable workability levels.

The setting time of mixtures is observed to increase with the addition of fibers (see Table 2). The initial setting time increased by as much as 25% and the final setting time by 39% with 2% mass fraction of kraft pulp.

Cellulose fibers are observed to reduce the specific gravity of fresh cement-based materials (see Table 2). The reduction in specific gravity was 12% when 2% mass fraction of kraft pulp was added. This may be attributed in part to the increased air content in the presence of fibers. The increase in fresh mix and hardened material air contents were 7% and 6%, respectively, with the addition of kraft pulp at 2% mass fraction. The increase in air content could be attributed to the difficulty in compacting cement composites incorporating fibers, which leads to increased entrapped air.

The specific gravity of hardened cement based materials is observed to decrease with the addition of fibers (see Table 2). At 2% fiber mass content the fiber reinforced composites had specific gravity of about 13% below that of plain matrix; similar trends were observed in the fresh mix specific gravity.

The water absorption capacity of the cement based materials is observed to increase with the addition of fibers (see Table 2). The increase in water absorption over that of plain cementitious matrix was 23% at 2% mass fraction. This could be attributed to the higher void content of matrix and also the relatively high absorption of water by cellulose fibers.

In order to see if there is any relationship between the fresh mix air content and the hardened material void content, specific gravity and water absorption, correlation coefficients were calculated and analyzed statistically. The results indicated a strong correlation (at 95% level of confidence) for all pairs of these properties.

FLEXURAL PERFORMANCE

The effects of cellulose fiber reinforcement on the flexural load-deflection behavior of cement-based materials are shown in Figures 4(a) and (b) before and after accelerated wetting-drying tests, respectively. The effects of cellulose fiber reinforcement on flexural strength and toughness for plain matrix and cellulose fiber reinforced composite at different wetting-drying cycles are presented in Tables 3, 4 and figures 5 and 6, respectively.

One may derive the following conclusions from the test data regarding the effects of fiber addition and ageing cycles on flexural strength and toughness.

1. The flexural strength of unaged fiber reinforced cement composites doubled and flexural toughness increased by more than 20 times over that of plain specimens.

2. In aged specimens (after 120 cycles of wetting-drying), the specimens with 2% cellulose fiber had flexural strength doubled and toughness increased by 8 times, when compared to plain specimens.

3. Wetting-drying cycles tend to increase the flexural strength of both plain and fibrous specimens. The increase in flexural strength after 120 cycles of wetting and drying was 39% for plain cement mortar and 12% for cellulose fiber reinforced cement composite. Analysis of variance of test results at 95% level of confidence, however, indicated that, considering the random experimental errors, changes in flexural strength of plain mortar and fibrous cement composites with wetting-drying cycles were not significant. Statistical time-series analysis with regression forecasting predicted continued increase in flexural strength with increased numbers of wetting-drying cycles for plain mortar as well as fibrous composites.

4. Accelerated wetting-drying cycles caused a drop in flexural toughness for both plain and fibrous specimens. On the average, drops of 44% and 77% for plain mortar and fiber reinforced composites, respectively, were observed after 120 cycles of wetting and drying. Analysis of variance of test data confirmed the significance of drop in flexural toughness only for fibrous composites at 95% level of confidence. In this case, it was also noted that, at 95% level of confidence, the initial 12 cycles of wetting-drying

caused significant drop in flexural toughness; consequent cycles caused only gradual drops in toughness. Statistical time-series analysis with regression forecasting predicted continued decrease in flexural toughness with increased numbers of wetting-drying cycles for plain mortar as well as fibrous composites.

SUMMARY AND CONCLUSIONS

An experimental study was conducted on cellulose fiber reinforced cement composites in order to assess the effects of accelerated weathering conditions representing repeated wetting and drying in outside exposure conditions. The cement composites incorporated 2% mass fraction of kraft pulp, and were manufactured using a conventional mortar mixer. Comprehensive test data was generated for various ages at different wetting-drying cycles and was analyzed statistically. The effects of cellulose fiber reinforcement on some physical properties of cement mortars in the fresh and hardened state were also investigated. The following conclusions could be derived from the generated test results.

1. Cellulose fiber reinforcement leads to increased water requirement, setting time, void content and water absorption capacity of cementitious materials; specific gravity was reduced in the presence of cellulose fibers;

2. The flexural strength and toughness of cellulose fiber reinforced cement composites, even after ageing, were higher than those of plain cementitious materials;

3. Repeated wetting-drying cycles caused an increase in the average flexural strength of both plain and fiber reinforced mortars. Analysis of variance test results at 95% level of confidence, however, indicated that the increase in flexural strength with ageing was not significant.

4. Repeated wetting-drying cycles tend to reduce the average flexural toughness of both plain and fibrous specimens. Analysis of variance of test results at 95% level of confidence, however, indicated that the reduction in toughness is significant only in fibrous composites.

5. Statistical time-series analysis with regression forecasting predicted continued improvement in flexural strength and drop in flexural toughness with increased number of wetting-drying cycles.

ACKNOWLEDGMENT

Financial support for the performance of this research project was provided by the U. S. Department of Agriculture (Eastern Hardwood Utilization Program) and the Research Excellence Fund of the State of Michigan. The fibers used in this project were provided by The Procter and Gamble Cellulose Company. These contributions are gratefully acknowledged. The authors are also thankful to Dr. Otto Suchsland from the Forestry Department of Michigan State University for his continuous support of research activities in this area of cellulose fiber-cement composites. The technical support provided by the Composite Materials and Structure Center of Michigan State University and also by Mr. Siavosh Ravanbakhsh are gratefully acknowledged.

REFERENCES

1. Vinson, K. D. and Daniel, J. I., "Specialty Cellulose Fibers for Cement Reinforcement", Thin Section Fiber Reinforced Concrete and Ferrocement, American Concrete Institute Publication SP-124, 1990, pp. 1-18.

2. Coutts, R. S. P., "Sticks and Stones", Forest Products Newsletter, (CSIRO Division of Chemical and Wood Technology (Australia), Vol. 2, No. 1, 1988, pp. 1-4.

3. CSIRO, "New-A Wood Fiber Cement Building Board", CSIRO Industrial Research News (Australia), 1981, pp.146.

4. Coutts, R. S. P., "Air-Cured Wood Pulp, Fiber/Cement Mortars," Composites, Vol. 18, No. 4, Sept. 1987, pp. 325-328.

5. Soroushian, P. and Marikunte, S.," Reinforcement of Cement-Based Materials with Cellulose Fibers", Thin Section Fiber Reinforced Concrete and Ferrocement, Publication SP-124, American Concrete Institute, 1990, pp. 99-124.

6. Gram, H. E., "Durability of Natural Fibers in Concrete," Swedish Cement and Concrete Research Institute, Stockholm, 1983, pp. 255.

7. Bentur. A. and Akers, S. S. S., "The Microstructure and Ageing of Cellulose Fiber Reinforced Cement Composites Cured in a Normal Environment," International Journal of Cement Composites and Light Weight Concrete, Vol. 11, No. 2, May 1989, pp. 99-109.

8. Akers, S. A. S. and Studinka, J. B., "Ageing Behavior of Cellulose Fiber Cement Composites in Natural Weathering and Accelerated Tests," International Journal of Cement and Light Weight Concrete, Vol. 11, No. 2, May 1989, pp. 93-97.

9. Procter and Gamble Cellulose Paper Grade Wood Pulp HP-11. Technical Bulletin, Memphis, Tennessee.

10. Coutts, R. S. P. and Ridikas, D., "Refined Wood Fiber Cement Products", Appita, Vol. 35, No. 5, March 1982, pp.

11. Coutts, R. S. P., "Autoclaved Beaten Wood Fiber Reinforced Cement Composites", Composites, Vol. 15, No. 2, 1984, pp. 139-143.

12. Japanese Concrete Institute, "JCI Standards for Test Methods of Fiber Reinforced Concrete", Report No. JCI-SF, 1984, pp. 68.

TABLE 1 — PROPERTIES OF CELLULOSE FIBERS

Type	Species	Average Length	CSF*
Kraft Pulp	Softwood	3.0 mm	700

* CSF = Canadian Standard Freeness

TABLE 2 — MIXTURE PROPORTIONS, FRESH MIX AND HARDENED MATERIAL PHYSICAL PROPERTIES

Mix	water/ Cement	Flow (%)	Setting Time (min.)		Air Content (%)		Specific Gravity (gm/cc)		Water Absorption (%)
			Initial	Final	Fresh	Hardened	Fresh	Hardened	
Plain	0.30	58±1	186±3	210±3	21.07±0.25	22.75±0.30	2.01±0.014	2.00±0.001	11.07±0.12
2% Kraft Pulp	0.43	48±1	233±3	293±4	22.50±0.26	24.18±0.07	1.77±0.018	1.75±0.041	13.66±0.06

TABLE 3 — FLEXURAL STRENGTH TEST RESULTS (MPa)

Mix	Wetting-Drying Cycles					
	0	**12**	**24**	**30**	**60**	**120**
Plain	2.2252 1.9280 0.9491 2.6479 1.5301 1.6169 0.7711 3.7156 1.5532 1.7423 **Mean** 1.8692 **Std. Dev.** 0.8510	2.2202 3.4488 1.5514 2.7662 2.9731 2.3236 4.9492 3.1290 3.0545 1.3376 **Mean** 2.7752 **Std. Dev.** 1.0270	3.9205 2.9097 2.8097 1.9499 3.3227 2.9517 3.9584 4.9616 1.2949 1.1273 **Mean** 2.9221 **Std. Dev.** 1.2121	3.8308 3.1510 3.3234 3.0503 3.3302 4.3480 1.7072 2.9097 2.3098 1.5720 **Mean** 2.9462 **Std. Dev.** 0.8750	9.4648 1.2983 3.0890 2.1099 10.405 6.9081 2.7511 3.7702 0.8901 1.5238 **Mean** 4.2211 **Std. Dev.** 4.1428	3.0890 4.1997 2.9855 4.8382 0.7357 4.8892 2.2477 6.2896 2.2202 6.7688 **Mean** 3.8260 **Std. Dev.** 1.9113
2% Kraft Pulp	6.2813 6.0373 5.2919 4.9409 6.0683 4.2590 5.7608 5.4002 5.5670 5.1175 **Mean** 5.4726 **Std. Dev.** 0.6095	7.7762 4.5362 5.4698 3.6840 5.5250 5.4339 5.7587 5.4077 5.6539 6.5213 **Mean** 5.5767 **Std. Dev.** 1.0798	6.7557 4.8175 5.7276 5.0947 4.6638 5.0243 6.9157 5.9138 4.8844 5.7304 **Mean** 5.5525 **Std. Dev.** 0.8010	8.7497 6.7199 5.3243 6.1572 7.0267 4.7486 4.7458 4.5183 5.2912 6.5771 **Mean** 5.7780 **Std. Dev.** 1.4482	5.8449 6.8123 4.3252 5.4395 5.2526 7.1108 8.4029 6.8329 5.1726 4.1777 **Mean** 5.9304 **Std. Dev.** 1.3294	7.7086 4.4349 3.9729 7.2604 8.3843 6.0352 6.7640 4.0832 5.6753 6.7088 **Mean** 6.1028 **Std. Dev.** 1.5459

TABLE 4 — FLEXURAL TOUGHNESS TEST RESULTS (N mm)

Mix	Wetting-Drying Cycles					
	0	**12**	**24**	**30**	**60**	**120**
Plain	1.1299	2.2598	3.3897	3.3897	2.2598	0.0000
	1.1299	2.2598	7.9092	0.0000	0.0000	1.1299
	1.1299	1.1299	1.1299	0.0000	0.0000	0.0000
	3.3897	1.1299	1.1299	3.3897	0.0000	5.6495
	2.2598	3.3897	2.2598	0.0000	3.3897	3.3897
	3.3897	12.428	2.2598	5.6494	4.5196	2.2598
	1.1299	3.3897	7.9092	3.3897	2.2598	2.2598
	7.9092	2.2598	0.0000	3.3897	0.0000	0.0000
	2.2598	1.1299	0.0000	2.2598	1.1299	1.1299
	1.1299	3.3897	1.1299	1.1299	3.3897	0.0000
	Mean	**Mean**	**Mean**	**Mean**	**Mean**	**Mean**
	2.8247	3.2767	2.7117	2.2598	1.6948	1.5818
	Std. Dev.	**Std. Dev.**	**Std. Dev.**	**Std. Dev.**	**Std. Var.**	**Std. Dev.**
	2.1467	3.3444	2.9264	1.9208	1.7061	1.8643
2% Kraft Pulp	132.17	46.325	46.325	65.534	39.546	12.428
	93.781	16.948	24.857	36.156	33.897	14.686
	62.144	23.728	11.299	29.377	27.117	19.208
	36.156	44.066	36.156	14.688	23.728	7.9092
	59.884	56.495	29.377	32.767	5.6495	5.6495
	48.585	28.247	69.793	23.728	2.2958	10.169
	83.612	30.507	48.585	18.078	7.9092	30.507
	65.533	45.196	16.948	23.728	11.298	6.7793
	65.533	39.546	29.377	24.858	16.948	20.338
	32.767	13.559	29.377	28.247	12.429	13.559
	Mean	**Mean**	**Mean**	**Mean**	**Mean**	**Mean**
	68.019	34.462	34.009	29.603	18.078	14.236
	Std. Dev.	**Std. Dev.**	**Std. Dev.**	**Std. Dev.**	**Std. Dev.**	**Std. Dev.**
	29.388	14.033	16.553	14.225	12.530	7.6832

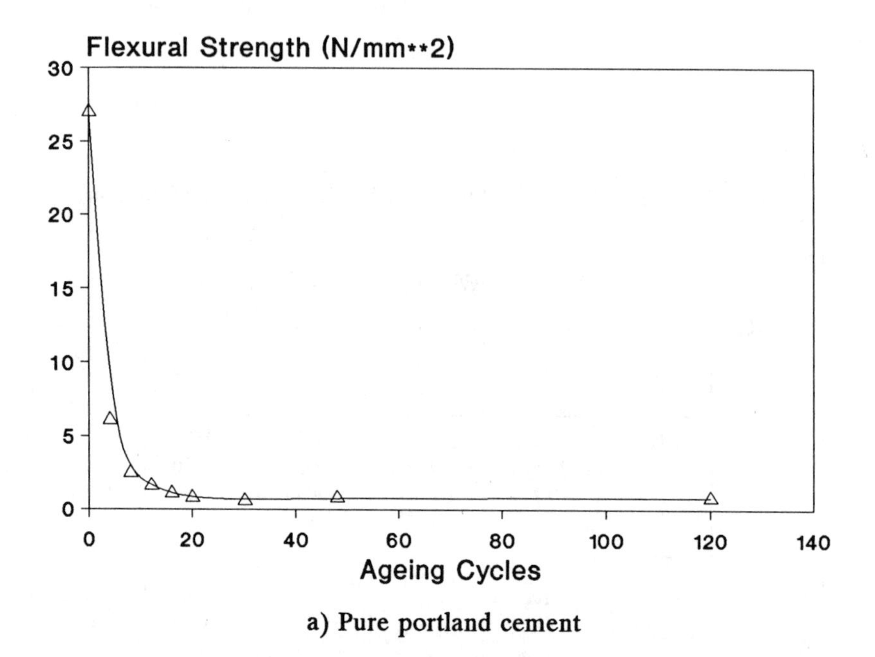

a) Pure portland cement

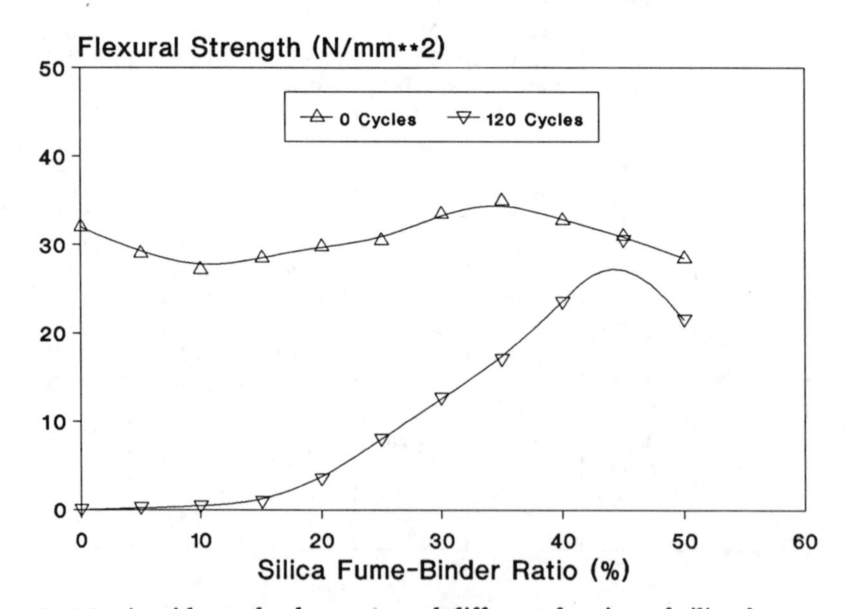

b) Matrix with portland cement and different fraction of silica fume

Fig. 1—Flexural strength of the sisal fiber reinforced concrete after wetting-drying cycles [6]

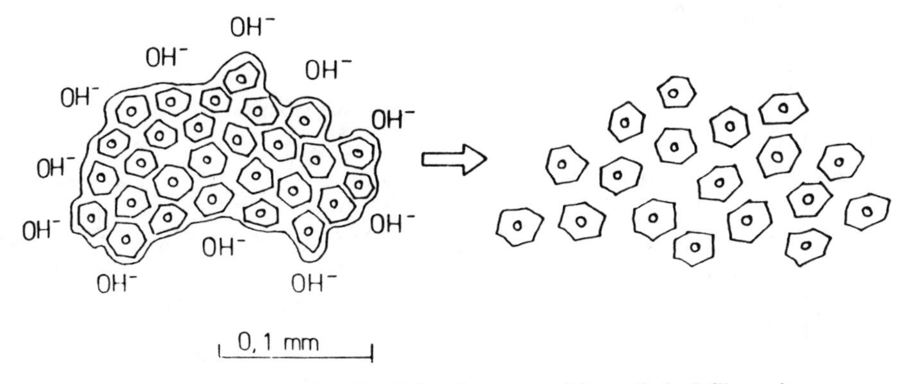

Fig. 2—Schematic sketch of the decomposition of sisal fibers in the alkaline pore water of concrete [6]

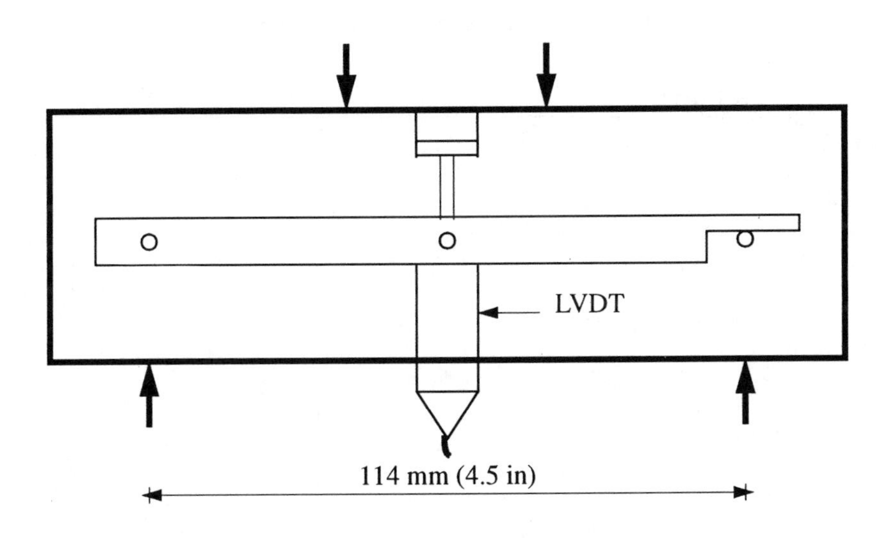

Fig. 3—Japanese standard flexural test set-up [12]

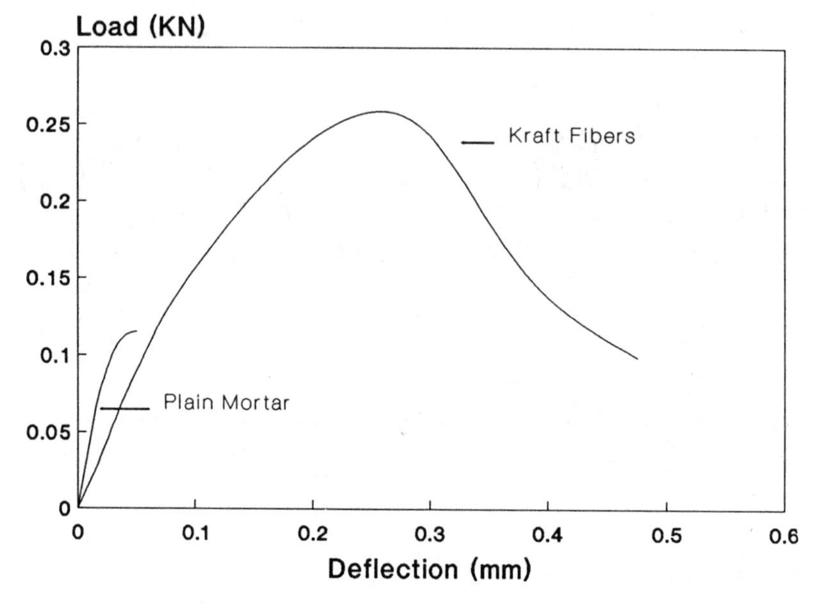

a) Unaged composites (0 cycles of wetting-drying)

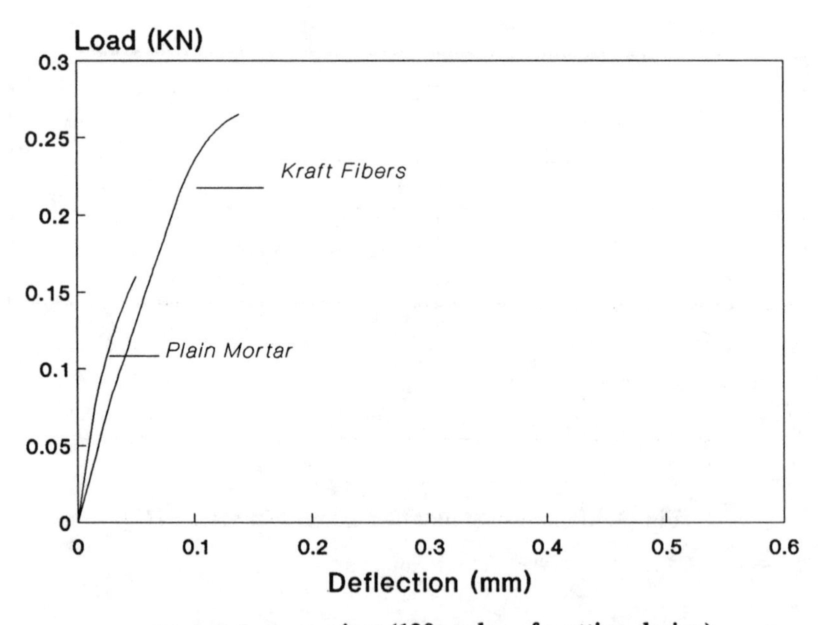

b) Aged composites (120 cycles of wetting-drying)

Fig. 4—Typical flexural load-deflection behavior

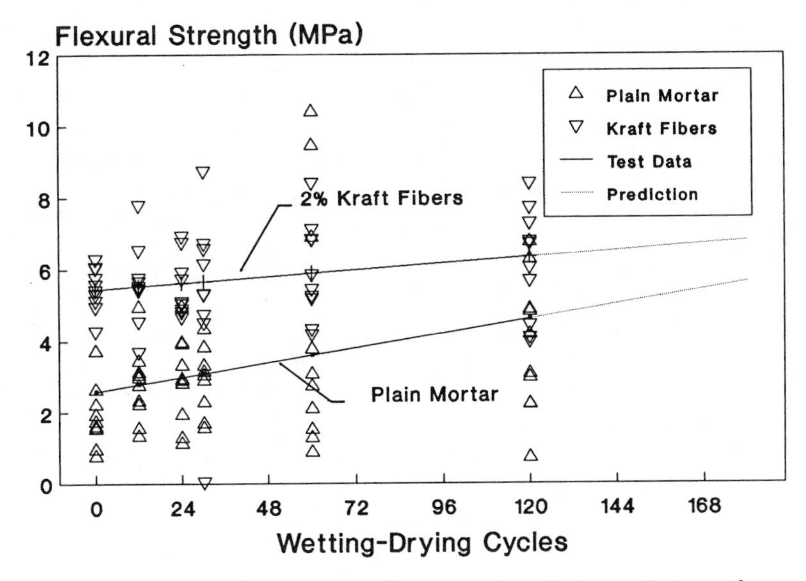

Fig. 5—Effects of accelerated weathering on flexural strength (regression analysis)

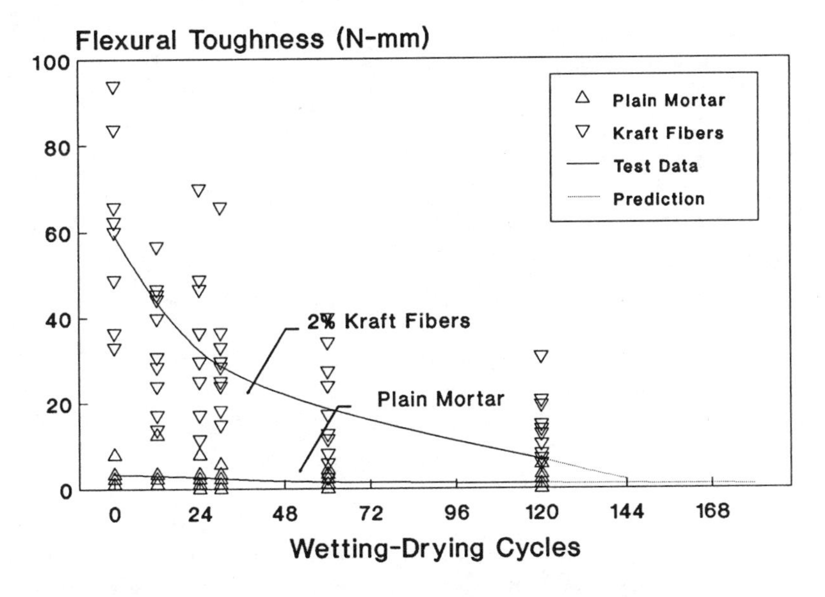

Fig. 6—Effects of accelerated weathering on flexural toughness (regression analysis)

SP 142-6

Carbon Fiber Cements: Structure, Performance, Applications and Research Needs

by N. Banthia

Synopsis: The improvements in the performance characteristics of cements due to carbon fiber reinforcement have been described. In particular, the structure, physical properties, mechanical behavior and durability aspects of carbon-cement composites using pitch-based fibers have been discussed. The various possible applications of these composites in structural and non-structural applications have been enumerated. The future research needs have been identified.

Keywords: Carbon fibers; composite materials; cracking (fracturing); durability; fiber reinforced concretes; mechanical properties; tensile strength; toughness

---

Associate Professor, Dept. of Civil Engineering, University of British Columbia, 2324 Main Mall, Vancouver, B.C., Canada V6T 1Z4

INTRODUCTION

Cement-based materials are undoubtedly the most used and most researched construction materials today. These inorganic materials are abundant, inexpensive and easy to produce and handle. These seemingly simple materials, however, are also very complex and far-reaching research efforts are underway (1,2).

Perhaps, the most important challenge encountered by the research community investigating cementitious materials is the poor tensile strength and low fracture toughness of these materials. These undesirable attributes lead to an easy nucleation and propagation of cracks restricting the range of their use. One effective method of improving the mechanical behavior of cementitious materials is by "fiber reinforcement". However, research conducted so far with large steel fibers (20-60 mm in length and about 0.3-1.0 mm in diameter) has indicated that although the toughness improvements are significant, the tensile strength of the composite is not greatly different from that of the host matrix (3,4). The inability of the large fibers to improve the tensile strength of the cement-based materials is often explained on the basis of the fact that tensile failure is caused by progressive extension of distributed microcracks that eventually coalesce into macrocracks and for the usual volume fractions, the large steel fibers are too far apart to blunt, arrest or modify these microcracks in any significant way (5,6). For an improvement in the tensile strength extremely fine fibers are needed. These fine fibers (collectively called "micro-fibers") have their diameters of the same order as the size of the cement particles ($<25\ \mu m$) and large volume fractions can be easily mixed. Carbon fiber is one of the most commonly used micro-fiber.

The advantage of carbon fiber reinforcement over steel, polypropylene or glass fibers is in finishability, thermal resistance, weatherability, ability to mix high volume fractions and long-term chemical stability in alkaline and other chemically aggressive environments. Further, the use of carbon fibers is not associated with any potential health hazards as does the use of asbestos fibers. These benefits along with the reported improvements in the mechanical properties make carbon fiber reinforcement a propitious proposition.

Historically, the first uses of carbon fibers in cement-based matrices were in the form of continuous high modulus polyacrylonitrile (PAN) fibers (7), whereby significant improvements in the mechanical properties were noted. But, this type of fiber reinforcement did not prevail because of the high cost of these fibers. In the early 1980s, the interest in the use of carbon fibers in cements was revived with the development of inexpensive pitch-based carbon fibers and the reported improvements in the composite properties. Table 1 gives a comparative account of the properties of PAN and pitch-based carbon fibers. This paper deals entirely with the inexpensive pitch-based low modulus carbon fibers in the discontinuous form. Carbon fiber reinforced cements and concretes are often abbreviated as "CFRC".

PRODUCTION OF CFRC

Given the high specific surface area of carbon fibers, the mixing by conventional means is usually difficult. Ordinarily, carbon fibers tend to ball and disperse non-uniformly. Using conventional mortar mixer and no dispersing agent, about 1% carbon fibers by volume may be evenly mixed in a normal ASTM Type I cement paste matrix. With a finer cement (ASTM Type III), however, fiber volume fractions may be increased to about 3% with substantial quantities of superplasticizer (8). Beyond this fiber volume fraction, a suitable dispersing agent is needed. The most commonly used dispersing agents are carboxyl methyl cellulose (9), condensed silica fume (10-11) and ground blast furnace slag (12). For CFRC, a silica-cement ratio of 0.2 or more, and a minimum superplasticizer content of 2% by weight of cement have been suggested (13). Alternatively, the availability of a specialized type mixer (omni-mixer) may facilitate uniform mixing and dispersion even at high fiber volume fractions. Some particular orders in which the ingredients should be introduced in the mixer for a better fiber dispersion have been recognized (9).

The workability of CFRC is often quantified by the *flow index*. The flow index is found to be proportional to the fiber diameter or inversely proportional to the specific surface area of the fibers used. The flow index, as well expected, is also inversely proportional to the fiber volume fraction (9). The flowability of CFRC mixes is not found to depend upon the length of the fibers used (10). Further, the size of the mixer is not found to have a particular effect on the observed flow index, i.e., smaller lab mixers produce flow indices reproducible in the field (9). One interesting observation is the inverse dependence of flow index on the tensile strength of the fiber itself. This dependence, however, stems from the fact that the tensile strength of the fiber, and not that of bulk carbon, is inversely proportional to fiber diameter (based on Griffith's Theory), and the flow index, as mentioned previously, is directly proportional to fiber diameter.

For a good fiber-matrix bond in CFRC, a dense packing of cement particles around the fibers is essential. This may be achieved by using cements with particle sizes less than 45 μm (14). For short carbon fiber composites, ground silica sand may be used as fine aggregate with particle size not exceeding 0.2 mm.

For CFRC mixes in the fresh state, although the flowability is only moderate, proper proportioning and mixing can assure appreciable moldability and finishability. CFRC mixes ordinarily require longer than usual compaction times.

STRUCTURE OF CFRC

Depending on the technique of mixing, carbon fibers can be dispersed in the cementitious matrix in a 3-Dimensional random fashion. Figure 1 shown a fractured surface of CFRC with silica fume used as the dispersant at a relatively low magnification. Good distribution of fibers may be noticed. Figure 2 shows the dense packing of cementitious matrix around the fibers.

The toughening and strengthening mechanisms furnished by carbon fibers in cementitious matrices is not so well understood. However, as seen in Figures 2 and 3, the operative mechanisms appear to be composed of fiber pull-out, fiber fracture and even a combination of the two modes where fiber fracture occurs within the embedded length and fiber pull-out follows. The intricate nature of the microstructural features insinuates the complexities involved in explaining the micromechanical and macromechanical observations. One can easily appreciate the need to conduct systematic and extensive microstructural investigations on CFRC with the aim of optimizing the composite properties, particularly the fracture behavior.

The carbon-cement composites produced using commercially available carbon fibers are distinctive in the sense that the number of fibers in a unit square centimeter may well exceed a few thousand. Compared with conventional steel fiber composites with 0.3-1.0 mm diameter steel fibers, at equal fiber volume fractions, the carbon-cement composites have almost three orders of magnitude greater number of fibers. The difficulties encountered during mixing and the observed distinctive behavior under mechanical loading all have their origins in this fact.

MECHANICAL PROPERTIES OF CFRC

Tensile Behavior

Uni-axial tensile tests on carbon fiber reinforced cement paste were conducted by Ohama, Amano and Endo (10) using 3 and 10 mm long fibers. Carbon fiber reinforced cement mortars were tested by Akihama, Suenaga and Banno (15) and Akihama, Suenaga and Nakagawa (16) using 10 mm long fibers. In both cases, the fibers used were 14.5 μm in diameter with a tensile strength of 767 MPa and a modulus of elasticity of 37 GPa. Their results are shown in Figure 4. Note that the curve in the case of paste has been plotted only until the occurrence of peak load. A substantial increase in the strength and toughness in direct tension brought about by the fibers may be noted. The curves for the mortar matrix composites become distinctly bi-linear at a fiber content of about 2% by volume. The somewhat stiffer response of paste matrix composites may be noticed. Such a response may be related to the considerably increased heterogeneity in mortars over pastes that allows for increased pre-peak deformability and non-linearity. Based on the assumption that if the fibers were failing by pull-out, the average fiber length projecting from the fractured surface would be $0.25l$ (l=length of the fiber), Akihama et al (16) argued that since the average projecting length in their case was considerably less than $0.1l$, most of the fibers in their tests had fractured.

Akihama et al (16) also tested lightweight CFRC (specific gravity of 1.0) under monotonic and cyclic tensile loading. Under cyclic loading the envelop of the stress-strain curve was found to resemble the shape of the stress-strain curve under monotonic loading indicating a satisfactory fatigue behavior (Figure 5).

Compressive Behavior

The compressive strength of cement pastes reinforced with carbon fibers was found to be somewhat superior than that of the base matrix (10). The strength was found to increase up to about 3% by volume of carbon fibers followed by a decrease at higher volume fractions. Also, shorter 3 mm fibers were found to impart a better compressive strength than the longer 10 mm fibers. In the case of the mortars reinforced with carbon fibers, Ohama and Amano (13) reported increases in the compressive strength with an increase in the silica fume-cement ratio. The compressive strength of unreinforced mortar, on the other hand, appeared to have the maximum value at a silica fume-cement ratio of 0.4. The quantity of superplasticizer in the mix, on the other hand, was not found to have any influence on the compressive strength. Overall, they concluded that the compressive strength of the mortars is almost unaltered by carbon fiber inclusion. Similar conclusions were drawn by Sheng (8).

The fatigue strength of carbon fiber reinforced alumina cements under a 12 hertz pulsating compressive load was determined by Kanno, Ohama, Kawai and Demura (17). Carbon-cement composites were mixed in vacuum using an omni-mixer with carbon fiber fraction of 4% and then pressure molded under 25 MPa into cylindrical specimens 50 mm by 100 mm. The plotted S-N curves are shown in Figure 6. A significant improvement in the fatigue behavior may be noticed.

Flexural Behavior

One of the simpler ways of studying fracture in CFRC as adopted by Ohama et al (10) and Banthia et al (6) is in flexure. The test setup adopted by Banthia et al is shown in Figure 7. Figures 8 and 9 show the load vs. load point displacement plots obtained. Figure 8 corresponds to 3 and 10 mm fibers (10) and Figure 9 corresponds to 6 mm fibers (6). These curves may be further analyzed by noting the peak elastic load (P_e) at the end of the linear portion of the curve, ultimate load (P_u), and by measuring the area under such a curve to obtain the magnitude of the fracture energy (E_f) consumed in a test as shown in Figure 7 (inset). The values of these quantities appear in Table 2 for the 6 mm fiber. Note that in Table 2, the peak value of the elastic load has been used to obtain the value of the first crack strength. A 3-fold increase in the first crack strength at high fiber volume contents may be noted. More important, perhaps, is the one to two orders of magnitude increase in the fracture energy consumption brought about by the fibers. An attempt to characterize the behavior of CFRC in flexure by *Toughness Indices* (ASTM C1018) has also been made with some success (18). Need is felt to find suitable means of characterizing the behaviour of CFRC under flexure with design considerations in mind.

The mechanical behavior of CFRC in flexure is influenced not only by the length of the fibers used but also by the other factors such as cement matrix strength, fiber elastic modulus, fiber-matrix bond, extent of fiber dispersion, etc. Improvements in the load behavior of CFRC due to polymer modification by styrene-butadiene rubber have also been reported (19).

Scale effects in CFRC load behavior under flexure were studied by Akihama et al (20). They reported a decrease in the flexural strength of CFRC beams as the width and the span increased and proposed a power law for estimating the factored decrease in the flexural strength as a function of specimen *l.d* (span x depth). The influence of curing conditions was studied by Soroushian et al (21) who reported a distinct improvement in the flexural strength of CFRC when cured under hot-water.

Impact Behavior

Ohama et al (10) loaded CFRC plate specimens 100 by 100 by 10 mm under impact on a bed of sand under a consecutive drop of a 80 g steel ball from a height of 20 cm. Number of blows to complete failure were recorded as shown in Figure 10. A remarkable increase in the number of blows due to fiber presence may be noted. Similar tests were performed by Soroushian et al (21) who also reported a notable improvement in the recorded number of blows due to fiber presence.

Instrumented impact tests in uni-axial tension mode were performed by Banthia and Ohama (11) using a trolley mounted specimen support system shown in Figure 11. Instrumentation provided included dynamic load cell in the striking tup, accelerometer on the specimen trolley and a velocity measuring photocell assembly at the base. Figures 12a and 12b show the observed tensile strength and the recorded fracture energies under impact, respectively. The remarkable improvements in the impact resistance may also be noted from the hammer-specimen contact load vs. time pulses of Figure 13 recorded in these impact tests for a hammer approach velocity of 2.3 m/s. A larger area under such curves indicates a bigger loss in the hammer momentum indicating a more energy consuming material.

Bi-axial Bending

One of the important uses of carbon-cement composites is in thin plate-like precast products like roofing sheets, tiles, etc. These products are usually loaded in the transverse direction which introduces bi-axial moments in the material. The material behavior, in such a case, may not be assessed correctly by the uni-axial flexural tests and proper plate tests are needed. Such tests were conducted by Banthia, Sheng and Ohama (22) on circular CFRC plates 200 mm in diameter and 10 mm thick. The simply supported plates were loaded by a transverse concentrated load at the center. The resulting load vs. load point displacement plots are shown in Figure 14. The differences in the load response of the plates (Figure 14) form that of the beams (Figure 9) may also be noticed. One further distinct difference between the beam and the plate behavior was in the manner in which failure occurred. While beams failed by propagation of the crack from the bottom face to the top, the plates, particularly at high volume fractions, failed by punching shear with the loading ball traversing the depth of the plate making a clean hole of the size of the ball itself. This type of failure produced no or very little damage to the rest of the plate and remarkable quantities of energy were absorbed. The observed load-displacement plots for the plates and the beams were further analyzed by means of the *Toughness Indices* (ASTM C1018) at various multiples of first crack displacements (18).

Bond with Old Concrete

One of the possible uses of carbon-cement composites is in thin repairs. Based on the uni-axial tensile tests conducted using the specimens shown in Figure 15, improvements in the apparent adhesion (including all possible modes of failure) have been reported (Figure 16) (23). It was suggested that the improvements in the calculated values of apparent adhesion are better in the case of CFRC because of the finer packing of the different phases due to the high dosages of superplasticizer and the reduced shrinkage cracking at the interface. The increased instances of the inclined cohesive failures observed in case of the CFRC also accounted for the improved apparent adhesion.

PHYSICAL PROPERTIES OF CFRC

Electrical Conductivity

Although cementitious materials are ordinarily poor conductors of electricity, there are instances where a high electrical conductivity is desirable. Carbon fibers being good conductors of electricity, the conductivity of carbon-cement composites is of considerable interest. Potential uses of conductive concrete are in the cathodic protection of reinforced concrete bridge decks as secondary anode systems (24), in conductive panels and also in non-structural applications including consumer electronics and automobiles (25).

Figure 17 shown a plot of the electrical resistivity of carbon fiber reinforced cements as a function of age for various fiber volume fractions (26). A reduction in the resistivity by two to three orders of magnitude may be noticed. It may also be noticed that conductivity improvements are proportional to the fiber volume fraction.

Dimensional Stability

The water absorption and drying shrinkage characteristics of autoclaved carbon fiber reinforced cements are shown in Figures 18a and 18b, respectively (10). It may be noticed that the dimensional stability of carbon-cement composites is superior to unreinforced cement matrix. The drying shrinkage values reduce with an increase in the fiber volume percentage and attain a nearly constant value at the age of 14 days. Results of drying shrinkage tests with carbon fiber reinforced lightweight mortars up to an age of one year have indicated that autoclaving produces the most stable composite (16).

DURABILITY OF CFRC

Superior chemical inertness of carbon fibers over all other high performance fibers is one of the important benefits. The pitch-based fibers are more than 90% elemental carbon and are not corroded in the alkaline cementitious environment like the ordinary glass fibers. Although, the fibers themselves are attacked by strong oxidizing agents such as nitric and sulfuric acids (27), their composites have been found to have no appreciable retrogression either in the strength or in the toughness when subjected to cyclic exposures of weak acids (pH = 4.0) for up to 90 days

(28) as shown in Figure 19. Carbon fibers tolerate heating of up to 2500°C in inert atmospheres but oxidize slowly at 300°C or more.

Limited data with regard to the freeze-thaw resistance of CFRC with tests performed in accordance with ASTM C666 after 300 cycles (Figure 20) have indicated that the diminution of dynamic modulus of elasticity is insignificant (16). However, considerable further effort is needed in this direction aimed at studying air bubble stability, etc., before a confident use of cement composites under the possible action of frost may be made.

APPLICATIONS OF CARBON-CEMENT COMPOSITES

Given the improvements in the mechanical properties of weak and brittle cement matrices by carbon fiber reinforcing and the physical properties of these composites, there are numerous possible uses.

One of the major uses of these composites is in thin precast products like roofing sheets, panels, tiles, curtain walls, ferrocements, wave absorbers, permanent forms, free-access floor panels, and I- and L-shaped beams. The first large scale application of CFRC was in the form of panels with tile cladding in the Al Shaheed Monument in Iraq. CFRC curtain walls have been used in Japan for some time now.

In the cast in place applications, CFRC has potential for use in mortars for external walls especially for structures in seismic regions, for thin repairs, for small machinery foundations, etc. The good conductivity of these composites may be put to use in the secondary anode system in the cathodic protection of reinforced concrete bridge decks, in conductive floor panel systems and also in the concrete for lightning arresters.

Numerous non-structural applications of CFRC have also been suggested. The potentially beneficial application include use in the electrical and electronics industries. On the highly unconventional side, the use of CFRC in the motorcycle engine as the cylinder head has also been attempted (17).

FUTURE RESEARCH NEEDS

Given the potential of carbon-cement composites and the possible applications, the following area where future research needs exist may be identified:

1) Fiber-Matrix bond studies and fundamental fracture studies including microscopic fracture observations using in-situ devices aimed at understanding the strengthening and toughening mechanisms in these composites with the objective of optimizing their mechanical properties.

The sensitivity of these composites to rate of stressing or loading should be investigated through variable stress-rate tests. In the same context, the impact resistance of these composites should be thoroughly assessed.

2) Durability studies aimed at understanding the long term performance of these composites under hostile environments. In particular, the stability of the network of air bubbles for proper frost resistance need be assessed. Equally important is the resistance to scaling under the influence of de-icing salts if these composites were to be used for bridge deck overlays or thin repairs. Resistance to abrasion may be of relevance in some applications.

In some other applications, the resistance to repeated heating and cooling cycles may be of pertinence. The long term embrittlement, if any, should be determined.

Permeability of these composites to water and other aggressive chemicals, to the Author's knowledge, has not been measured yet. In the context of permeability, the influence of damage due to pre-loading should also be looked into.

ACKNOWLEDGEMENTS

The Author wishes to thank Kureha Chemical Company of Japan for supplying the fibers for some of the work reported here. Thanks are also due to Prof. Yoshihiko Ohama of Nihon University Japan for valuable support and advice.

REFERENCES

1. Portland Cement Association, *National Canadian Research Program on High Performance Concrete Gets under Way,* PCA Progress, Vol. 4, No. 3, 1990, p. 8.

2. Shah, S.P., and Young, J.F., *Current Research at NSF Science and Technology Center for Advanced Cement-Based Materials,* Amer. Ceramic Soc. Bulletin, Vol. 69, No. 8, August 1990, pp. 1319-1331.

3. Banthia, N., Mindess, S. and Bentur, A., *Impact Behavior of Concrete Beams,* Mater. & Struc. (RILEM), 20(119), 1987, pp. 293-302.

4. Shah, S.P. and Rangan, B.V., *Fiber Reinforced Concrete Properties,* ACI J., Proc., 68(2), Feb. 1971, pp.126-134.

5. Bayasi, Z. and Peterson, G. in Fiber Reinforced Cements and Concretes: Recent Developments (Eds. R.N. Swamy and B. Barr) Elsevier Appl. Sci. Publishers, 1989, pp. 200-208.

6. Banthia, N. and Sheng, J., *Micro-Reinforced Cementitious Materials,* Mater. Res. Society Symp. Proc., Vol. 211 (Eds. S. Mindess and J. Skalny), Boston, Nov. 1990, pp. 25-32.

7. Ali, M.A., Majumdar, A.J. and Rayment, D.L., *Carbon Fiber Reinforcement of Cement,* Cement & Concrete Res., 2, 1972, pp. 201-212.

8. Sheng, J., *Fracture of Micro-reinforced Cements,* Ph.D. Thesis, Laval University, Quebec, Canada, in preparation.

9. Ando, T., Sakai, H., Takahashi, K., Hoshijima, T., Awata, M. and Oka, S., *Fabrication and Properties for a New Carbon Fiber Reinforced Cement Product,* in Thin Section Fiber Reinforced Concrete and Ferrocement (Eds. J.I. Daniel and S.P. Shah) Amer. Concr. Inst., SP-124, 1990, pp. 39-60.

10. Ohama, Y., Amano, M. and Endo, M., *Properties of Carbon Fiber Reinforced Cement with Silica Fume,* Concrete Int., March 1985, pp. 58-62.

11. Banthia, N. and Ohama, Y., *Dynamic Tensile Fracture of Carbon Fiber Reinforced Cements,* Fiber Reinforced Cements and Concretes: Recent Developments (Eds. R.N. Swamy and B. Barr) Elsevier Appl. Sci. Publishers, 1989, pp. 251-260.

12. Furukawa, S. Tsuji, Y. and Miyamoto, M., In Review of the 41st General Meeting/Technical Session (CAJ Review 1987), Cement Assoc. of Japan, Tokyo, 1987, pp. 336-339.

13. Ohama, Y. and Amano, M., *Effects of Silica Fume and Water Reducing Agent on Carbon Fiber Reinforced Mortar,* Proc., 27th Japan Congress on Mater. Res., Society of Mater. Sci., Kyoto, 1984, pp. 187-191.

14. Briggs, A. *Carbon Fiber Reinforced Cement,* J. Mater. Sci., 12, 1977, pp. 384-404.

15. Akihama, S. Suenaga, T. and Banno, T., *Mechanical Properties of Carbon Fiber Reinforced Cement Composites,* Int. J. of Cement Composites & Lightweight Concr., 8(1), Feb. 1986, pp. 21-33.

16. Akihama, S., Suenaga, T. and Nakagawa, H., *Carbon Fiber Reinforced Concrete,* Concrete Int., 10(1), Jan. 1988, pp. 40-47.

17. Kanno, M., Ohama, Y., Kawai, H. and Demura, K., *Fatigue Strength of Carbon Fiber Reinforced Paste and it Application to Machine Parts,* Proc., 32nd Japan Congress on Mater. Res., Soc. of Mater. Sci., Kyoto, Japan, 1989, pp. 209-212.

18. Banthia, N., Sheng, J., Mindess, S. and Ohama, Y., *Toughness Characterization of Carbon Fiber Reinforced Cements,* Proc., 3rd Int. Symposium on Brittle Matrix Composites, Poland, Sept. 1991, pp. 318-327.

19. Ohama, Y., Demura, K. and Sato, Y., *Development of Lightweight Carbon Fiber Reinforced Fly Ash-Cement Composite,* Proc., Int. Symp. on Fiber Reinforced Concrete, (Eds. V.S. Parameswaran and T.S. Krishnamoorthy), Oxford & IBH Publishing, New Delhi, Vol 1., 1987, pp. 3.23-3.31.

20. Akihama, S., Kobayashi, M., Suenaga, T., Nakagawa, H. and Suzuki, K., *Mechanical Properties of Carbon Fiber Cement Composites and the Application to Buildings (Part 2),* Kajima Inst. of Constr. Tech., Report No. 65, Tokyo, Oct. 1986, 54 pp.

21. Soroushian, P., Bayasi, Z. and Nagi, M., in Fiber Reinforced Cements and Concretes: Recent Developments (Eds. R.N. Swamy and B. Barr) Elsevier Appl. Sci. Publishers, 1989, pp. 167-178.

22. Banthia, N., Sheng, J. and Ohama, Y., *Carbon Fiber Reinforced Cement Plates under Transverse Loading,* Proc., 5th Tech. Conf. on Composite Mater. (Amer. Soc. for Composites), Michigan, 1990, pp. 709-718.

23. Banthia, N. and Dubeau S., "*Micro-Reinforced Cementitious Composites for Thin Repairs*", Proc., ACI Int. Conf. on Evaluation and Rehabilitation of Concr. Struct. & Innovation in Design, Hong Kong, Dec. 1991.

24. Clemena, G.G., *Electrically Conductive Portland Cement Concrete,* Materials Performance, Nat. Assoc. of Corrosion Engrs., March 1988, pp. 19-25.

25. Ohama, Y., *Carbon-Cement Composites,* Carbon, 27(5), 1989, pp. 729-737.

26. Banthia, N. Djeridane, S. and Pigeon, M., *Electrical Resistivity of Cements Reinforced with Microfibers of Carbon and Steel,* Cement & Concr. Res., 22(5), 1992, pp. 804-814.

27. Ohama, Y., *Durability and Long Term Performance of FRC,* Proc., Int. Symp. on Fiber Reinf. Concr., (Eds. V.S. Parameswaran and T.S. Krishnamoorthy), Oxford & IBH Publishing, New Delhi, Vol. 2, 1987, pp. 5.3-5.16.

28. Banthia, N. and Sheng, J., *Durability of Carbon Fiber Reinforced Cements in Acidic Environments,* CANMET-ACI, 2nd Int. Conf. on Durability of Concrete, Montreal, 1991 (accepted).

TABLE 1 — PROPERTIES OF PAN AND PITCH-BASED COMMERCIAL CARBON FIBERS

Fibre Type	Diameter (μm)	Specific gravity (kg/L)	Tensile strength (MPa)	Young's modulus (GPa)	Approx. cost ratios
PAN-based	7-8	1.6-1.7	3000-4000	250-400	7
Pitch-based	14-18	1.7-1.8	600-2000	30-200	1

TABLE 2 — FLEXURAL BEHAVIOR OF CFRC* (see Fig. 7 for definitions)

Carbon Fiber (% vol.)	P_e (N)	P_u (N)	E_f (N.mm)	First Crack Strength† (MPa)	Ultimate Strength‡ (MPa)	Specific Fracture Energy§ (x10^3 N.mm/mm^2)
0	79	79	3	4.6	4.6	13
1	197	272	102	11.4	15.7	453
3	285	365	229	16.5	21.1	1017
5	296	525	686	17.1	30.3	3048

*Beams 15x15x150 (mm) tested over a 130 mm span.
†Using elastic analysis and P_e.
‡Using elastic analysis and P_u.
§Dividing E_f by the specimen cross-sectional area.

Fig. 1—Fractured surface of CFRC showing random distribution of carbon fibers

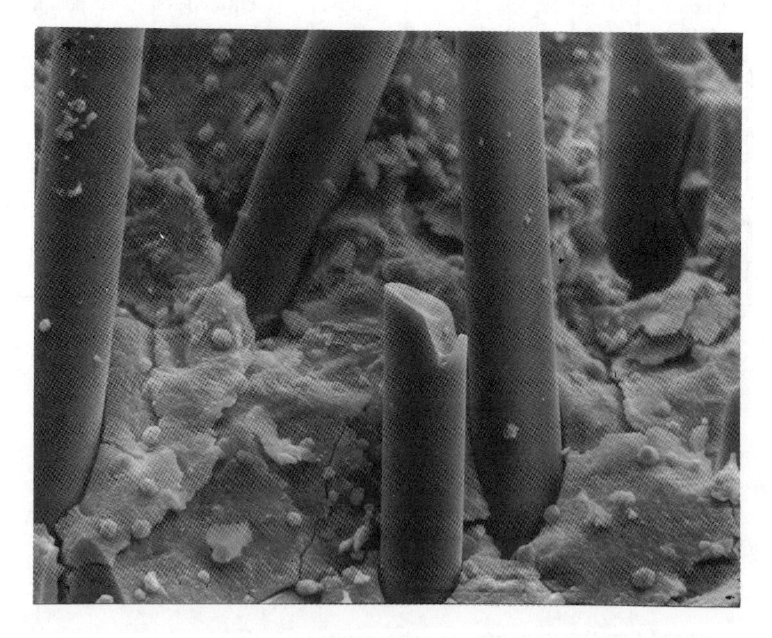

Fig. 2—Dense packing of hydration products around the carbon fibers

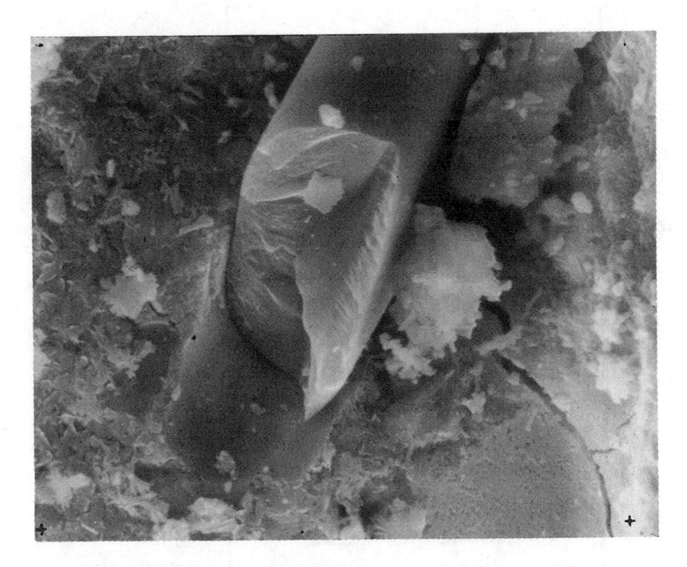

Fig. 3—A fractured fiber of carbon under load. Note the occurrence of fracture mode of fiber failure followed by fiber pull-out

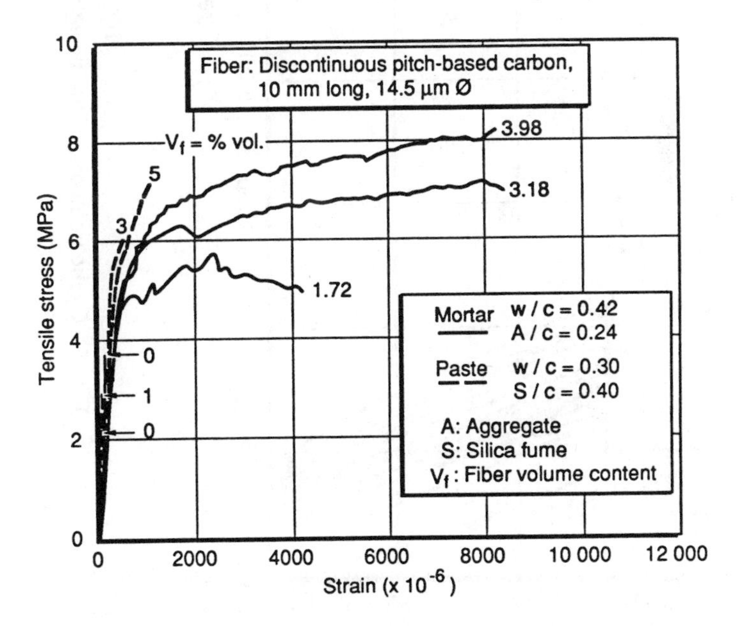

Fig. 4—Response of carbon fiber reinforced paste (10) and mortar (15) subjected to uniaxial tensile load

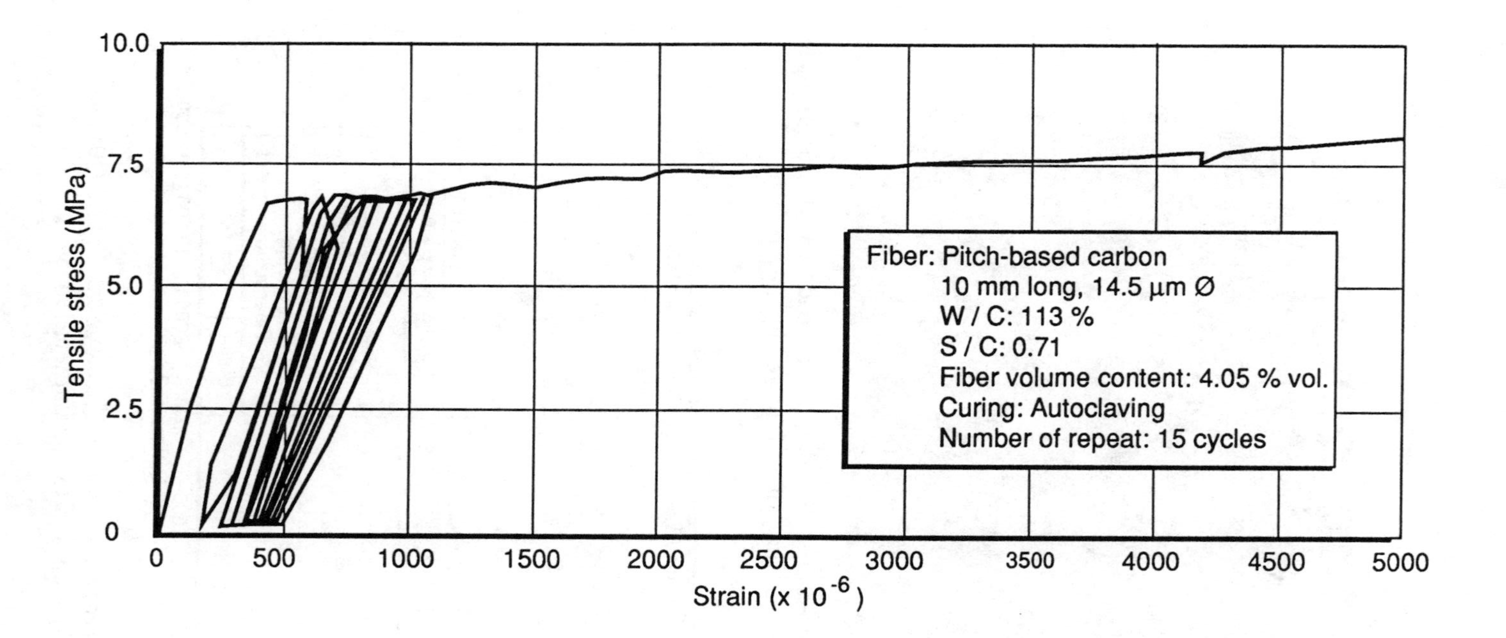

Fig. 5—Cyclic behavior of lightweight CFRC under uniaxial tensile load (16)

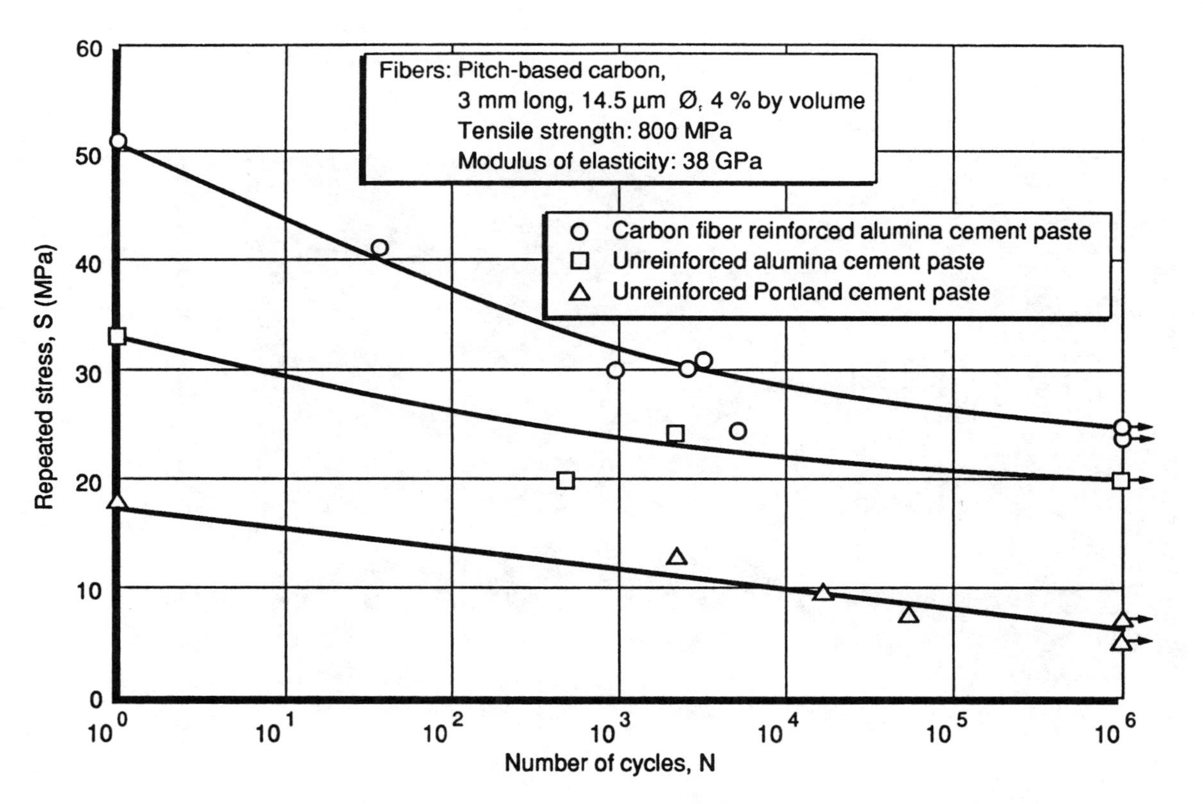

Fig. 6—S-N curves for pressure molded CFRC under cyclic compression (17)

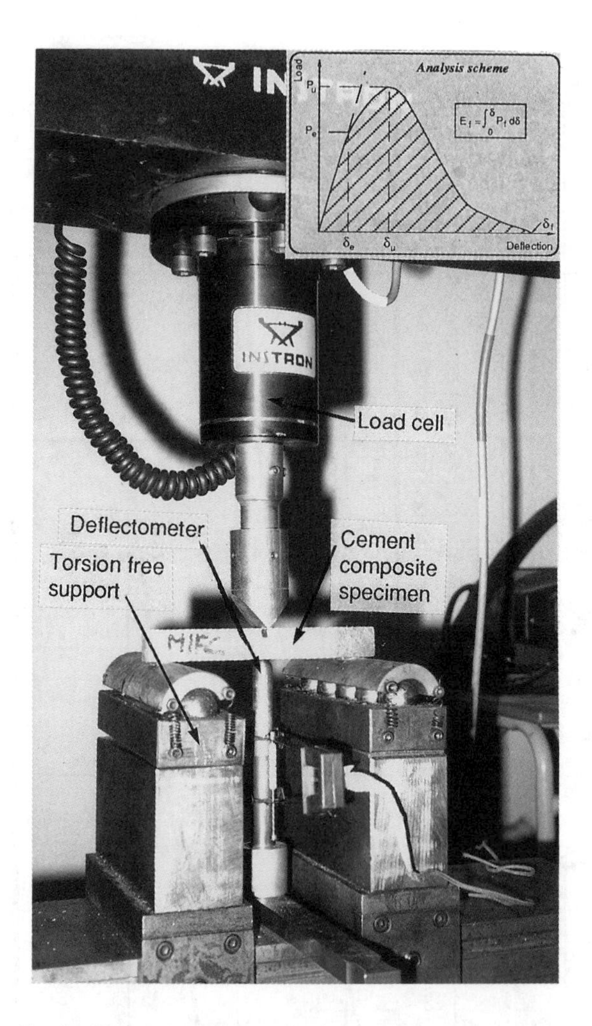

Fig. 7—A CFRC beam under three-point flexural test (6)

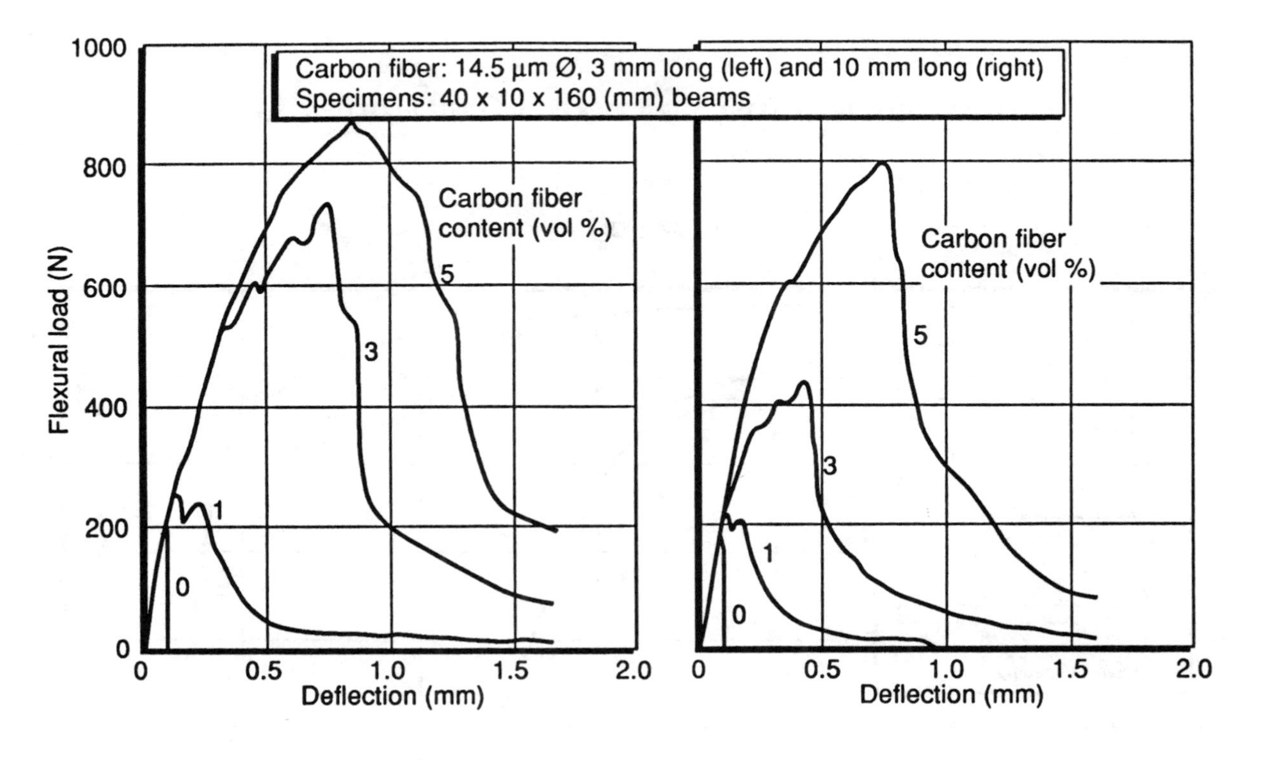

Fig. 8—Load-deflection plots for CFRC using 3 and 10 mm carbon fibers (10)

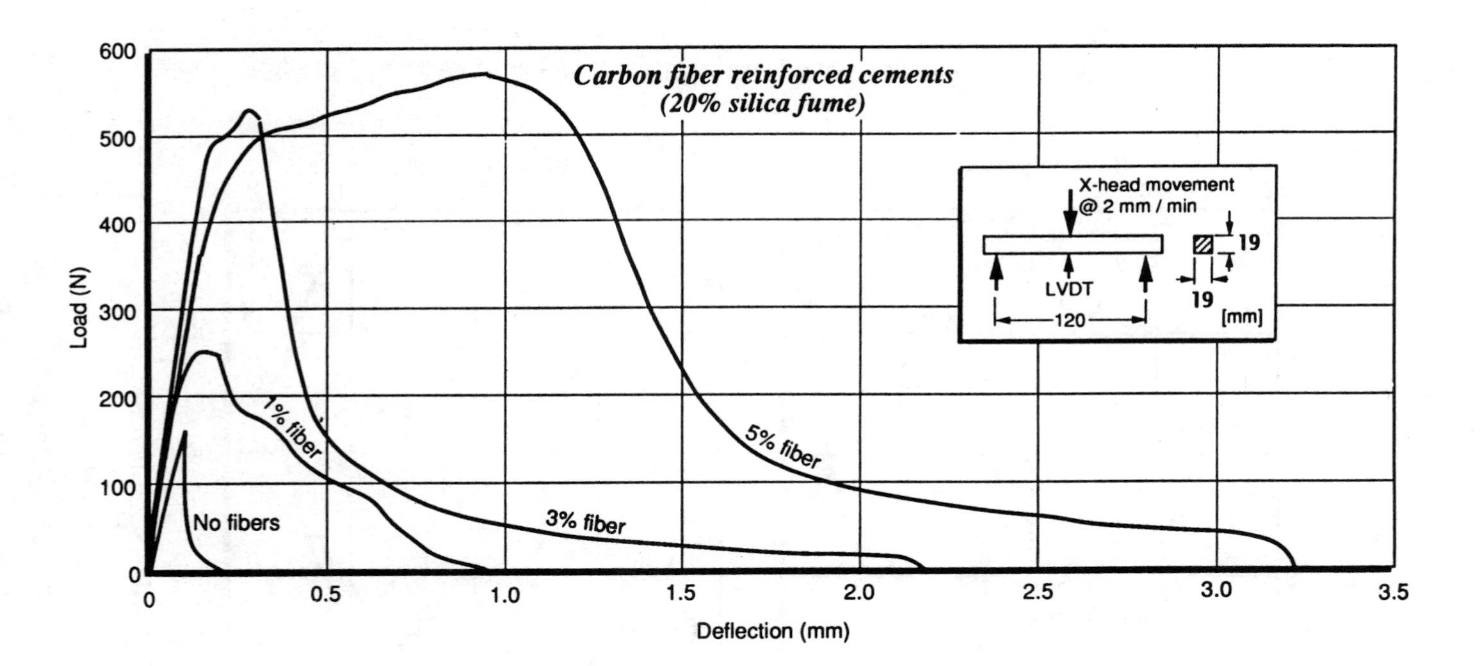

Fig. 9—Load-deflection plots for CFRC using 6 mm carbon fibers (6)

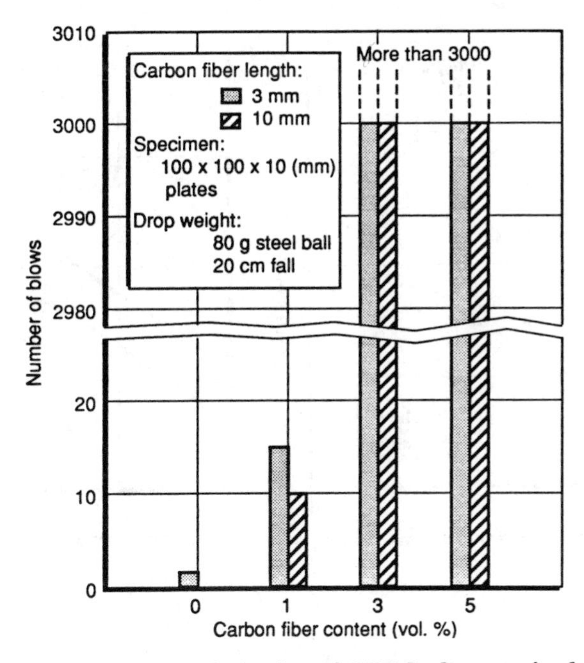

Fig. 10—Impact behavior of CFRC characterized using multiple drop-weight tests (10)

Fig. 11—Instrumented impact test set-up for testing CFRC under uniaxial tensile impact (11)

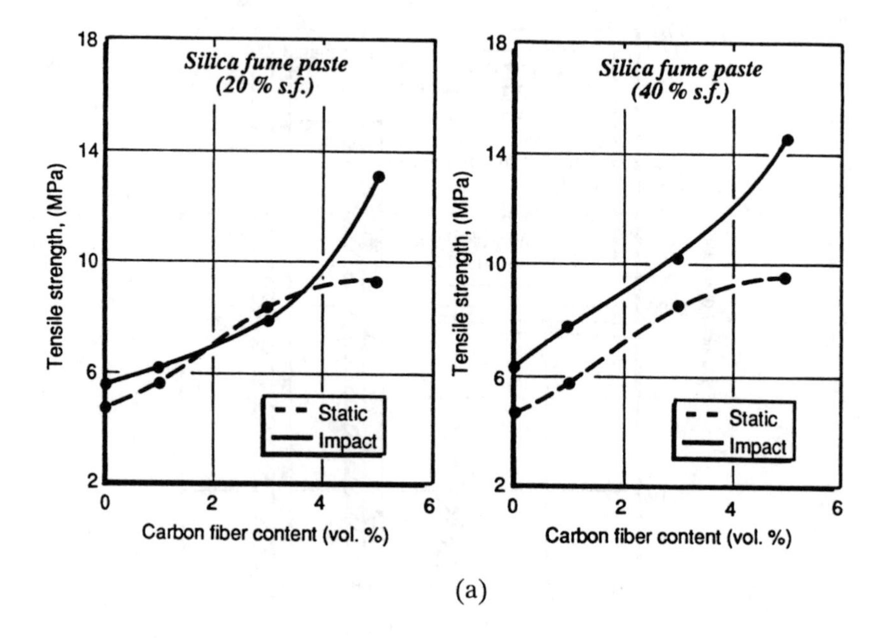

(a)

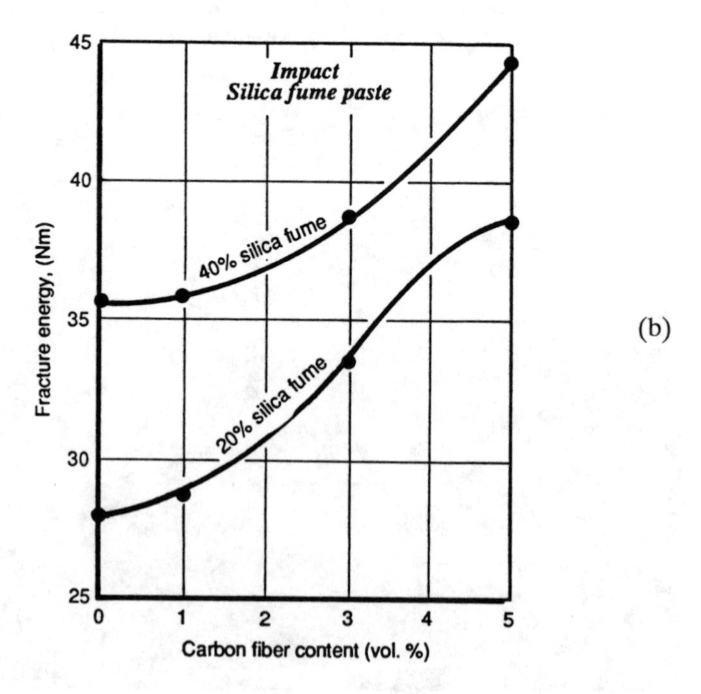

(b)

Fig. 12—(a) Tensile strength, and (b) fracture energy of CFRC under impact (11)

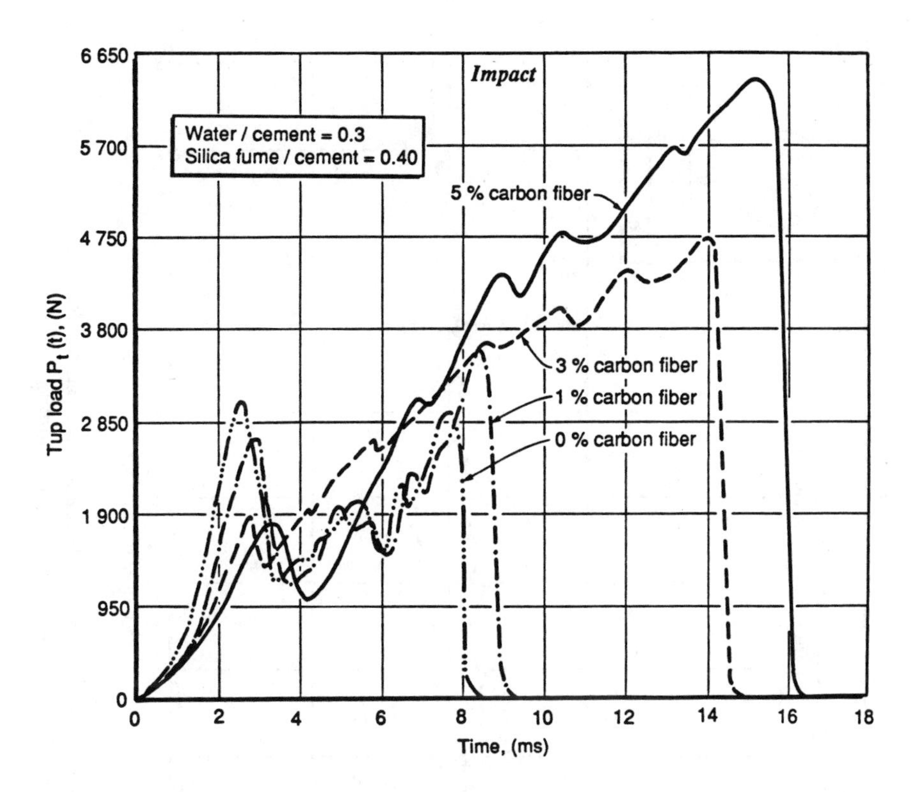

Fig. 13—Hammer-specimen contact load pulses under impact with the same hammer approach velocity of 2.3 m/s for CFRC with variable carbon fiber fractions (11)

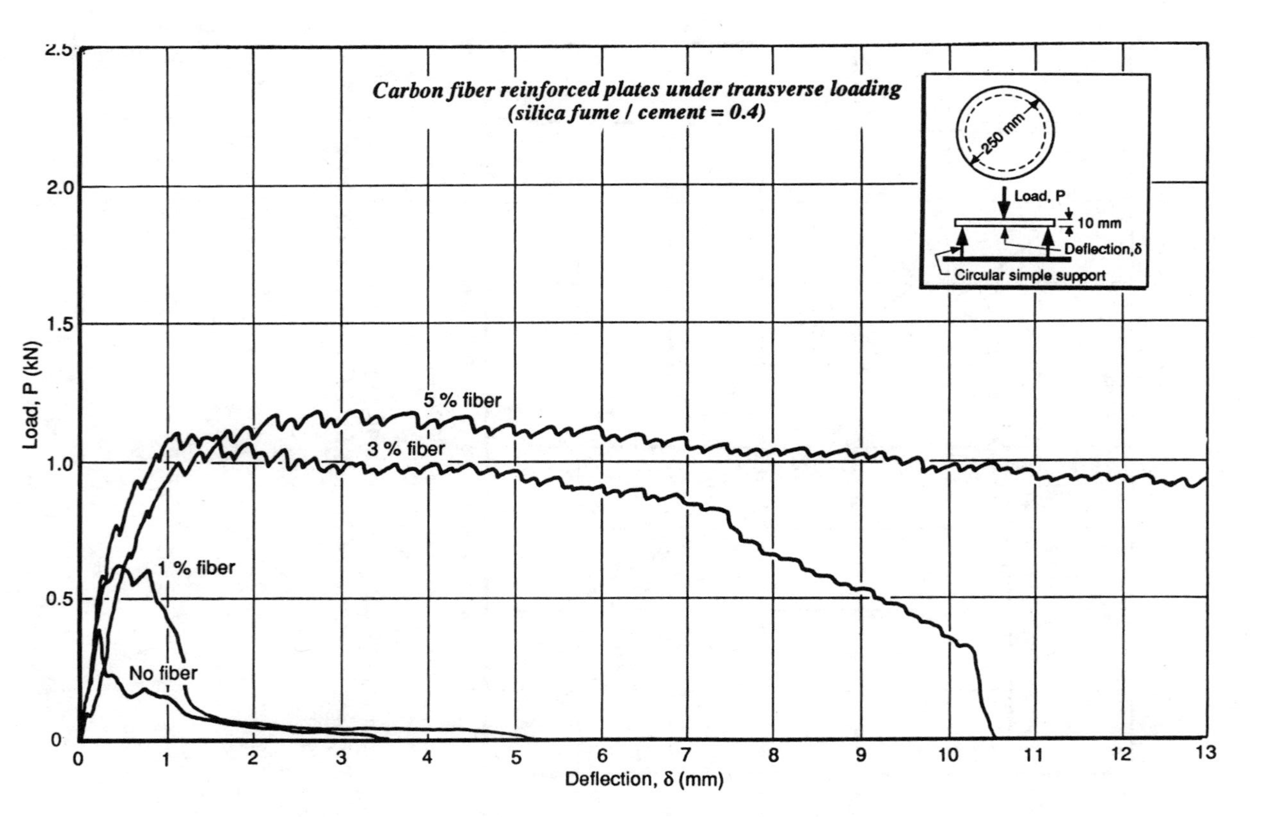

Fig. 14—Load versus load point displacement plots obtained for CFRC circular plates under center-point loading (22)

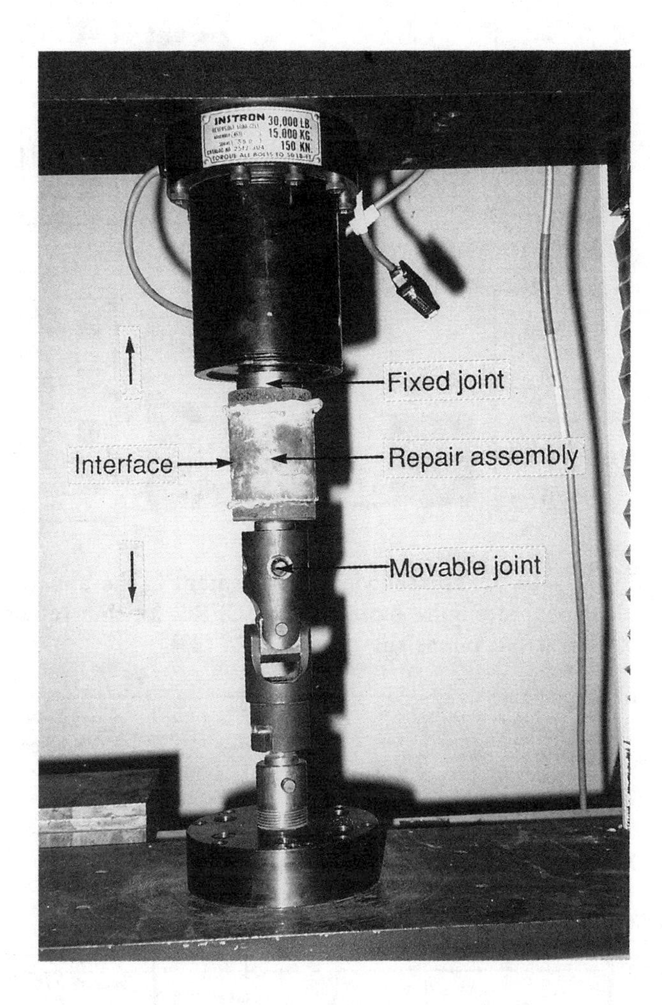

Fig. 15—A repair assembly under uniaxial adhesion test (23)

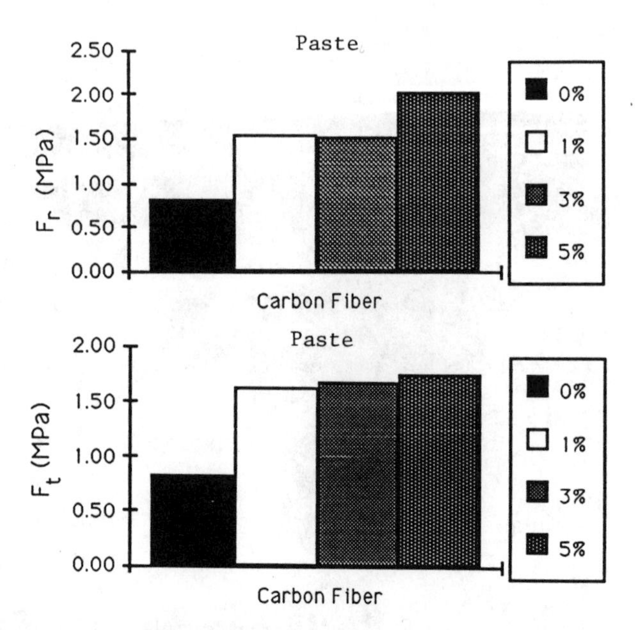

Fig. 16—Bar charts showing improvement in the apparent adhesional strength obtained using CFRC for thin repairs using test specimens shown in Fig. 15 (23)

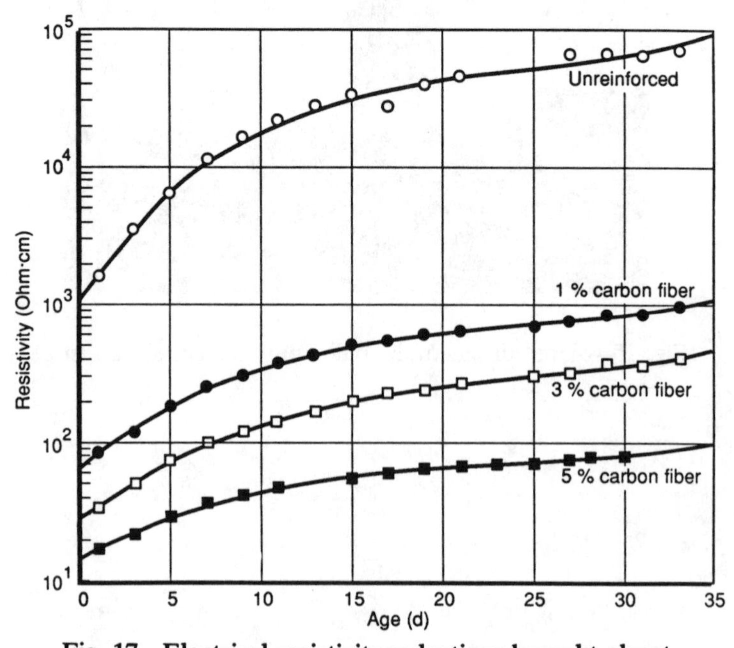

Fig. 17—Electrical resistivity reductions brought about by carbon fiber inclusion (26)

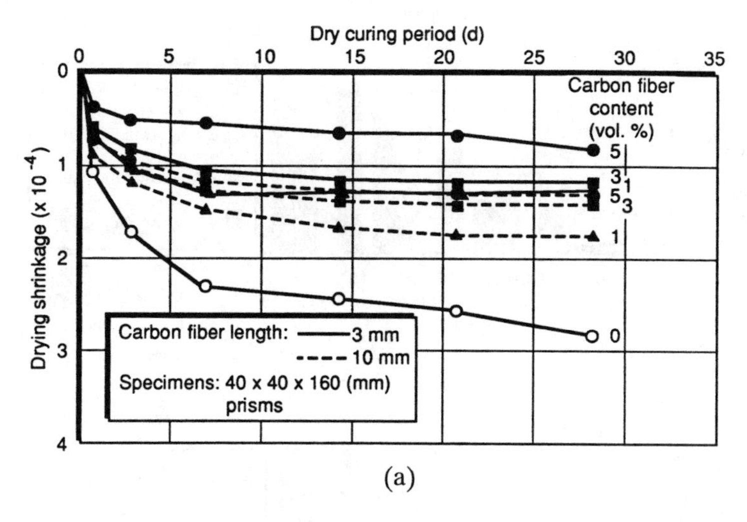

(a)

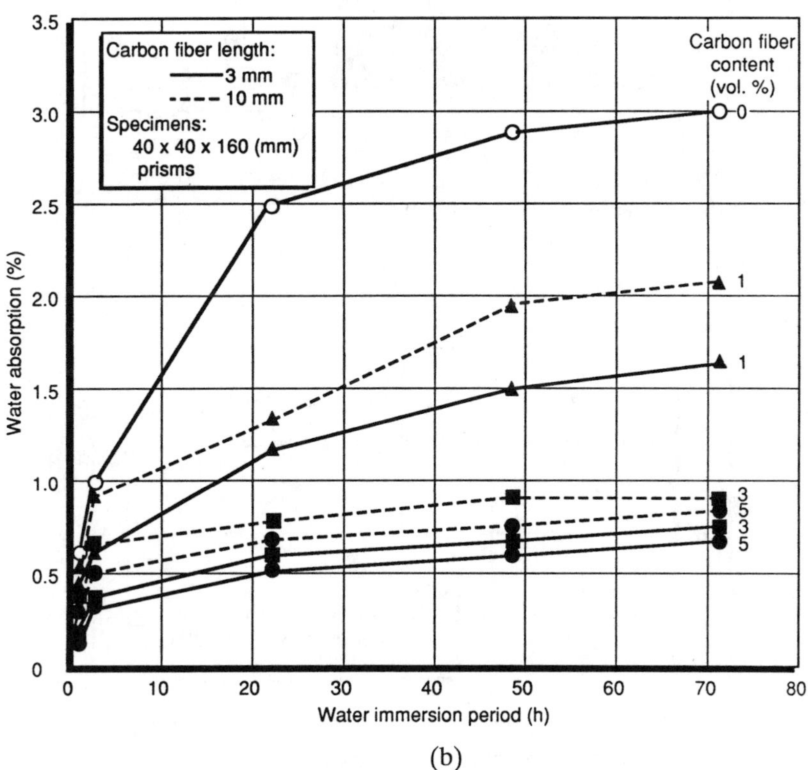

(b)

Fig. 18—(a) Drying shrinkage, and (b) water absorption results for CFRC (10)

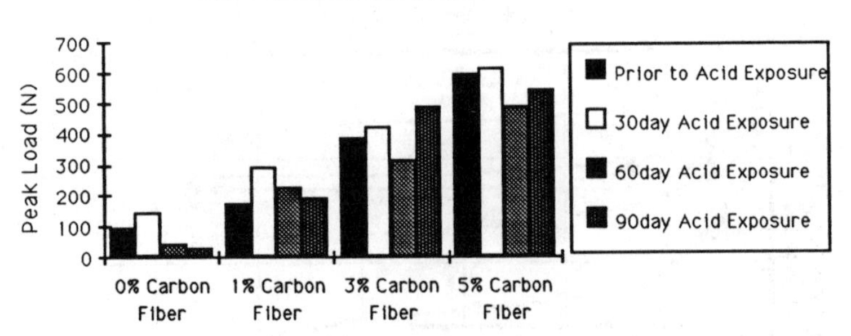

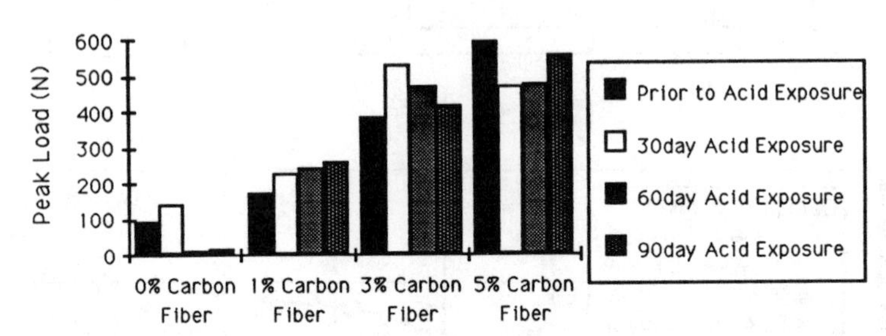

Fig. 19—Influence of acid exposure (pH = 4.0) on the load carrying capacity of CFRC up to 90 days (28)

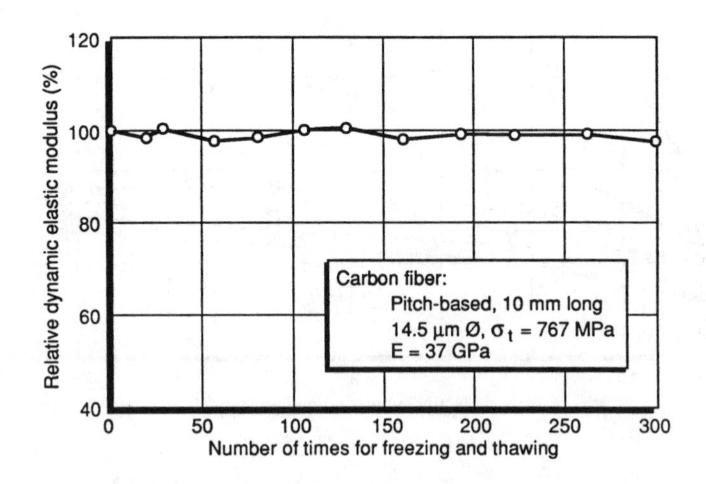

Fig. 20—Changes in the dynamic modulus of CFRC subjected to freeze-thaw cycles (16)

SP 142-7

Flexural Behavior of Carbon Fiber Reinforced Cement Composite

by H. Sakai, K. Takahashi, Y. Mitsui, T. Ando, M. Awata, and T. Hoshijima

Synopsis:CFRC(Carbon Fiber Reinforced Cement Composite) has outstanding advantages in its dynamic characteristics and durability. Among others, it has a flexural strength three to four times higher than that of ordinary concrete. Taking advantage of this characteristics of CFRC in designing curtain walls, manufacturing of thin, light-weight curtain wall is possible. This paper describes experimental studies conducted using CFRC specimens to exmine the effects of mixing and placing conditions upon the flexural strength of CFRC, scale effects and the fatigue of CFRC subject to repetitive loads. Furthermore,based on the results of these experiments, allowable bending stress in designing curtain walls was determined, and its authenticity was verified by having a full-scale composite panel undergo a wind resistance test. Also, several examples of CFRC used as curtain walls are introduced.

Keywords: Carbon fibers; composite materials; curtain walls; durability; fatigue (materials); fiber reinforced concretes; flexural strength; mixers; mixing; scale effects; vibrators (machinery)

Mr.Hiromichi Sakai,an ACI member,is a manager of Engineering Department,Kurosaki Plant,of Mitsubishi Kasei Corporation(MKC), Japan. He received his M.Eng. from Kumamoto University in 1975 and is responsible for the engineering development of carbon fiber cement composite. He was also the speaker at the ACI symposium on FRC in Atlanta,1989.

Mr.Keisuke Takahashi,an ACI member,is an assistant manager and has been engaged in carbon fiber reinforced composites at the Head office,MKC,Tokyo. He received his M.Eng. from Kumamoto University in 1981.

Dr.Yoshiyuki Mitsui is Professor of structural Eng. at Kumamoto University,Japan. He received his D.Eng.degree in structural engineering from Oosaka University in 1974. He has authored numerous publications and reports relating to fiber reinforced concrete.

Mr.Tatsuo Ando,an ACI member of manager responsible for technicalservices of composite materials at Mitsubishi Kasei America Inc.,Chesapeake,Virginia. He received his M.Eng.from Tokyo University in 1976 and has been engaged in research and developement of composite building materials.He was also the speaker at the ACI symposium on FRC in Atlanta,1989.

Mr.Mitsuru Awata,an ACI member,is a senior reserch scientist at the Reseach Center,MKC,Yokohama,Japan. He received his B.Eng.from Kanazawa University and has been engaged in research and developement of inorganic fiber reinforced composites.

Mr.Tokitaro Hoshijima is a senior manager responsible for carbon fiber reinforced composite at the Head Office,MKC,Tokyo. He received his B.Eng. from Tokyo Institute of Technology in 1971.

INTRODUCTION

Carbon fiber reinforced cement composite (CFRC) is lighter in weight and higher in tensile and flexural strengths than ordinary concrete. Therefore many researches are under way in Japan to find applications of CFRC as construction material. Among other applications,the possibility of using CFRC to make thin and light-weight curtain walls taking advantage of its higher flexural strength has been verified in experiments by many researchers. Our previous report discussed that it is important to grasp its required flexural strength in designing a curtain wall and the flexural strength of CFRC is affected largely by the volume fraction and properties of CF(1).

Successively, this discussion exhibits the results of experiments on the following four subjects. First, the effects of mixing and placing conditions upon the flexural strength of CFRC is reported. Because each type of mixer has its own optimum time for mixing CFRC, an accurate understanding is necessary of the mixer we use. In this paper, two types of mixers, omni-mixer and ordinary mortar mixer, are discussed for relationship between mixing time and flexural strength. Next, while a casting method is employed for placing CFRC into a formwork, the effects of vibrational direction of the vibrator at compaction upon the flexural strength of CFRC is discussed.

Second, scale effects upon the flexural strength of CFRC when it is formed into panels are discussed. So far, there have been many reports made of the scale effects of steel fiber reinforced concrete. Akihama's report on an experiment using CFRC specimens of general pitch-based carbon fiber showed a correlation between the flexural strength of CFRC and the mathematical product of the height and bending span of the specimens(2). We conducted an experiment based on the high stressed volume theory, using the product of panel width and panel height and bending span length (called the volume of specimen for the sake of convenience) and the results are reported.

Third, the fatigue of curtain walls subjected to repetitive stress by wind load and the flexural fatigue characteristics of CFRC curtain walls are discussed. We conducted a one-direction bending test on CFRC panel specimens to examine their flexural fatigue characteristics and also studied their residual strength after the bending test.

Fourth, based on the results from the above-mentioned experiments, an allowable bending stress to be used in designing curtain wall was determined, and full-scale panels were made accordingly for a wind load test. The results are reported herein. At the end of this report, several actual cases where CFRC is used as curtain walls are described. The carbon fiber used in our experiments was high-performance pitch-based carbon fiber. Continuous threads of the fiber were given a special sizing treatment and cut to a specific size for the experiments.

EXPERIMENTS

Effects of mixing and placing conditions

Based on the results of our previous report(1), the mix proportion of CFRC for this experiment was determined as in Table 1. Two types of mixers were used, omni-mixer (30 liters) and ordinary mortar mixer (70 liters). A batch of CF, cement, aggregate and dispersant was dry-mixed for thirty seconds and then, water and water reducing agent were added for succeeding mixing. Relationship between mixing time and flexural strength is shown in Fig. 1. The mixing time refers to the time of mixing after water is added. It is revealed from the figure that the optimum mixing times of the omni-mixer and the ordinary mortar mixer are 60 and 150 seconds respectivery. All specimens were air-cured at 20℃ and 60%RH after being cast for a week and underwent the bending test. The flexural strength of CFRC was obtained by a three-point bending test of a 4 × 4 × 16 (cm) specimen (span: 10 cm). Different types of mixers can be used for mixing CFRC and they will give a similar level of flexural strength of CFRC batches provided their optimum mixing times are observed. The longer the mixing time, the lower the flexural strength. This is because the ordinary mortar mixer is effective for dispersing carbon fibers at its initial stage and thereafter determinal. Therefore, it is necessary to observe strictly the optimum mixing time of the mixer for mixing CFRC to achieve a desired flexural strength.

Casting is an efficient placing method for manufacturing curtain walls of CFRC. Since a vibrator is used to compact CFRC uniformly inside a formwork, the effects of the vibrational direction of the vibrator upon the flexural strength of CFRC was examined.It has been known that steel fibers in SFRC take a two-dimensional orientation as it is vibrated by a vibrator because of a large difference in specific gravity between steel fiber and concerte matrix. Our study was made of CFRC how carbon fibers behave when vibrated by a vibrator, where carbon fiber has the same specific gravity as the matrix.

Fig.2 shows two casting methods, the method A with the formwork placed horizontally against up-down vibration and the method B with the formwork placed vertically. Mix proportions were as per Table 1,and an ordinary mortar mixer(70 liters) was used. All specimens were air-cured at 20℃ and 60%RH after being cast for a week and underwent the bending test. Fig.3 shows relationships between vibrational direction and flexural sterngth for both the methods A and B. The flexural sterngths were results from the three-point bending of specimens measuring 4 × 4 × 32 cm with a span of 26 cm. Looking at Fig.3,while flexural strength increases as volume fraction (Vf) increase with the method A, no trend of increaseing flexural strength was observed with the increase in Vf with the method B. Observation of the fractured sections of the specimens showed that those by the method A had their broken carbon fibers oriented at right angles with the fractured face,but those by method B had their carbon fibers oriented in parallel with the fractured face,indicating that with the method B,there is a tendency of carbon fibers being oriented at right angles with the vibrational direction of the vibrator. Therefore, all specimens therafter were made by the method A.

Scale Effects

It is known that the flexural strength of the CFRC panel is largely affected by its demensions including width, height and the length of bending span. Specimens as shown in Table 2 were made and the effects bending span length has upon the flexural strength of the panel were studied. The mix proportion is given in Table 1. An ordinary mortar mixer (500 liters) was used. The properties of green CFRC are given in Table 3. The dispersion of carbon fibers in the specimen was visually observed. All specimens were air-cured at 20℃ and 60%RH after being cast for four weeks and underwent the bending test. The specimen of 10 × 10 × 40 cm was subjected to four-point bending test and other specimens of different size were bent by a three-point bending apparatus. Fig.4 shows how the specimens were loaded. Table 4 shows the results of the bending tests.

Akihama,et al deduced from the results of the bending test of general pitch-based carbon fiber reinforced cement composite specimens an equation to estimate the flexural sterngth σ_{b1} of CFRC, taking account of the scale effects of the specimens(2).

$$\sigma_{b1} = \beta_1 \ (D \times \ell)^{-\alpha 1} \qquad (1)$$

In the meantime, based on the high stressed volume theory, Torrent has proposed an estimation equation for the tensile and flexural strength σ_{b2} of cement-based composite materials and substantiated that the equation gives values closely corresponding with the results of experiments(3),

$$\sigma_{b2} = \beta_2 \ (b \times D \times \ell)^{\alpha 2} \qquad (2)$$

In the equations, letters b, D and ℓ stand for the width, height and bending span length of the specimen respectively and $\beta_1, \beta_2, \alpha_1$ and α_2 stand for given constants. Figs.5 and 6 show the scale effects of CFRC plotted in a logarithmic bi-axial graph with its y-axis representing flexural strength σ_b, and its x-axis $(D \times \ell)$ and $(b \times D \times \ell)$ respectively. Both the figures show a tendency of experimental values neariy making a straight line and give the following regression equations.

$$\sigma_b = 485 \ (D \times \ell)^{-0.272} \qquad (3)$$

Correlation coefficient $\gamma = 0.83$

$$\sigma_b = 417.8 \ (b \times D \times \ell)^{-0.174} \qquad (4)$$

Correlation coefficient $\gamma = 0.85$
Units are in kg and cm.
Comparing the equations (1) with (2), equation (2) has a higher correlation coefficient, indicating the possibility of applying the theory of high stressed volume in evaluating the scale effects upon flexural strength of CFRC. However, since the

applicable range this experiment is limited, further study is necessary.

Fatigue strength

Considering the fact that curtain wall is subjected to constant and repeated wind load, it is necessary to study the flexural fatigue strength of CFRC if it is to be used as a material of curtain walls. For this experiment, mix proportion was as per Table 1 and an omni-mixer (30 liters) was used. Specimens used were square columns, each measuring 10×10×40 cm, air-cured at 20℃ and 60%RH for four weeks after casting.

In order to locate the position of the specimen where fatigue crack originate from, a 0.5cm deep notch was cut at the center of the specimen using a metal saw (blade thickness:0.64mm). An oil hydraulic servo type tester was used for applying from one side only a bending load at three point (span length : 30cm) of the specimen. The maximum load applied was approximately 90% of the maximum static load ,and the minimum load applied was 200 to 400 kgf. The measurement method used is given in Fig.7. The control waveform was sine wave and the loading speed 1 to 4 Hz. A magnifier with 10 magnifications was used to observe crack propagation. An example of progressive cracking is shown in Fig.8. A crack originated at the tip of the notch and propagated as loading is repeated. Another crack appeared at a point close to the tip of the first crack after reaching a certain length. Afterwards, both cracks developed without combining with each other. Also,while cracks developed at both sides of the notch,the crack at a side alone grew larger until it was about a half of the height of the specimen and then, stopped growing. Therefore, the test was terminated after repetitive loading of 800,000 times,and the residual flexural strength at the point was determined measured by means of the static bending test. Fig.9 shows the results of the fatigue test,with its y-axis representing maximum residual load/maximum static load and x-axis times of repetitive loading (N), delineating the relationship between S and N. In Fig.9, the S-N relationship of ordinary concrete is also given(6).

With this experiment stopped before the specimen reached to fatigue failure,the S-N relationships of CFRC and ordinary concrete is hardly comparable. It is clear,however,that CFRC has by far a higher fatigue strength than ordinary concrete. Table 5 shows residual flexural strength determined after completing the fatigue test. The table verifies that being subjected to 800,000 times of repetitive loading of the maximum load as high as 90% of the maximum static load, CFRC does not lose its flexural strength, though it develops fatigue cracks.

Wind Load Test Using Full-Scale Curtain Wall Specimen

A wind load test was conducted of a 357 by 565 cm curtain wall panel to confirm the flexural behavior of CFRC discussed in the preceding section. Assuming a curtain wall is installed at a height of 100 m from the ground level, positive and negative wind pressures applied in this experiment were made 390 and 580 kgf/m² respectively. Figs.10 and 11 show the method of loading employed and the view of the experiment respectively. Deflection and strain taking place at specific points of the panel specimen under the load were measured using a displacement gage and strain gage respectively. Fig.12 shows the shape of the specimen, which had a thickness of 17 cm including 10 cm rib and 7 cm slab. An ordinary mortar mixer (500 liters) was used to mix the CFRC with ingredients at proportions shown in Table 1. The panel was air-cured at 15 to 20℃ for four weeks before it was tested.

All stresses were examined in accordance with the allowable stress design method. The allowable bending stress σ_a was given by the equation below(4).

$$\sigma_a = \sigma_b - 1.73S \qquad (5)$$

where; σ_b: Flexural strength obtained by the equation (4)
S : Standard deviation of 10.4 kgf/cm² from Table 4
For obtaining ,bending span was made 364 cm according to Fig. 10. For width b, three different widths, i.e. the total width, the width of rib section and a width obtained by a formula to obtain the effective width of slab (Refer to Fig.13.) given in the AIJ Standard(5). The respective calculation results of σ_b are shown in Table 6.

Table 6 shows the experimental values of mid-span deflection and stress measured at the center (A) of the specimen subjected to the maximum wind load of 580 kgf/m². Though the actual data were a little lower than the calculated values with the total width of the curtain wall as its effective width, both show a close correspondence. In designing an actual curtain wall, it is possible to obtain the panel section by regarding the total width of the panel as the effective width.

APPLICATION OF CFRC

Both panel type and spandrel type curtain walls are described here as examples of CFRC applications. Fig.14 shows an eleven-story hotel building where a panel type external curtain walls were used. Benefits of CFRC being light in weight, superior in moldability were specifically considered in designing this curtain wall. Fig.15 shows a spandrel type curtain wall employed for the external walls of ten-story office building. For this application, benefits of CFRC being light in weight and cheaper in cost than the aluminum counterpart were considered. Two to four years after completion,these buildings demonstrate an excellent performance as expected at the design stage, experiencing several times of earthquakes and typhoons.

CONCLUSIONS

This study was conducted to verify the possibility of exploiting the superb flexural behavior of CFRC in designing and manufacturing precast concrete panels. The following conclusions were drawn from the study.

(1) Each mixer used for mixing CFRC has its own optimum mixing time to achieve uniform dispersion of carbon fibers in CFRC and give maximum flexural strength to the CFRC.

(2) With the casting method,carbon fibers in CFRC has an inclination of being oriented at right angles with the vibrational direction of the vibrator.

(3) As for the scale effect of CFRC,the flexural strength of the specimen is predictable using the following equation deduced from regression analysis of the relationship between the volume and the flexural strength of CFRC specimens.

Thanks to this equation,it has been made possible to obtain the flexural strength of a large span panel from that of a small specimen.

(4) The flexural behavior of CFRC is so superior that the residual strength is not reduced even when it has minute cracks.

The application of the allowable bending stress of CFRC to designing curtain walls was made possible through a wind load test of full-scale wall panels.

ACKNOWLEDGMENT

The authors are thankful to Dr.Kiyoshi Murakami, asst. professor at Kumamoto University for his contribution of valuable suggestions to this paper and also all the staff of the Engineering Department, Mitsubishi Kasei Corp. for their cooperationin conducting the experiments.

REFERRENCES

(1) Ando,T.; Sakai,H.; Takahashi,K.; Hoshijima,T.; Awata,M. and Oka,S.,"Fabrication and Properties for a New Carbon Fiber Reinforced Cement Product ",ACI SP-124,1990

(2) Akihama, S. ; Kobayasi, M. ; Suenaga, H. and Suzuki, K. , " Experimental Study of Carbon Fiber Reinforced Cement Composites (Part4) --Scale Effect of CFRC Test Specimen on Flectural Properties--, " Annual Report No.32, 1984, Technical Research Institute, Kajima Corp.

(3) R.J.Torrent, " A General Relation between Tensile Strength and Specimen Geometry for Concrete-Like Materials ", Materials and Structures-Reserch and Testing, Vol.10, No.58 July/August 1977.

(4) JAPANESE ARCHITECTURAL STANDARD SPECIMEN FOR REINFORCED CONCRETE - WORK (JASS5) Revised 1986

(5) AIJ STANDARD FOR STRUCTURAL CALCULATION OF REINFORCED CONCRETE STRUCTURES (revised in 1988)

(6) U.Ohlsson.P.A.Daerga, L.Elfgren;"Fracture Energy and Fatigue Strength of Unreinforced Concrete Beams at Normal and Low Temperature " , Engineering Fracture Mechanics, Vol.35, No.1/2/3, 1990.

TABLE 1 — MIX PROPORTION OF CFRC

W/C (%)	S/C (%)	Water Reducing Agent (%)	Dispersant (%)	CF/vol. (%)
66	56	3	0.25	2.0

CF:High-performance Pitch-based Carbon Fiber
Size:17Φmm×18mmℓ, Specific Gravity:1.9
T.S:180 kgf/mm^2
T.M:18 tf/mm^2
C:High-early-strength Portland Cement
S:Silicate Sand:shirasu(light-weight sand)=2:1(weight ratio)
Water Reducing Agent:High-condensation triazine-base compound
Dispersant:Methyl-cellulose

TABLE 2 — SPECIMEN FOR SCALE EFFECT TESTING

Specimen b×D×L (cm)	Loading span (cm)	Loading	Quantity
10×10×40	30	Four-point bending	35
30×10×140	100	Three-point bending	15
30×10×240	200	〃	15
30×10×340	300	〃	5

TABLE 3 — PROPERTY OF GREEN CFRC

Flow Index* (mm)	Air Content** (%)	Weight per Unit Volume	CF Dispersion
140/142	4.4	1.6t/m^3	good

*Flow Index to JIS R5201
**Air Content to JIS A1128

TABLE 4 — RESULTS OF FLEXURAL TEST

	size(cm)	10×10×40	30×10×140	30×10×240	30×10×340
Flexural Strength at the occurrence of Initial Crack	Mean Value (kgf/ cm^2)	–	64	58.3	53.0
	Standard deviation	–	9.8	9.54	9.34
Flexural Strength	Mean Value (kgf/ cm^2)	105.5	65.9	65.8	57.2
	Standard deviation	14.2	10.5	10.5	10.3

Flexural Strength at the occurrence of Initial Crack=Mc/Z
Flexural Strength=M_{max}/Z
Mc,M_{max} :Bending moment at the occurrence of initial crack and at the max.load
Z:Section modulus

TABLE 5 — RESIDUAL FLEXURAL STRENGTH

Number of Repetition	Flexural Strength (kgf/ cm²)
Static Loading	104
440000(1.9t) times	100
800000(1.8t) times	106
850000(1.8t) times	100

*Nominal flexural Strength of beam with notch(5mm deep)

Figure in brackets stands for the max. repetitive load

TABLE 6 — RESULTS OF WIND LOAD TEST (Negative pressure 580 kgf/m^2)

	Effective Flange width in design			Experimental Value
	Rib	AIJ Std.	Overall width	
Deflection (mm)	1.04	0.66	0.52	0.50
Flexural Stress (kg/ cm²)	74 (35)	35 (35)	22 (35)	18

Values in parentheses means allowable bending stress obtained by equation(5)

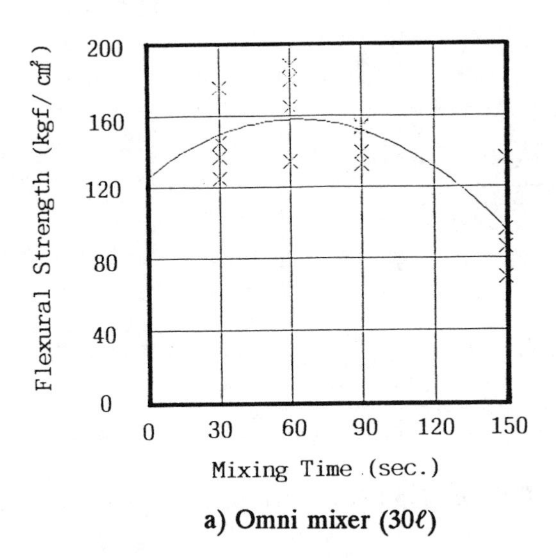

a) Omni mixer (30ℓ)

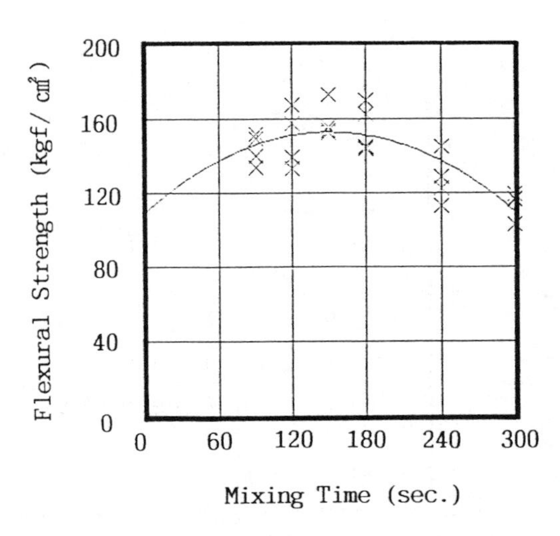

b) Ordinary mortar mixer (70ℓ)

Fig. 1—Relationship between mixing time and flexural strength

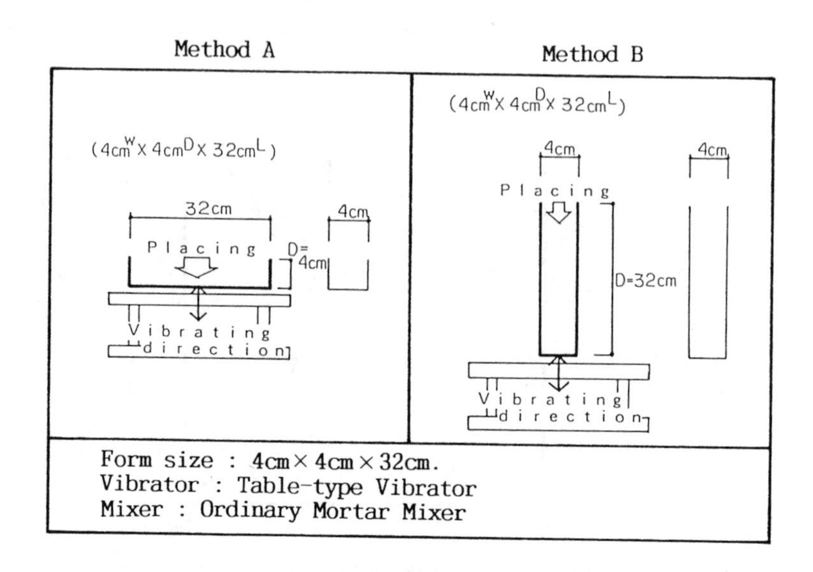

Fig. 2—Relationship between vibration direction and form

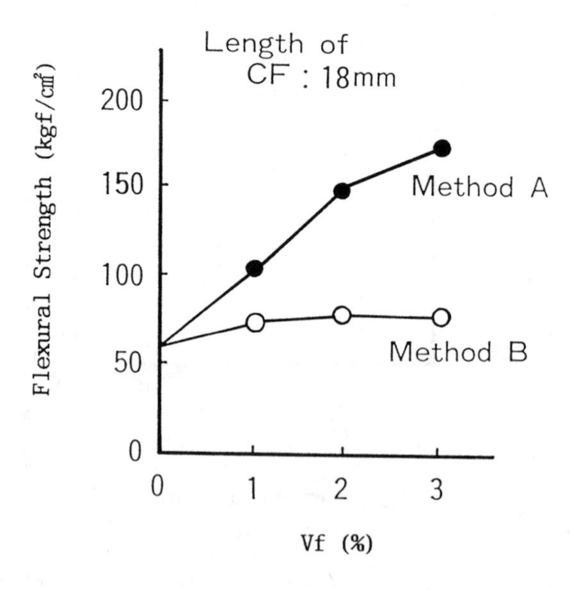

Fig. 3—Relationship between vibration direction and flexural strength

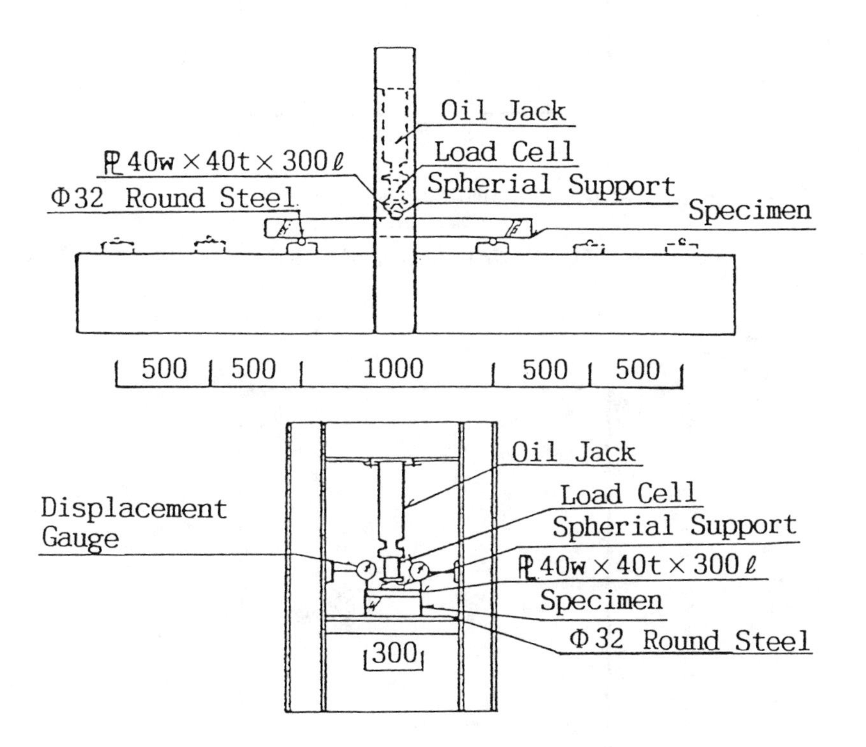

Fig. 4—Bending test of panel

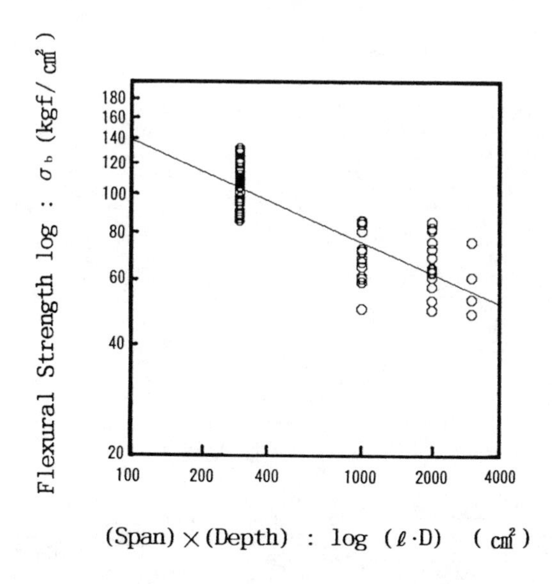

Fig. 5—Scale effect of CFRC

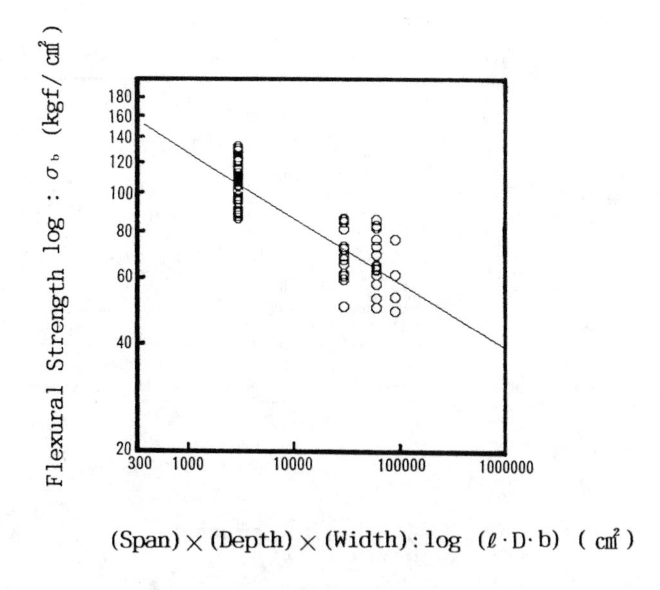

Fig. 6—Scale effect of CFRC

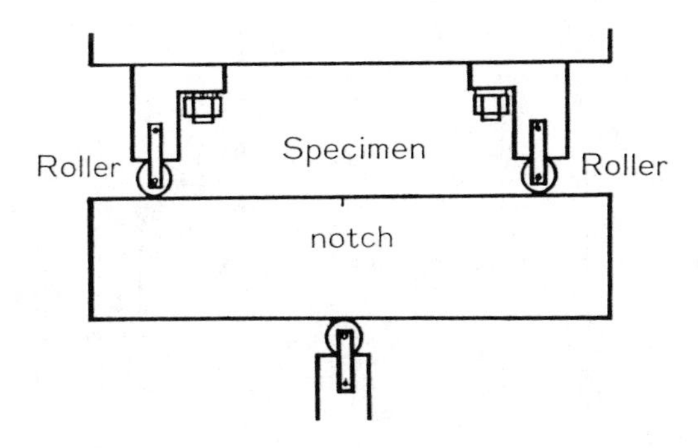

Fig. 7—Bending fatigue test

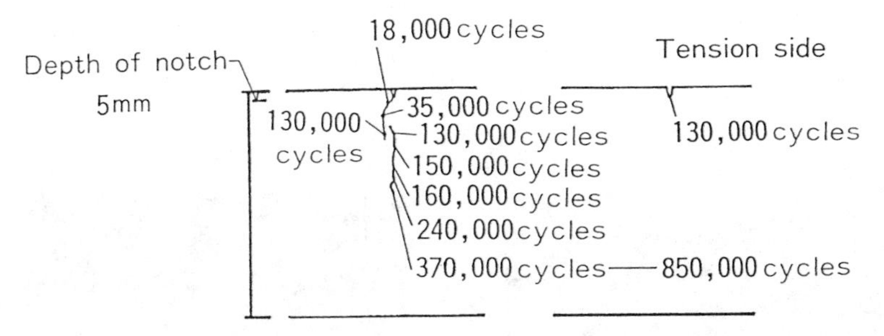

Fig. 8—Progress of fatigue crack progress

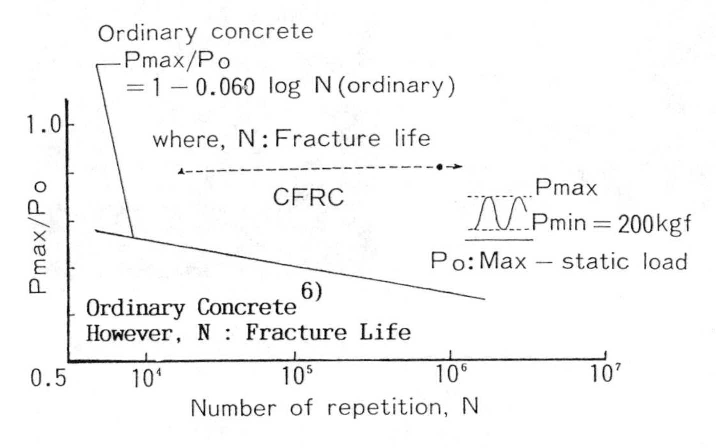

Fig. 9—S-N relationship of CFRC

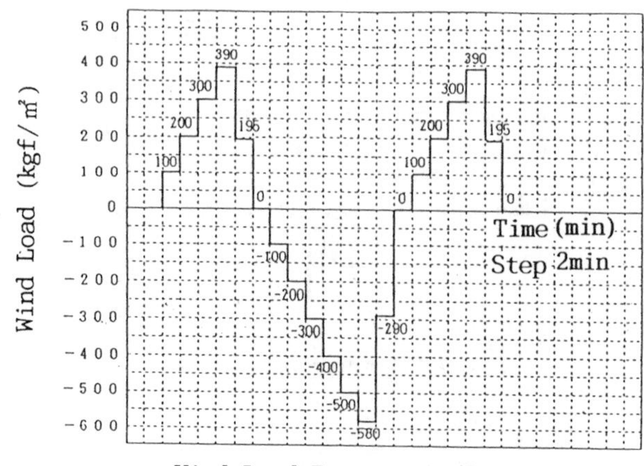

Fig. 10—Wind load resistance test

a) Installation of CFRC panel

b) Measurement

Fig. 11—Wind load test of full-scale panel

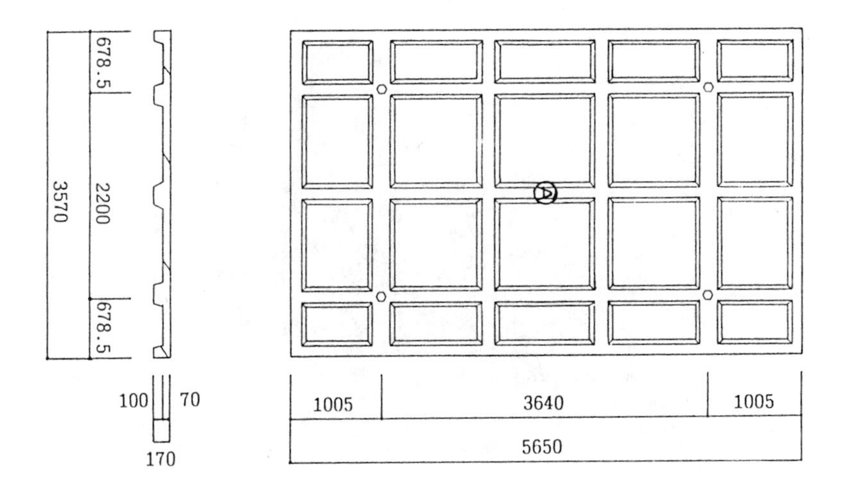

Fig. 12—Shape of curtain wall panel (in mm)

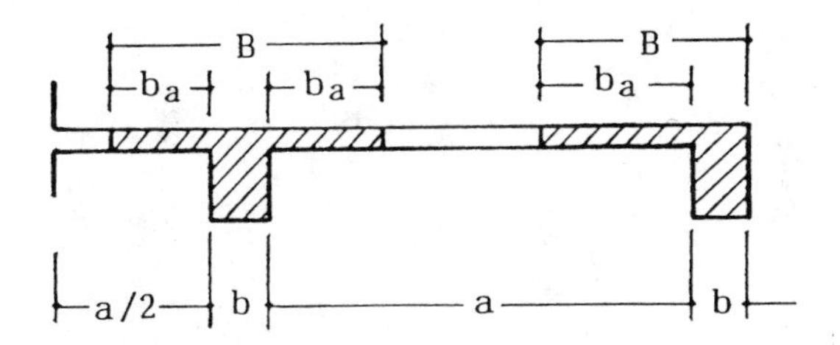

For simple beams

$$b_a = \begin{cases} (0.5-0.3a/\ell_0)a & \text{in which } a<\ell_0 \\ (0.2\ell_0) & \text{in which } a\geq\ell_0 \end{cases}$$

where B: effective flange width

a: distance from side of beam to side of parallel T beam, or sum of flange widths on both sides of individual T beam

ℓ : span length of frame or continuous beam

ℓ_0 : span length of simple beam

Fig. 13—Concept of effective width according to AIJ standard

a) Panel type

b) Spandrel type
and panel type

Fig. 14—Examples of CFRC curtain walls in Japan

SP 142-8

Shear Capacity of Fiber Reinforced Concrete Based on Plasticity of Concrete: A Review

by G.B. Batson and A.G. Youssef

Synopsis: The effectiveness of steel fibers as shear reinforcement to replace and/or augment conventional stirrups in concrete beams with flexural reinforcement has been demonstrated by Batson et al (1972), J. Craig (1984) and other researchers. The current thinking within ACI Committee 544, Fiber Concrete, is to adjust the limiting values of the empirical equations for shear design in ACI 318 Building Code Requirements for Reinforced concrete. However a rational basis for the design or analysis of steel fibers as shear reinforcement has not been developed. Possible approaches can be based on the plasticity of concrete, Chen (1978) and Nielsen (1984) limit state analysis and the modified compression field theory, Marti (1986) and Collins (1984). Test data for flexural reinforced concrete beams using steel fibers as the shear reinforcement matches the lower bound solution for the shear strength as a function of the shear span-depth ratio based on limit states analysis of concrete by Nielsen and Braestrup (1978) and Kemp and Al-Safi (1981). The test data agree well with the theoretical predicted strength assuming the steel fiber concrete is rigid-plastic with a modified Coulomb failure criterion for the yield condition, no tensile strength and the compressive strength is the effective compressive strength.

The plasticity assumption for steel fiber reinforced concrete is supported by research reported on its torsional strength by Narayanan et al (1979 and 1983) where the torsional strength was best predicted by the Nadai's "sand heap" plastic model for a variety of steel fiber volumes in the concrete. The random distribution of the steel fibers at relatively close spacing provides a very ductile mode of failure that is in good agreement with strength theories based on plasticity theory and limit states. The initial test results suggest that a rational design procedure for the shear strength of steel fiber concrete can be based on a modified compression field theory that will be accepted by design engineers.

The paper briefly reviews the current thinking on shear design of beams using steel fibers as the shear reinforcement, plastic material response of steel fiber concrete and test data that agrees with the plasticity properties and limit theorems proposed by Nielsen and Braestrup and by Kemp and Al-Safi for reinforced and prestressed concrete beams without shear reinforcement.

Keywords: Beams (supports); compressive strength; fiber reinforced concretes; metal fibers; plasticity; shear strength; stirrups

Dr. Gordon Batson is a Professor of Civil and Environmental Engineering at Clarkson University, Potsdam, New York. He has been active in research of steel fiber reinforced concrete for over 30 years and has been chairman of ACI 544 and ACI 549.

Mr. Alber Youssef was a graduate research assistant in the CEE Department of Clarkson University.

INTRODUCTION

Steel fibers mixed into concrete have been shown to be effective as shear reinforcement in laboratory tests on beams (Batson et al '72 and Batson and Alguire '87, Sharma '86, Narayanan and Darwish '87, Swamy and Bahia '85, Craig '84). Steel fibers can replace stirrups or augment widely space stirrups for shear reinforcement and also increase the flexural strength of concrete due to the rebars. However, two problems currently hinder the use of steel fiber concrete as a cost effective construction and structural material. First is the lack of a rational design procedure to calculate the quantity of steel fibers required for shear reinforcement that can be easily applied with confidence by the designer. The second is getting steel fiber concrete accepted by code writing bodies, such as ACI 318. The purpose of this paper is to demonstrate that plasticity concepts for concrete can be used to develop a design procedure for shear design of reinforced concrete beams using steel fibers for the shear reinforcement.

The incorporation of steel fibers directly into the concrete mix for shear reinforcement can provide cost and labor saving tradeoffs between the costs of bending and placing of stirrups which is labor intensive and the direct incorporation of steel fibers into the concrete mix. In a sense the steel fibers provide a dispersion of reinforcement throughout the volume of the concrete. Steel fiber concrete can be mixed, transported, placed and consolidated with existing concrete construction equipment, but some prior training of the construction workers in proper mixing, handling, and finishing is required.

The ACI 318-89 Code for the design of shear reinforcement does not consider the compression field theory or truss model. ACI 318-89 shear design equations are empirical and they generally provide a conservative design compared to a similar design based on the 1984 Canadian Code (CSA '84) or the European Model Concrete Code (CEB-FIP '78). The adoption of a modified compression field theory along with the plasticity theory of concrete, truss model and limit analysis is most likely too complicated a design procedure for the usual shear and flexural beam designs, but it is useful for unusual loadings, beam shapes or when a more thorough design is required (Vecchio and Collins '88). For steel fiber reinforced concrete beams with flexural reinforcement, plasticity concepts of concrete and the modified compression field theory may provide a rational design procedure that is simple and reliable enough for the usual beam shear design.

PROPOSED SHEAR DESIGN PROCEDURE

The proposed shear design procedure is based upon established concepts of plasticity, limit state analysis and the compression field theory of concrete (Chen '82, Nielsen '84, Collins and Mitchell '86). These concepts can be adapted for steel fiber reinforced concrete by taking advantage of its ductility and toughness to develop a rational design procedure for the shear strength of concrete beams reinforced with flexural steel and using steel fibers to replace the conventional vertical or inclined stirrups shear reinforcement. The concepts of concrete plasticity can be extended to steel fiber reinforced concrete because steel fiber reinforced concrete develops significant ductility and toughness, (area under the stress strain curve), upon the incorporation of 0.5 to 2.0 volume percentage of fibers. Figures 1 and 2 from previous research (Batson et al '72 and Craig '84) show that steel fibers mixed into concrete can replace conventional vertical stirrups as shear reinforcement in beams subjected to flexural loading or to augment the shear capacity of widely spaced stirrups (Batson and Alguire '87). The volume percentage of fibers for the transition from a shear failure to a moment failure depends on the type and volume percentage of fiber and the shear-span depth ratio of the beam. Darwish and Narayanan '90 have recently published a procedure to predict the shear capacity along with charts for the shear design of reinforced and prestressed steel fiber reinforced concrete beams. Umoto '83 developed an equation to predict the shear strength of reinforced concrete beams with steel fibers in the concrete that is in good agreement with wide range of test data. The current thinking within ACI Committee 544, Fiber Reinforced Concrete, is simply to modify the current stress limits of the empirical ACI 318 Code '89 shear capacity equations. The development of a shear design procedure for steel fiber reinforced concrete beams based on accepted concepts of concrete plasticity would be more widely accepted than current empirical equations.

The current research directions for shear design of reinforced concrete beams considers a modified compression field theory and concepts from the truss analog model and plasticity theory of concrete. This is the basis of the European Concrete Committee Model Code and the 1984 Canadian Code (Marti '82a, '86b, Nielsen et al '78, Collins and Mitchell '86). Similar procedures are being considered by ACI 318 for future editions of the code.

The attractiveness of plasticity theory of concrete and the upper and lower bound theorems of limit state analysis for the shear strength of concrete beams is that a single parameter, called the effectiveness or efficiency factor related to the compressive strength of the concrete, needs to be determined from laboratory experiments or for some simple loadings can be determined theoretically (Nielsen '84, Nielsen and Braestrup '78). The effectiveness factor can be thought of as a parameter that reflects the limited ductility of plain concrete. A rigid-plastic constitutive model is assumed for the steel fiber concrete represented by a modified Coulomb material with zero tensile cutoff, shown in Figure 3. The constitutive model can be modified to account for the tensile strength of the steel fiber concrete (Vecchio and Collins '88) for the modified compression field theory, but will not be done for this paper.

PLASTICITY OF STEEL FIBER REINFORCED CONCRETE

Figure 4 shows the tensile strength versus displacement for a range of steel fiber volume percentages (Gopalaratnam and Shah '87). In particular the strain softening after the peak load, negative sloping portion of the stress strain curve, depends on the volume percentage and shape of the fibers. For fibers with good mechanical resistance to pullout, the post peak residual strength is increased.

The load-deflection curve for a steel fiber reinforced concrete beam can exhibit elastic-plastic behavior. The toughness of a material is the area under the load deflection curve and represents the amount of energy a material can absorb before failure. The ASTM C1018 standard test method has been developed to compare the material behavior of steel fiber concrete based on a toughness index evaluated from the load deflection data for third point (four point) flexural loading of beams. The toughness index is computed by dividing the area under the load deflection curve at a specified multiple of the first crack deflection by the area up to the first crack deflection (Johnston '82a, '82b). The toughness index of plain concrete is 1 and for an elastic-plastic material behavior the toughness indices are 5, 10 or 30 at deflections 3, 5.5 or 15.5 times the first deflection respectively. Depending on the shape and volume percentage of the fibers, the toughness indices can equal or exceed the values for the ideal elastic-plastic behavior as shown in Figure 5.

Additional evidence for the appropriateness of plasticity theory for steel fiber reinforced concrete can be found in the test results for the torsion tests of beams. Test data (Narayanan and Toorani-Goloosalar '79 and Narayanan and Kareem-Palanjian '83) for the torsion of steel fiber concrete beams show the ultimate torsional strength to be much greater than predicted by either the ACI or CP 110 codes and is closely predicted by Nadai's sand-heap analog (plastic theory) using the split cylinder test for the tensile strength of the steel fiber concrete. The ultimate torsional strength for 21 torsion tests (Mansur and Paramasivam '82) are best predicted by the sand-heap model of plasticity. Figure 6 is the correlation of the predicted torsion versus the torsion test data from Narayanan and Toorani-Goloosalar '79, Narayanan and Kareem-Palanjian '83, and Mansur and Paramasivam '82 which covers a wide range of steel fiber types and volume percentages. (Contrary results are reported by Mindess '80. He states that there is no significant increase in the torsional strength based on small test specimens about 3/4 x 3/4 x 13 inches (20 x 20 x 330 mm) sawed from a large cast slab to minimize the alignment effects of fibers near the cast surfaces.

The material behavior of steel fiber concrete after the peak stress in the strain softening region can be modified by the fiber shape and volume to exhibit elastic-plastic behavior. Therefore it appears that the assumed material behavior and the solutions from plasticity theory and limit state analysis used by Nielsen and Braestrup '78 and Kemp and Al-Safi '81 to determine the ultimate shear strength of beams without stirrups can apply to the evaluation of the shear capacity of steel fiber reinforced concrete beams in flexure subjected to concentrated loads.

PLASTICITY CONCEPTS FOR CONCRETE

Theoretically a perfectly rigid-plastic material will deform continuously after the yield stress is reached. The load capacity of a structure for such a material can be found by limit state analysis and the upper and lower bound theorems of plasticity. A short history of the development and application of plasticity theory to reinforced and plain concrete has been presented by Nielsen '84. Concrete structures with a low flexural reinforcing steel content are controlled primarily by the yielding of the reinforcing steel, such as slabs and beams, are logical applications of concrete plasticity theory. Examples are the yield line theory for slabs (Johansen '62 and Wood '61) and the yield hinges for beams and frames (Baker '56). However, structures that are over reinforced and controlled by the compressive strength of the concrete, the applicability of plasticity is not as obvious. Nevertheless plasticity theory has provided good solutions when compared to test results if a reduced concrete strength, termed the effective concrete strength, is used in the plasticity solutions. The effective strength is defined as a fraction of the uniaxial compressive or tensile strength of the concrete.

$$f_c = \nu f_c' \tag{1}$$

$$f_t = \nu f_t' \tag{2}$$

where ν is the effectiveness factor and has a value between 0 and 1. The effectiveness factor, ν, can be determined analytically for a few simple cases such as the pure bending of beam with tensile reinforcement. The analytical solution for ν is a function of the compressive strength of the concrete f_c', the yield stress of the steel, f_y, and the percentage of reinforcement, ρ. For low values of ρ, ν is approximately proportional to the inverse square root of the compressive strength of the concrete as shown in Figure 7 (Nielsen '84). Generally the effectiveness factor, ν, has to be determined from experiments which depend on the material properties, geometry and loading conditions. The geometrical effects arise from stress concentrations around the reinforcing bars which may be neglected for most practical conditions (i.e. sufficient development length and cover of the flexural steel) and the size of beam. Also it has been shown that ν decreases with increasing dimensions of the structure (Roik-jaer et al '78, Bazant and Sun '87).

The analytical solutions (Narayanan and Toori-Goloosalar '79, Narayanan and Kareem-Palanjian '83, Mansur and Paramasivam '82) that predict the ultimate torsional strength of the steel fiber concrete beams requires knowing the tensile strength of the steel fiber reinforced concrete and these data are obtained from empirical relationships between compression and split tension tests. Mansur and Paramasivam '82 suggest that the biaxial stress state data for steel fiber concrete should be used in place of the split cylinder data that are empirically related to the compression cylinder test data. Yin, Su, Mansur and Hsu '89 report data for the biaxial compression of steel fiber concrete that shows increases in the compressive strength up to 35 percent compared to the uniaxial compressive strength. For biaxial compression, the stiffness increases in the major principal stress direction and slows down the development of tensile stresses in the unloaded direction. Also there is an increase in the ductility for the biaxial stress state.

PLASTICITY SOLUTION AND EXPERIMENTAL RESULTS FOR BEAMS WITHOUT SHEAR REINFORCEMENT

Nielsen and Braestrup '78 obtained the upper and lower bound solution for a rectangular concrete beam without stirrups supporting concentrated loads as shown in Figure 7. Later, Kemp and Al-Safi '81 presented a revised upper bound solution which gave a slightly lower collapse load, established the minimum amount of reinforcement required for yielding, a range of values of ν and the shear-span depth ratio. The assumptions used by Nielsen and Braestrup '78 can be summarized as follows:

1) Beam is in a state of plane stress and bond failure does not occur between the reinforcement and the concrete.

2) Reinforcement is rigid-plastic and unable to resist lateral forces.

3) Concrete is rigid-plastic with a modified Coulomb failure criterion as the yield condition and the associated flow rule. Tensile strength of the concrete is neglected and the compressive strength is the effective strength $\nu f_c'$.

4) Elastic deformations and work hardening are neglected and dowel action by the flexural reinforcement does not contribute to the shear strength of the concrete.

The lowest upper bound solution by Nielsen and Braestrup '78 is given by:

$$\frac{\tau}{f_c} = \frac{\nu}{2}\left[\sqrt{\left(\frac{a}{h}\right)^2 + \frac{4\,\phi\,(\nu - \phi)}{\nu^2}} - \frac{a}{h}\right] \tag{3}$$

for $\phi \leq \nu/2$, and

$$\frac{\tau}{f_c} = \frac{\nu}{2}\left[\sqrt{\left(\frac{a}{h}\right)^2 + 1} - \frac{a}{h}\right] \tag{4}$$

for $\phi \geq \nu/2$ and a/h is the shear-span depth ratio. ϕ is defined as the degree of reinforcement given by:

$$\phi = \frac{A_s\, f_y}{b h f_c} \tag{5}$$

The highest lower bound solution by Nielsen and Braestrup '78 is given by:

$$\frac{\tau}{f_c} = \frac{\nu}{2}\left[\sqrt{\left(\frac{a}{h}\right)^2 + \frac{4\phi\,(\nu - \phi)}{\upsilon^2}} - \frac{2}{h}\right] \tag{6}$$

for $\phi \leq \nu/2$ and

$$\frac{\tau}{f_c} = \frac{\nu}{2}\left[\sqrt{\left(\frac{a}{h}\right)^2 + 1} - \frac{a}{h}\right] \tag{7}$$

for $\phi \geq \nu/2$.

Nielsen and Braestrup '78 upper and lower bound solutions are the same, therefore the ultimate shear load is the correct plasticity solution. Their experimental data shown in Figure 8 are in excellent agreement with the theoretical results. Figure 9 shows the shear strength as function of the shear-span depth ratio for $\nu = 0.6$ and $\phi = 0.3$. Figure 10 shows the shear capacity as a function of the shear-span ratio with curves for three values for ϕ.

An important result from the tests by Nielsen and Braestrup '78 is that the value of the effectiveness factor, ν, can be given for all practical purposes by:

$$\nu = 0.7 - f_c / 200 \quad (f_c \ in \ M \ P_a) \tag{8}$$

It is expected that Equation (8) should be modified for steel fiber concrete because the constant may depend on the volume percentage and possibly the shape of the fiber.

Kemp and Al-Safi '81 show that the upper bound solution of Nielsen and Braestrup '78 did not completely satisfy equilibrium and for certain conditions the ultimate shear load is lower. Kemp and Al-Safi '81 upper bound solution is complex and can only be expressed conveniently as two equations which reduce to Equation 3 or 4 for the value of $\phi = \phi_b$ which is the critical amount of tensile flexural steel required for yielding. The critical value, ϕ_b, ranges from $\nu/4$ for $a/h = 0$ to $3\nu/8$ for $a/h = \infty$, but for $a/h \geq 0.5$ the range of ϕ is restricted to between 0.32ν and 0.375ν. Figure 11 shows very little difference between the two solutions for a beam with tension reinforcing steel only

Because the Kemp and Al-Safi '81 upper bound solution reduces to the Nielsen and Braestrup '78 solution for the critical amount of steel required for yielding, a theoretical value for the effectiveness factor, ν, can be obtained from Equation (7) as:

$$\nu = \frac{\left(\frac{\tau}{f_c}\right)^2 + \phi^2}{\phi - \left(\frac{a}{h}\right)\left(\frac{\tau}{f_c}\right)} \tag{9}$$

where ϕ is the degree of reinforcement for bottom (tension) steel defined by Equation (5). Equation (9) shows very good agreement with a series of prestressed concrete beams without shear reinforcement tested by Roik-jaer '78 for a $\nu = 0.46$.

Figure 12 shows the data from Table 1 plotted on the curves for the upper bound solution by Nielsen and Braestrup and by Kemp and Al-Safi '81 with $\nu = 1.0$ and $\phi = 0.18$. Curves for ν less than 1.0 plot below the curves shown for the same value of ϕ and for the curves to be higher would imply that ν is greater than 1.0. The graph suggests that the contribution of the tensile strength of the fiber concrete needs to be considered along with the actual yield stress of the flexural steel (not the nominal ASTM stress grade) and possibly the position of the flexural steel in the cross section of the beam. Solutions for a beam without shear reinforcement taking into account these refinements are available (Nielsen '84).

Test data by other researchers are consistent with results shown in Figure 12. Batson and Alguire '87 data for three T-beams without stirrups, span-depth ratio of 3.6, average value of $\phi = 0.20$, fiber volume percentages of 0.2, 0.3, and 0.5 have computed values for the effectiveness factors, ν, of 0.40, 0.46, and 0.44, respectively. Test data from Swamy and Bahia '85 for four beams with a shear span-ratio of 4.5, average value of $\phi = 0.47$, fiber volume percentages of 0.0, 0.4, 0.8, and 1.2 have computed values for the effectiveness factor, ν, of 0.55, 0.74, 1.0 and 0.94. Additional data on the shear capacity of steel fiber beams can be found in Sharma '86, Narayanan and Darwish '86 and Narayanan and Darwish '88.

Youssef '89 data in Tables 2 and 3 are for 12 beams, 8 x 6 x 78 inches (203 x 152 x 2000 mm) larger than those plotted in Figure 12; three beams with 0.4 and three beams with 0.8 steel fiber volume percentage and singly reinforced with 3-#5 bars. These data are plotted in Figure 13 and good show agreement with the Nielsen and Braestrup '78 solution for ν of 1.0.

Exceptions to the trend of data in Figures 11 and 12 can be found. Williamson '75 tested two prototype size beams, 12 x 21.5 inches by 21 foot simple span (304 x 546 x 6400 mm) with three concentrated loads, shear span-depth ratio of 5.18, 7-#8 rebars, and 1.5 volume percentage of fibers. For $\phi = 0.31$, the computed value for ν was larger than 1.0. The shear strength was 39 percent greater than companion beams without stirrups, however the steel fiber reinforced beams failed in shear even though the flexural steel reached the theoretical yield stress. Bollana '80 test data for six two span continuous beams do not apply because the displacement field assumed by Nielsen and Braestrup '78 only applied to determinate beams.

The few cases were the effectiveness factor, ν, is theoretically greater than one indicates that the assumed constitutive model, modified Coulomb material with zero tensile cut off, needs to be revised for steel fiber concrete perhaps to include the tensile strength.

The preliminary success of predicting the shear capacity of steel fiber reinforced concrete beams without stirrups based on concepts for concrete plasticity suggests that an analysis and design procedure can be developed similar to the modified compression field theory used in the Canadian concrete code. An alternate approach based on crack arrest mechanics (Romualdi and Batson '63) and fracture mechanics (Hawkins et al '77 and Hawkins '84) for the analysis and design of steel fiber reinforced concrete is not being readily accepted by code writing bodies. The reluctance of code writing bodies and engineers to adopt radical changes in established design procedure that impact on public safety leaves fracture mechanics at a significant disadvantage at the present time. Perhaps the plasticity of concrete and related developments will be more readily accepted.

CONCLUSIONS

Tension, torsion and flexure test data show that steel fiber reinforced concrete can exhibit elastic-plastic behavior depending on the shape and fiber volume percentage. The ASTM C1018 toughness indices for fiber concrete provide a relative comparison of ductility among various fiber types and volume percentages.

Also it has been shown that steel fibers can be effective as shear reinforcement; replacing stirrups or augmenting the shear capacity of widely spaced stirrups in beams with flexural reinforcement.

The shear capacity of reinforced and prestressed concrete beams without stirrups has been solved using limit analysis states and the plasticity of concrete for simple beams with concentrated loads. Limit analysis and plasticity solutions require the determination of one parameter for the concrete, the effectiveness factor. The value of the effectiveness factor is applied to the tensile or compressive strength of the concrete and its value ranges for zero to unity. The effectiveness factor can be determined analytically for a few simple load cases or experimentally (Nielsen and Braestrup '78). The test results for the shear capacity of flexural reinforced steel fiber reinforced concrete beams without stirrups agree very well with the plasticity and limit analysis solutions. The effectiveness factor for the steel fiber reinforced concrete is nearly one. For a few cases the theoretical computed values are greater than one, which indicates that assumed constitutive model, modified Coulomb material with zero tensile cut off, needs to be adjusted for steel fiber concrete to include its tensile strength.

The good agreement in predicting the shear capacity of steel fiber reinforced concrete beams using concrete plasticity concepts indicates that a design and analysis procedure can be developed like the modified compression field theory of the Canadian concrete code that will be accepted by code writing bodies and the design engineers.

REFERENCES

American Concrete Institute, "Building Code Requirements for Reinforced Concrete ACI 318-89," American Concrete Institute, Detroit, Michigan, 1983.

ASTM "Standard Test Method for Flexural Toughness and First-Crack Strength of Fiber Reinforced Cocnrete", C1018-89, Vol. 04.02, Philadelphia, PA.

Baker, A.L.L., The Ultimate Load Theory Applied to the Design of Reinforced and Prestressed Concrete Frames, Concrete Publications, Ltd., London, 1956.

Batson, G., J. Jenkins, R. Spatney, "Steel Fibers as Shear Reinforcement in Beams," J. of American Concrete Inst., Proceedings. Vol. 69, October 1972, pg. 640-644.

Batson, G.B., C. Alguire, "Steel Fibers as Shear Reinforcement in Reinforced Cocnrete T-Beams," Proc. International Symposium Fibre Reinforced Concrete," Vol. I, Structural Engineering Research Center, Madras, India, 1987, pg. 1,113-1,123.

Bazant, Z.P., H.H., Sun, "Size Effect in Diagonal Shear Failure: Influence of Aggregate and Stirrups," ACI Material Journal, Vol. 84, No. 4, July-August 1987, pg. 259-272.

Bollana, R.D., "Steel Fibers as Shear Reinforcement in Two Span Continuous Reinforced Concrete Beams," Unpublished MS Thesis, Clarkson University, Potsdam, NY, May 1980.

Chen, W.F., Plasticity in Reinforced Concrete, McGraw-Hill Book Company, N.Y., 1982.

Collins, M.P., D. Mitchell, "A Rational Approach to Shear Design - The 1984 Canadian Code Provisions," J. of ACI, Nov.-Dec. 1986, No. 6, Proc. Vol. 83, pg. 925-933.

Craig, R.J., "Structural Applications of Reinforced Fibrous Concrete," Concrete International, Vol. 6, No. 12, Dec. 1984, pg. 28-32.

CSA, "Design of Concrete Structures for Buildings," (CAN 3-A23.3-M84), Rexdale, Ontario, Canada, 1984, 281 pp.

Darwish, I. Y., R. Narayanan, "Design Charts for Reinforced and Pressed Fibre Concrete Elements", The Structural Engineer", Vol 68, No 2, 23 Jan 1990, pg 34-39.

Gopalaratnam, V.S., S.P. Shah, "Tensile Failure of Steel Fiber-Reinforced Mortar," Proc. ASCE, J. of Engineering Mechanics, Vol. 113, No. 5, May 1987, pg. 635-652.

Johansen, K.W., Yield-Line Theory, Cement and Concrete Association, London, 1962.

Johnston, C.D., "Definition and Measurement of Flexural Toughness Parameters for Fiber Reinforced Concrete," Cement, Concrete and Aggregates, ASTM,

Winter 1982, pg. 53-60.

Johnston, C.D., "Precision of Flexural Strength and Toughness Parameters for Steel Fiber Reinforced Concrete," Cement, Concrete, Aggregates, Winter 1982, pg. 61-67.

Kemp, K.O., M.T. Al-Safi, "An Upper Bound Rigid-Plastic Solution for the Shear Failure of Concrete Beams Without Shear Reinforcement," Magazine of Concrete Research, Vol. 33, No. 115, June 1981, pg. 96-102.

Mansur, M.A. and Paramasivam, P., "Steel Fibre Reinforced Concrete Beams in Pure Torsion," The Int. Journal of Cement Composites and Lightweight Concrete, V. 4, No. 1, Feb. 1982, pg. 39.

Mansur, M.A., Ong, K.D.G., Paramasivam, P., "Shear Strength of Fibrous Concrete Beams Without Stirrups," Journal of Structural Engineering, ASCE, Vol. 112, No. 9, September 1986, pp. 2066-2079.

Marti, P., "Basic Tools of Reinforced Concrete Design," J. ACI, Jan.-Feb. 1985, No. 1, Proc. Vol. 82, pg. 46-56.

Mindess, S., "Torsion Tests of Steel-Fibre Reinforced Concrete," International Journal of Cement Composites, Vol. 2, No. 2, May 1980, pg. 85-89.

Narayanan, K. and Toorani-Goloosalar, Z., "Fibre Reinforced Concrete in Pure Torsion and in Combined Bending and Torsion," Proceedcings of the Institute of Civil Engineers, Part 2, 1979, 67, Dec., pg. 987.

Narayanan, R. and Kareem-Palanjian, A.S., "Steel Fibre Reinforced Concrete Beams in Torsion," The Int. Journal of Cement Composite and Lightweight Concrete, V. 5, No. 4, Nov. 1983, pg. 235.

Narayanan, R., Darwish, T.Y.S., "Use of Steel Fibers as Shear Reinforcement," ACI Structural Journal, Vol. 84, No. 3, May-June 1987, pp. 216-227.

Narayanan, R. and Darwish, T.Y.S., "Fiber Concrete Deep Beams in Shear," ACI Structural Journal, Vol. 85, No. 2, March-April 1988, pg. 141-149.

Nielsen, M.P., M.W. Braestrup, and F. Bach, "Rational Analysis of Shear in Reinforced Concrete Beams," Int. Assoc. Bridge and Structural Engineering, Proc. P-15178, May 1978, 16 pp.

Nielsen, M.P., M.W. Braestrup, "Shear Strength of Prestressed Concrete Beams Without Web Reinforcement," Magazine of Concrete Research, Vol. 30, No. 104, Sept. 1978, pg. 119-127.

Nielsen, M.P., Limit Analysis and Concrete Plasticity, Prentice Hall, Englewood Cliffs, N.J., 1984.

Roik-jaer, M., C. Pedersen, M.W. Braestrup, M.P. Nielsen, F. Bach, "Load-carrying Capacity of Beams Without Shear Reinforcement," (In Danish) Danmarks tekniske Hojskole, Afdelinyen for Baerende Konstruktioner, Rapport

Nr. I-62, 1978, 44 pp.

Romualdi, J. P., G.B. Batson, "Mechanics of Craxk Arrest in Concrete," Proc. ASCE, Vol.89, N0. 6, June 1964, pg. 147-168.

Sharma, A.K., "Shear Strength of Steel Fiber Reinforced Concrete Beams," J. of American Concrete Institute Proceedings, Vol. 83, No. 4, July-August 1986, pp. 624-628.

Swamy, R.N., H.M. Bahia, "The Effectiveness of Steel Fibers as Shear Reinforcement," Concrete International, March 1985, Vol. 7, No. 3, pg. 35-40.

Vecchio, F.J. and Collins, M.P., "Predicting the Response of Reinforced Concrete Beams Subjected to Shear Using Modified Compression Field Theory," ACI Structural Journal, May-June 1988, pg. 258-268.

Kobayashi, K., "Development of Fibre Reinforced Concrete in Japan",The International Journal of Cement Composites and Ligthweight Concrete, Vol 5, No 1, Feb 1983, pg 27-40.

Williamson, G.R., Knab, L.I., "Full Scale Fibre Concrete Beam Tests," Fibre Reinforced Cement Concrete RILEM Symposium 1975, Editor A. Neville, The Construction Press Ltd., England.

Wood, R.H., Plastic and Elastic Design of Slabs and Plates, Thames and Hudson, London, 1961.

Yin, W.S., Su, E.C.M., Mansur, M.A., Hsu, T.C., "Biaxial Tests of Plain and Fiber Concrete," ACI Materials Journal, Vol. 86, No. 3, May-June 1989, pg. 236-243.

Youssef, A., Steel Fibers Shear Reinforcement in Reinforced Concrete Beams, Unpublished MS Thesis, CEE Department, Clarkson University, Potsdam, N.Y., 13676, April 1989.

TABLE 1 — ANALYSIS OF TEST DATA, BATSON (1972)

Beam	a/d	τ psi	% Fibers	f_c' psi	τ/f
B3	4.4	236.3	0.22	4817	0.049
C2	4.2	208.5	0.22	4817	0.043
D2	4.3	221.1	0.22	4817	0.046
F1	4.0	247.5	0.44	5830	0.042
G3	4.4	201.2	0.22	4817	0.042
L1	4.0	225.0	0.22	4817	0.047
M1	4.6	193.2	0.22	4817	0.040
M3	4.4	192.0	0.22	4817	0.040
N1	5.0	182.0	0.22	4817	0.038
N2	4.8	201.2	0.22	4817	0.042
P2	4.2	243.0	0.44	5830	0.043
R1	3.2	274.0	0.88	5760	0.048
R2	3.4	254.1	0.88	5760	0.044
S3	3.4	295.2	0.88	5760	0.051
W1	1.2	1085.5	1.76	5770	0.188
W2	1.2	1042.5	1.76	5770	0.181
U1	2.8	420.3	1.76	5770	0.073
V2	1.8	575.9	1.76	5770	0.100

Note $\phi = 0.18$ 1 psc = 6.895 kPa

TABLE 2 — BEAM TEST RESULTS OF YOUSSEF

Beam	a/d	% Fiber	f_c' ksi	Failure Load k	Failure Mode
A1	2.37	0.4	5.3	26.0	S
A2	3.56	0.4	5.3	21.0	S
A3	4.74	0.4	5.3	18.4	S
B1	2.37	0.8	5.4	36.2	S
B2	3.56	0.8	5.4	24.0	S
B3	4.74	0.8	5.4	20.2	F
C1	2.37	0.4	6.2	38.0	S
C2	3.56	0.4	6.2	31.0	S
C3	4.74	0.4	6.2	28.0	S
D1	2.37	0.8	5.8	39.0	S
D2	3.56	0.8	5.8	31.0	S
D3	4.74	0.8	5.8	29.0	F

S - Shear Failure
F - Flexure Failure

1 ksi = 6.895 MPa
1 k = 4.448 kN

TABLE 3 — ANALYSIS OF THE TEST RESULTS OF YOUSSEF RELATED TO THE EFFECTIVE DEPTH, *d*

Beam	P k	ϕ	τ ksi	τ/f_c'
A1	13.0	0.285	0.321	0.060
A2	11.5	0.285	0.259	0.049
A3	9.2	0.285	0.227	0.043
B1	18.1	0.280	0.447	0.082
B2	12.0	0.280	0.296	0.055
B3	10.1	0.280	0.249	0.046
C1	19.0	0.223	0.469	0.076
C2	15.5	0.223	0.383	0.062
C3	14.0	0.223	0.315	0.056
D1	19.5	0.238	0.481	0.083
D2	15.5	0.238	0.382	0.066
D3	14.5	0.238	0.358	0.061

1 ksi = 6.895 MPa
1 k = 4.448 kN

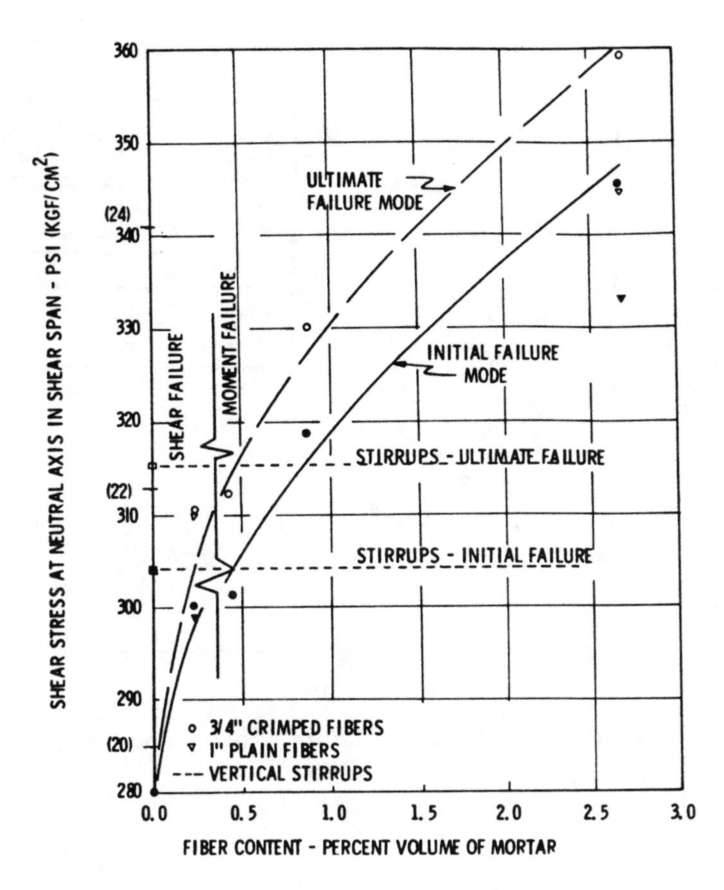

Fig. 1—Shear stress versus fiber volume (Batson et al 1972)

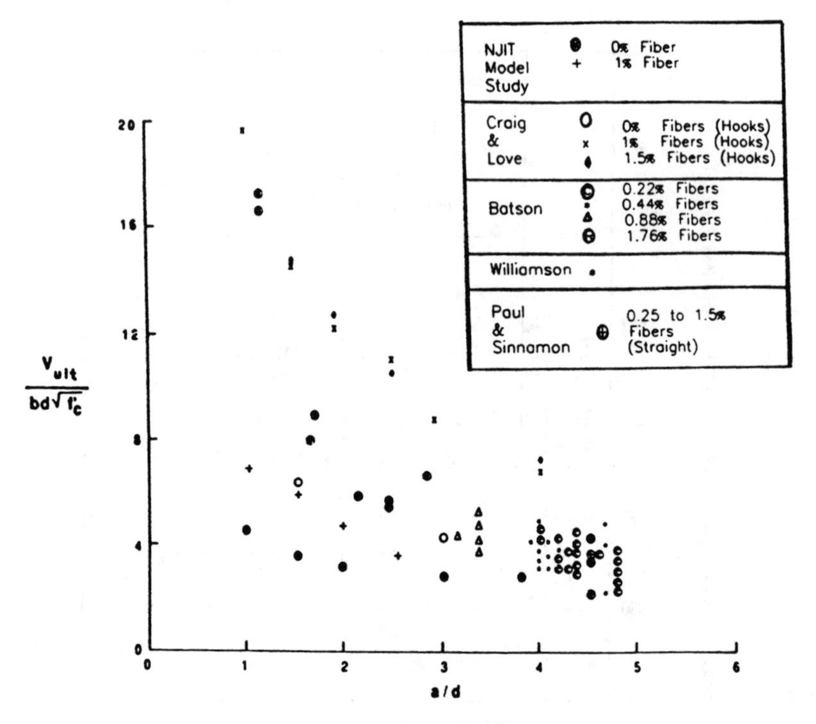

Fig. 2—Shear behavior of reinforced fibrous concrete beams (Craig 1984)

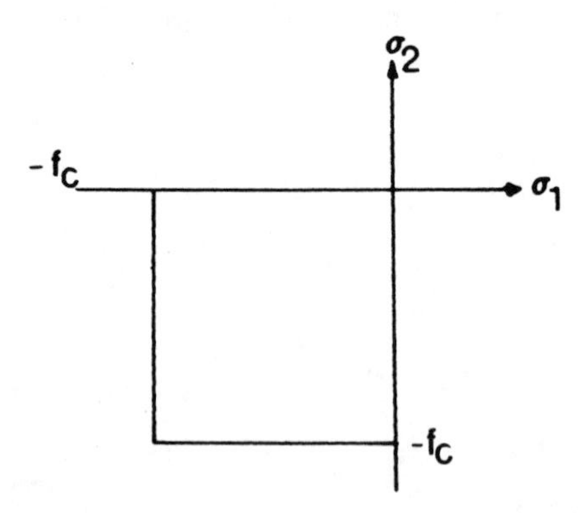

Fig. 3—Modified coulomb failure criterion for fiber concrete (Nielsen and Braestrup 1978)

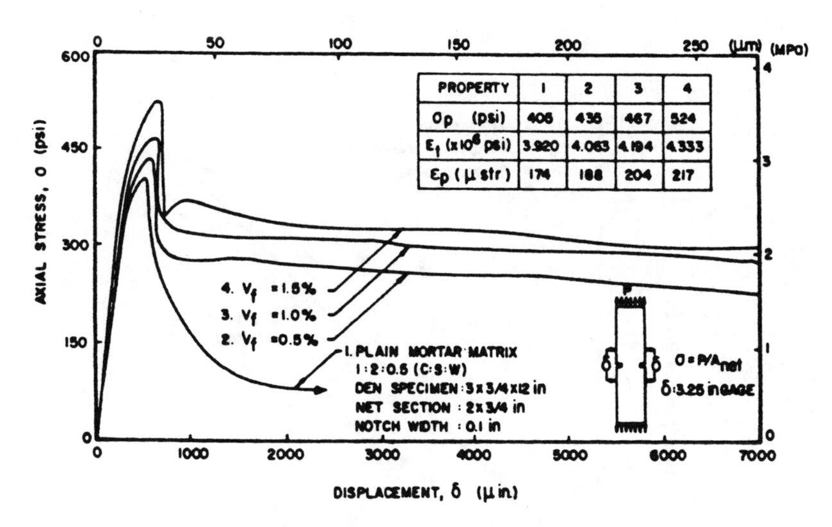

PROPERTY	1	2	3	4
σ_p (psi)	405	435	467	524
E_t ($\times 10^6$ psi)	3.920	4.063	4.194	4.333
ϵ_p (μ str)	174	188	204	217

Fig. 4—Tensile stress versus displacement (Gopalaratnam and Shah 1987)

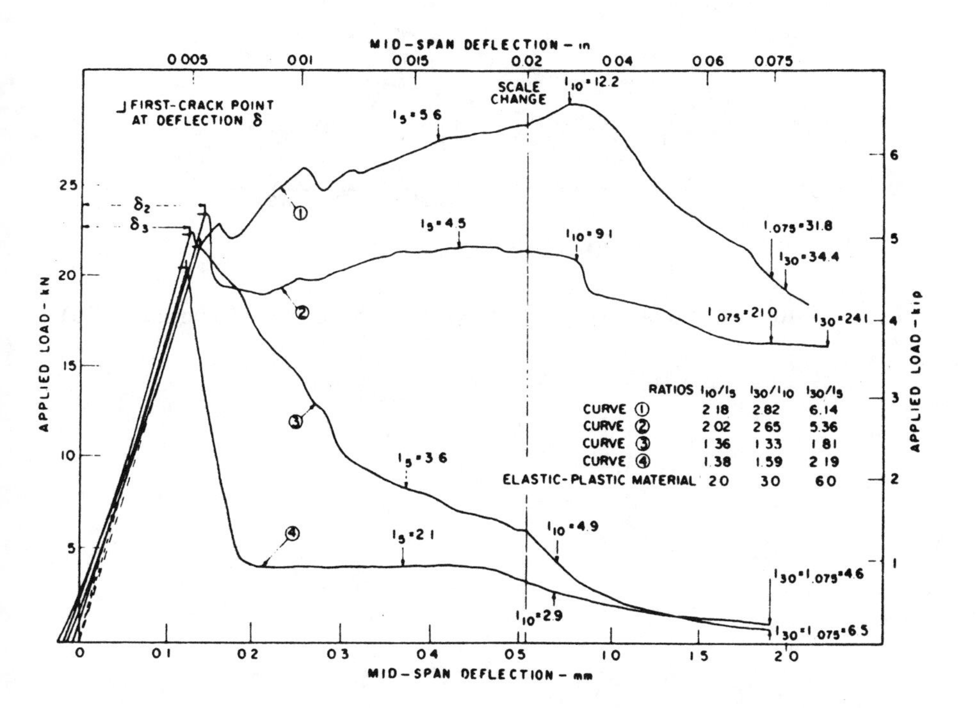

Fig. 5—Toughness indices for fiber concrete (Johnson 1982)

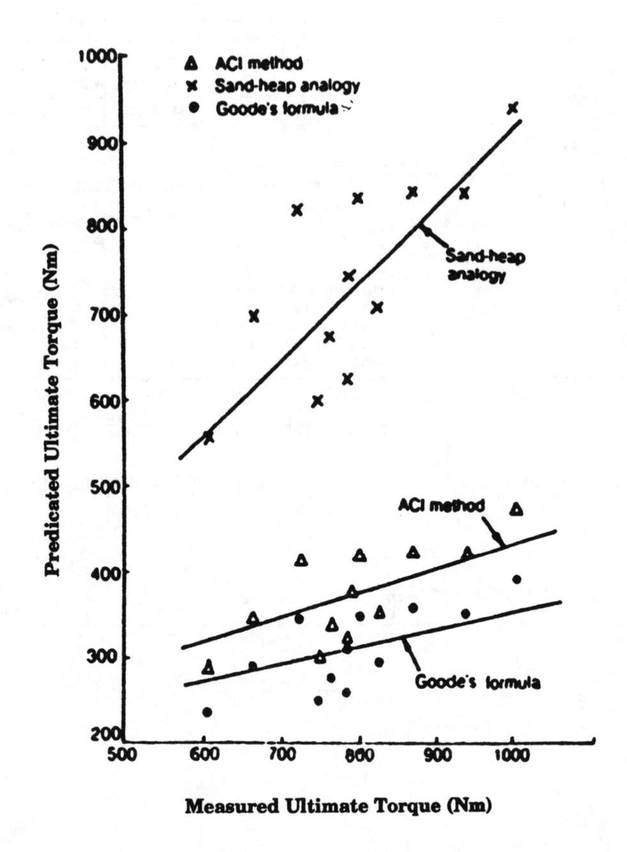

Fig. 6—Ultimate torsion test data (Narayanan and Toorani-Goloosalar 1979)

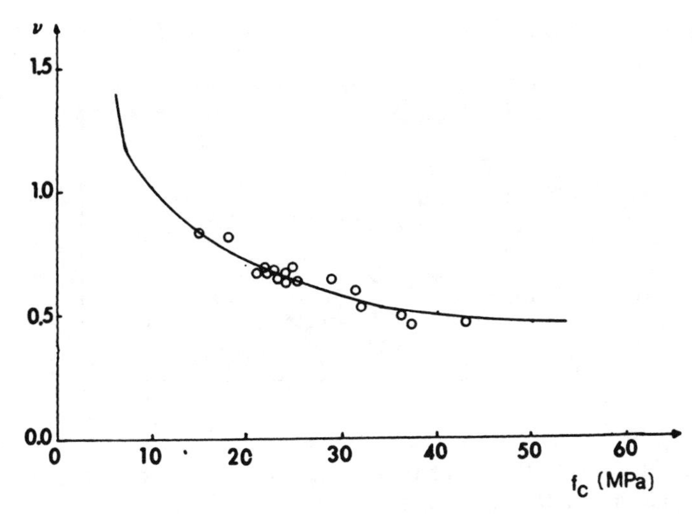

Fig. 7—Effectiveness factor versus compressive strength (Nielsen 1984)

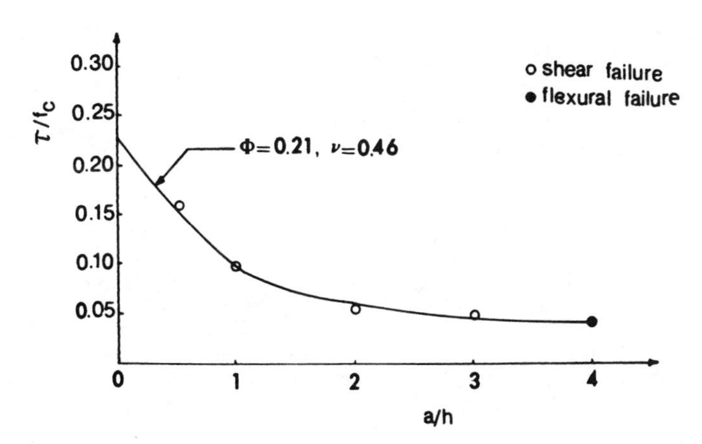

Fig. 8—Test data for shear strength versus shear span-depth ratio (Nielsen and Braestrup 1978)

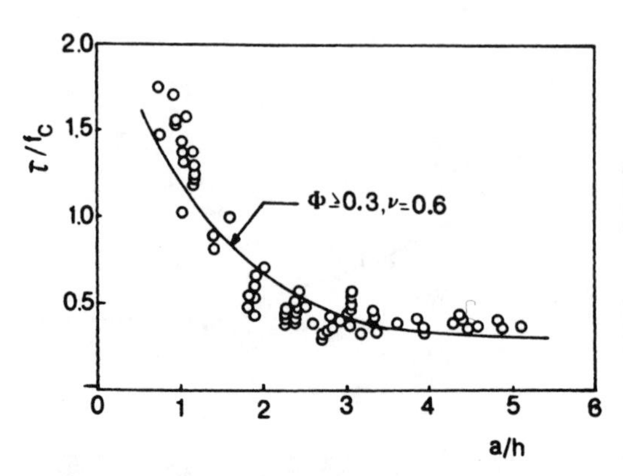

Fig. 9—Test data for shear strength versus shear span-depth ratio (Nielsen and Braestrup 1978)

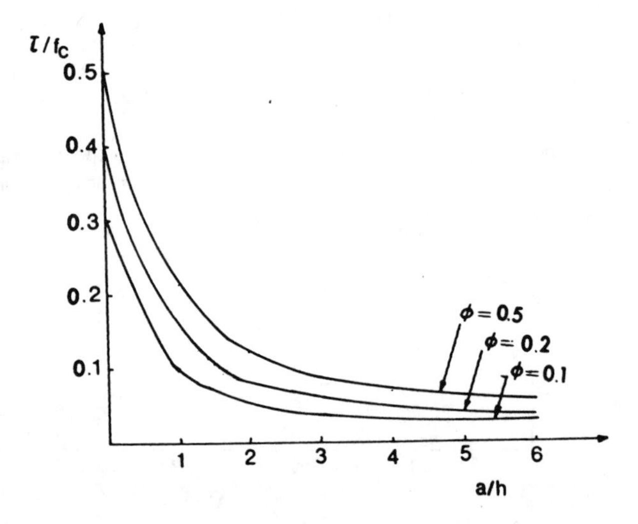

Fig. 10—Shear capacity versus shear span-depth ratio for degrees of reinforcement (Nielsen 1984)

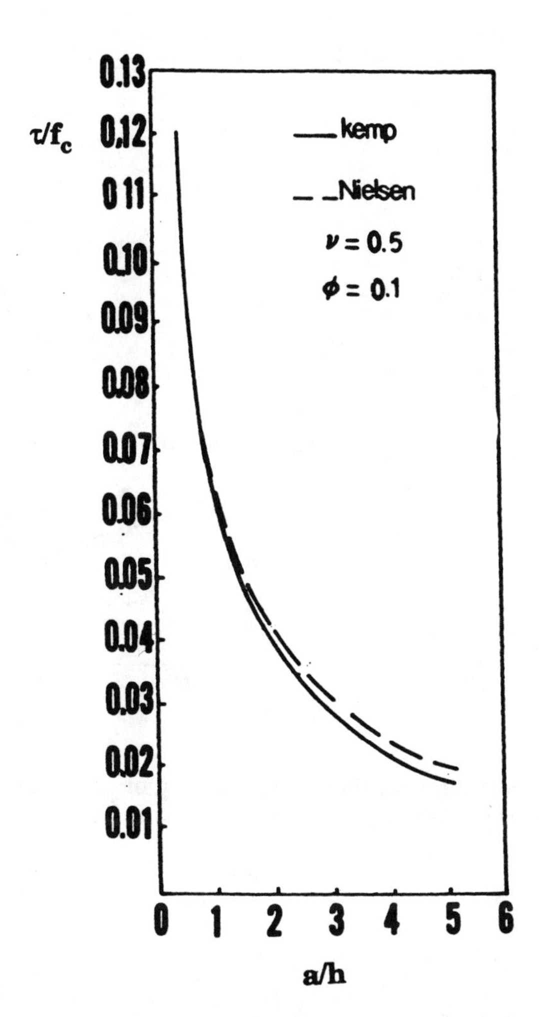

Fig. 11—Difference between Nielsen-Braestrup and Kemp-Al-Safi solution (Kemp and Al-Safi 1981)

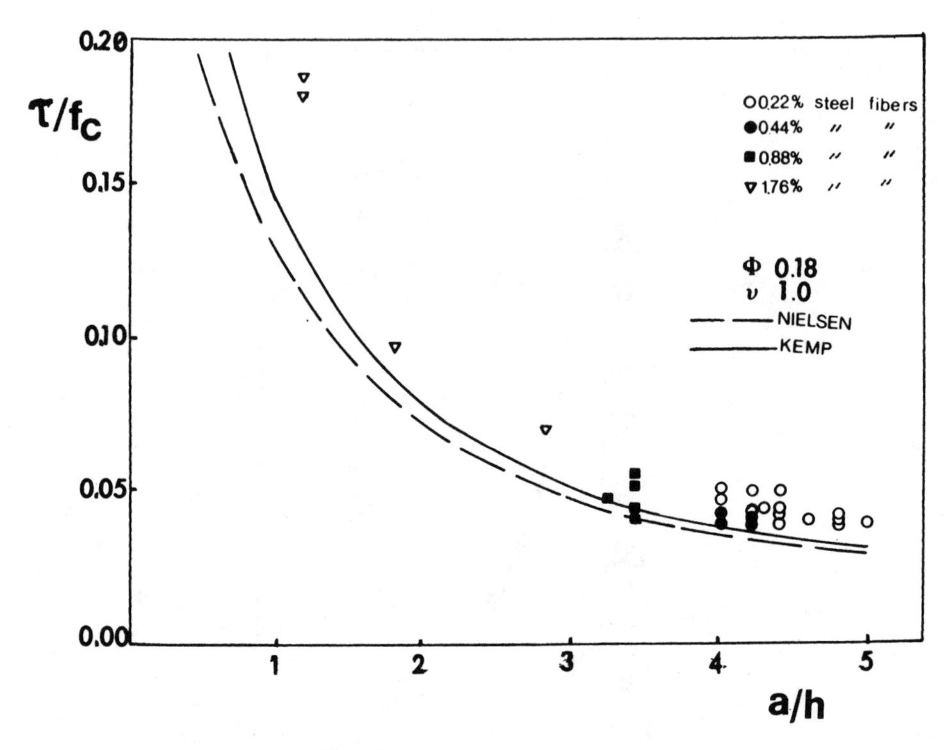

Fig. 12—Shear strength data Batson et al plotted on the Nielsen and Braestrup solution

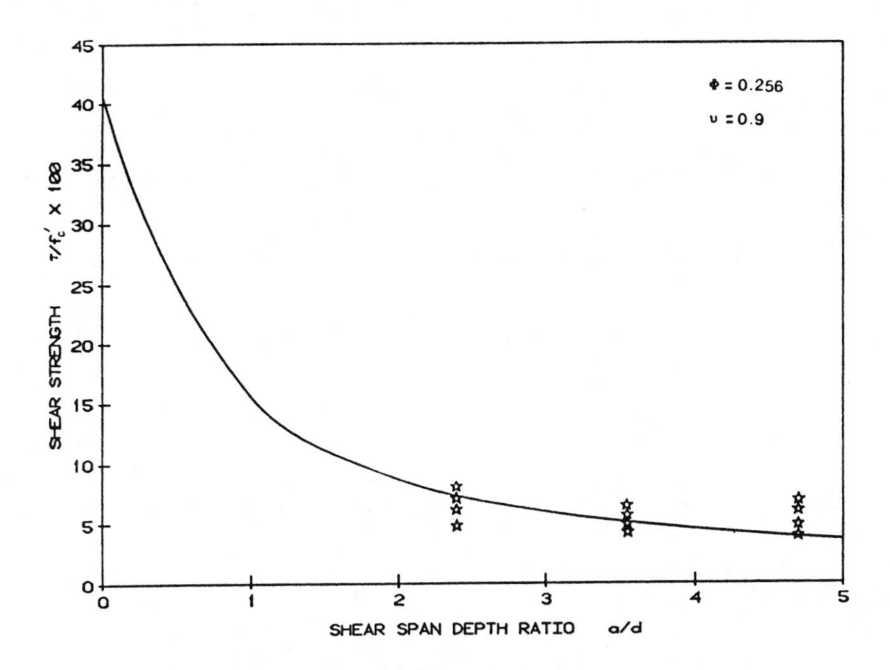

Fig. 13—Shear strength data Youssef plotted on Nielsen and Braestrup solution (Youssef 1989)

SP 142-9

Influence of Test Control on the Load-Deflection Behavior of FRC

by A. Khajuria, Z. El-Shakra, S. Gopalaratnam, and P. Balaguru

Synopsis: Load-deflection responses obtained using deflection control and crack-mouth opening displacement (CMOD) control are compared. CMOD control provides a more stable response in the immediate post-peak regime of the load-deflection response than deflection control. The differences in the responses recorded using these two types of test control are more pronounced for the more brittle mixes. Results reported and discussed in the paper were obtained using third-point loading in flexure. Deflection controlled tests were performed using manual control on a stiff million pound capacity machine. This is similar to the manner in which most commercial laboratories perform deflection controlled tests on concrete specimens. CMOD controlled tests were conducted using a servo-controlled machine. Normal and light-weight aggregate concrete mixes were evaluated with polymeric fiber loadings of 1, 2, 3 and 4 lb/yd^3 [0.6, 1.2, 1.8, 2.4 kg/m^3]. Overall load-deflection reponse and material toughness values are compared and discussed. Beams reinforced with low volume contents of polymeric fibers typically exhibit a sharp drop in load carrying capacity after first-crack. The shape of the load-deflection response in the initial portion of the softening regime is important for toughness computations, particularly for the smaller ASTM indices such as I_5 and I_{10}. Since the type of test control and the level of post-peak stability provided by the test set-up influence the shape of the load-deflection response in this regime of interest, there are questions regarding the objectivity of toughness indices computed at small limiting deflections.

Keywords: Beams (supports); concretes; crack-mouth opening displacement; deflection; fiber reinforced concretes; fibers; flexure; lightweight concretes; strength; tests; toughness

ACI member Anil Khajuria is a graduate student working towards his Ph.D. at Rutgers, The State University of New Jersey. His research interests are new construction material and use of expert system and neural networks for quality control and modelling of material properties.

Zeyad El-Shakra is a graduate student at the University of Missouri-Columbia where he is pursuing his Ph.D. degree. His research interests are modelling and testing of cement and fiber composites.

Vellore S. Gopalaratnam is an associate professor of civil engineering at the University Missouri-Columbia. His current research interests include failure of brittle matrix composites, fracture mechanics, experimental stress analysis, and response of wood-framed structures to wind loads. He is Secretary of ACI Committee 446, Fracture Mechanics, and ACI Committee 544, Fiber Reinforced Concrete.

ACI member P. Balaguru is a professor of civil engineering at Rutgers, The State University of New Jersey. He is the chairman of ACI Committee 549, Ferrocement and Other Thin Sheet Products. He served as Secretary of ACI Committee 214, Evaluation of Results of Tests Used to Determine the Strength of Concrete, and is a member of ACI Committees 215, Fatigue of Concrete; 544, Fiber Reinforced Concrete; and 440, FRP Bar and Tendon Reinforcement. Dr. Balaguru is the co-author of the book, "Fiber Reinforced Cement Composites." In addition, he has authored more than 125 publications on concrete structures and construction management. His research interests are reinforced and prestressed concrete and the development of new construction materials. He serves as a board-of-director for the New Jersey ACI.

INTRODUCTION

The ability to absorb relatively large amounts of energy before complete failure, superior resistance to crack propagation, significant post-cracking residual strength, and the ability to withstand large deformations are characteristics that distinguish fiber reinforced concrete from plain concrete. In recent years, substantial amount of research has been conducted in the development of standardized test procedures to evaluate the improvement in the mechanical performance resulting from the addition of fibers to plain concrete [1-4]. One of the important properties of the resulting composite, generically termed as fiber reinforced concrete (FRC), is its energy absorption capacity or toughness. In general, the area under the static load-deformation curve is used as a measure of toughness. Flexural toughness is often measured and reported although other test configurations have also been used [4,5].

Toughness can be defined in terms of the energy absorbed by a specimen and is typically computed using the area under the load-deflection (P-δ) curve. The P-δ curve is influenced by; (a) the specimen size (depth, span, and width, with depth and span significantly influencing the response recorded); (b) the loading configuration (midpoint versus third-point); (c) the type of control (load, load-point or midpoint deflection, crosshead displacement, and CMOD; (d) the machine stiffness; and (e) the loading rate (static, dynamic, and impact). Also governing the levels of these influences are composition parameters such as the type of fiber (steel-smooth, indented, hooked, and polypropylene-single filament, fibrillated, etc.), volume content and aspect ratio of the fibrous reinforcement, the matrix quality, and the fiber-matrix interface characteristics. To minimize some of these effects, normalization of the energy absorption capacity has been suggested resulting in a nondimensional toughness index [1], or indices that can be related to different levels of serviceability and/or performance [2,3].

Previous investigations have demonstrated the influence of specimen size, loading configuration (notched versus unnotched third-point flexural specimens), and rate of loading on the load-deflection characteristics of FRC [6-8]. Results obtained for the load-deflection response using deflection and CMOD control are compared and discussed in this paper.

EXPERIMENTAL PROGRAM

The primary variables for this investigation are matrix type and fiber content. The two types of matrix were made using normal weight and light-weight aggregates. The fiber content ranged from 1 lb/yd^3 to 4 lb/yd^3 (0.6 kg/m^3 to 2.4 kg/m^3). Seven mixtures were cast for this investigation (four mixtures of normal weight concrete and three mixtures of lightweight concrete). Three specimens each were tested under deflection control and under CMOD control, for each of the seven mixtures. Specimen size used was 4x4x14 in. tested over a 12 in. outer span (102x102x356 mm, 305 mm). Single filament polymeric fibers nominally 23 microns in diameter and 0.75 in. long (19 mm, Nylon 6) were used in this investigation. The low fiber content is typical of commercially used polymeric fiber reinforced concrete mixtures in applications such as slabs. Such mixtures are quite brittle and as a result are relatively more sensitive to the type of test control used. Hence, the mixtures discussed above were studied in the present investigation.

MATERIALS, MIXTURE PROPORTIONS AND SPECIMEN PREPARATION

Materials

The constituent materials used consisted of ASTM Type I cement, natural sand, crushed stone (normal weight), or expanded shale (lightweight), water, water-reducing and air-entraining admixtures, and polymeric fibers. Sieve analysis was performed on the fine aggregate, and normal and lightweight coarse aggregates in accordance with the ASTM specification. Aggregate gradation met ASTM C-33 requirements. The Nylon 6 single filament polymeric fibers were 23 microns (nominal) in diameter and 0.75 in. (19 mm) long. The mechanical and physical properties of the fibers are presented in Table 1.

Mixture Proportions

Concrete was proportioned to obtain approximate 28-day compressive strengths of 3,000 psi (21 MPa) for normal and lightweight mixtures. The matrix composition for both mixtures are presented in Table 2.

The fiber contents used in this investigation were 1, 2, 3, and 4 lb/yd^3 (0.6, 1.2, 1.8, and 2.4 kg/m^3) for the normal weight concrete and 1, 2, 3 lb/yd^3 (0.6, 1.2, and 1.8 kg/m^3) for the lightweight concrete. As mentioned earlier, the fiber contents were intentionally chosen to be low. This ensured that the specimens were brittle. In addition these fiber contents reflect the fiber volume fractions used in most practical application such as slab on grade.

Specimen Preparation

All of the specimens were fabricated at Rutgers University. The coarse and fine aggregates were first thoroughly mixed with 2/3 of the water required, for one minute, in a three cubic foot (0.9 m^3) conventional laboratory mixer. ASTM Type I cement, water-reducing and air-entraining admixtures, and the remainder of the water were added later. The ingredients were mixed for another three minutes. Following this, the fibers were hand dispersed into the mixer while the mixer was operating at the normal mixing speed. Mixing was continued for another ten minutes. The lightweight aggregates were soaked in water for at least twenty-four hours prior to mixing. They were added to the mixture in a saturated surface dry condition. The beams were cast using 4x4x14 in. (102x102x356 mm) plexiglas molds. The molds were vibrated to reduce air voids using a conventional laboratory table vibrator. The specimens were then kept in the molds and were covered with polyethylene sheets for approximately twenty-four hours to prevent loss of moisture. The specimens were later stripped out of the molds and were placed in a humidity room (98% relative humidity) for 27 days. Companion 6x12 in. (152x305 mm) cylinders were tested to confirm average 28-day compressive strengths of 3,000 psi (21 MPa).

DETAILS OF THE TEST SET-UP AND TESTING PROGRAM

Normal, and lightweight concrete, flexural beams were tested in a third-point loading configuration using both deflection and crack mouth opening displacement (CMOD) for controlling the tests. The beams tested under deflection control were unnotched. The beams tested under CMOD control were notched, with a notch-depth to beam-depth ratio of 1:8.

The tests conducted using deflection control were carried out at Rutgers University using a stiff million pound capacity machine. A dial gage with a resolution of 0.0001 in. (0.0025 mm) was used to measure net-deflection of the beam at midspan. The rate of deflection was manually maintained in the range of 0.0025 to 0.003 in/min. (0.063 to 0.075 mm/min). Such manual control is typically used in most commercial laboratories and is allowed in the test procedure described by ASTM C 1018-89 (Note 6, Section 9.3). The dial gage was mounted between the beam and the supporting frame, Fig. 1. Deflections were recorded at regular load increments until the first-crack. After first-crack, loads were recorded for chosen midspan deflections.

A special deflection measuring system was used in order to exclude extraneous deformations at the beam supports, Fig. 1 [9]. Net-deflection at beam midspan was measured using a dial gage mounted between the tension face of the beam and the bottom plate of the supporting frame and attached to the middepth of the specimen (to minimize the effect of twisting). The frame was mounted on the specimen using four screws, two on each side, located exactly over the supports. A schematic of the flexural test set-up used at Rutgers University is shown in Fig. 1.

The tests conducted using CMOD control were carried out at the University of Missouri-Columbia. A servo-controlled MTS testing machine and associated electronics permitted closed-loop flexural testing of notched beams under CMOD control. A standard full-bridge strain-gage-based clip-on gage was used to measure crack-mouth opening displacement. The signal from the clip-on gage was used to control the test. The compressed gage length of the clip-on gage was 0.2 in. (5 mm). Clip-on gage had a maximum displacement range of +0.1 in. (+3 mm). The clip-on gage was mounted between two aluminum lips, 0.2 in. (5 mm) apart, glued across the notch to hold the clip-on gage in place. Three specimens were tested for each series using beam midpoint net-deflection rate of approximately 0.004 in/min. (6 mm/s). The tests were stopped at a crack-mouth opening displacement of 0.08 in. (2 mm).

Net-deflection at the beam midspan was measured in relation to the beam supports using a simple yoke design [6]. The yoke consists of a frame made from aluminum. Two rigid rectangular aluminum bars and a raised aluminum channel section permit the mounting of the displacement transducer (LVDT or other similar devices) at the midpoint (span-wise as well as width-wise) on the compression face of the beam. This mounting scheme also provides for easy zeroing of the displacement transducer. The frame is supported on the compression face of the beam using two cylindrical pins located directly over the beam supports. Since the yoke rests on the beam, it poses no practical difficulty in setting up the net-deflection measurement device. The self weight of the yoke is adequate for lending stability to the set-up and providing necessary precompression for the spring-loaded LVDT or other similar displacement measuring devices. A schematic of the flexural test set-up used at the University of Missouri-Columbia is shown in Fig. 2.

TEST RESULTS AND DISCUSSIONS

Typical load-deflection response obtained using deflection control and CMOD control are plotted in Fig. 3. The smaller load-carrying capacity of the beam tested under CMOD control is due primarily to the smaller net-depth of the specimens tested using CMOD control (3.5 in. versus 4 in. depth for the beams tested using deflection control - 89 mm and 102 mm respectively). However, when the stress levels are compared based on elastic behavior assuming notch insensitive behavior, specimens tested using CMOD control exhibited slightly smaller strengths than those tested under deflection control

It can be observed in Fig. 3 that the precrack load-deflection response is approximately the same for deflection and CMOD control. At the initiation of the crack (at peak-load), the load capacity of the beam reduces substantially because of low fiber contents. In the deflection control test, the midspan deflection rapidly increases until the load drops back to the reserve capacity of the beam. Since the load-deflection response between the peak-load and the reserve capacity could not be measured, these two points are connected by dotted lines. The actual response lies between the shown dotted line and a vertical drop from the peak-load to the reserve capacity of the beam. The CMOD control provides a smooth transition from the peak to post-peak reserve capacity. Since the rate of crack mouth opening displacement (CMOD) is controlled, the machine does not allow a rapid increase in CMOD and hence, the corresponding displacement. At large displacements, both systems provide a continuous line.

Fig. 4 shows the influence of the mixture composition and type of test on the ultimate strength of the specimen. Each point on this and subsequent figures (Figs. 5-6) represents the average result from three tests. The lines plotted in Figs. 4 to 6 represent the averages and show the general trends of the variations. As mentioned earlier, strengths obtained using notched specimens under CMOD control are somewhat lower than those obtained using unnotched specimens under displacement control. Further testing of notched specimens under deflection control in a continuing study, is expected to provide information that will help isolate the influences of test control and probable notch sensitivity of brittle FRC mixtures. FRC specimens made with lightweight matrix were weaker than similarly reinforced specimens made with normal weight matrix in all instances. Although, in the present investigation, only three specimens were tested for each mixture in each test configuration, observations of the scatter in the test results for the CMOD controlled and deflection controlled tests follow trends reported by Gopalaratnam et al [8].

Fig. 5 shows plots of ASTM indices (a) I_5 and (b) I_{100} (computed at a limiting deflection of $50.5\delta_f$, where δ_f is the deflection at first-crack) versus mixture composition parameters. As observed in earlier studies [8,9] toughnesses computed at small limiting deflections, are insensitive to the fiber content (Fig. 5a). In addition it can be seen that I_5 for FRC composites made with normal and lightweight matrices are comparable in all instances. Even at very large limiting deflections such as the one used to compute I_{100}, the ASTM type index can only marginally distinguish between FRC composites made with normal and lightweight matrices. Influence of the type of test control on the ASTM toughness index on the other hand is more readily apparent even at the small limiting deflections (Fig. 5a). This difference is more pronounced for toughness computed at the larger limiting deflections (Fig. 5b).

Energy absorbed by the specimen per unit net cross-sectional area, computed up to a prescribed limiting deflection or until failure (using application specific criteria to define failure) can be used as an alternate method to characterize toughness of

FRC composites [10]. This measure can, with some analytical effort, be related to the more fundamental definitions of fracture energy used in the fracture of concrete. Fig. 6 presents energy absorbed by the different composites using a limiting deflection of 0.06 in. (1.5 mm) as an example. This measure, like the ASTM toughness indices, is sensitive to the type of test control. In addition, this measure is better in distinguishing differences in energy absorption capacity of specimens made with different fiber contents, and different matrix types.

CONCLUSIONS

- Post-peak response of the flexural test depends upon the type of test control. This is particularly true for the more brittle FRC compositions.

- ASTM indices computed at small limiting deflections are insensitive to the fiber or matrix parameters. Indices computed at large limiting deflections are, however, more sensitive to these parameters.

- Energy absorbed per unit cross-sectional area appears to be reasonably sensitive to the fiber and matrix parameters.

- The type of test control significantly influences the load-deflection response recorded for FRC composites. This issue needs to be addressed if we need to obtain reproducible toughness measures on machines with vastly different stiffness characteristics and mechanisms of control.

ACKNOWLEDGEMENTS

The authors would like to thank Allied Fibers (Mr. Kailash Bohra and Ms. Marsha Feldstein) for their contributions to this study. The authors at the University of Missouri-Columbia would also like to acknowledge support received from the National Science Foundation (Structures and Building Systems Program, Ken P. Chong - Program Director, Grant No. MSM-8819803).

REFERENCES

1. American Concrete Institute Committee 544, "Measurements of Properties of Fiber Reinforced Concrete," ACI Materials Journal, Vol. 85, No. 6, Nov-Dec. 1988, pp. 583-593.

2. American Society for Testing and Materials, "Standard Test Method for Flexural Toughness and First-Crack Strength of Fiber Reinforced Concrete (Using Beam with Third-point Loading) (C1018-89)," Annual Book of Standards, Part 04.02, ASTM, Philadelphia, 1991, pp 507-513.

3. American Society for Testing and Materials, "Standard Specification for Fiber Reinforced Concrete and Shotcrete (C 1116-89)," Annual Book of Standards, Part 04.02, ASTM, Philadelphia, 1991, pp. 578-585.

4. Balaguru, P., and Shah, S.P., Fiber Reinforced Cement Composites, McGraw-Hill, 1992, 530 p.

5. Cho, B.S., El-Shakra, Z.M., and Gopalaratnam, V.S., "Failure of FRC in Direct and Indirect Tensile Test Configurations," Proceedings of the International Symposium on Fatigue and Fracture in Steel and Concrete Structures, Ed. A.G. Madhava Rao and T.V.S.R. Appa Rao, Vedam Books International, New Delhi, 1991, 16 p.

6. El-Shakra, Z.M. and Gopalaratnam, V.S., "Deflection Measurements and Toughness Evaluations for FRC," submitted for publication, 1991, 26 p.

7. Gopalaratnam, V.S., and Shah, S.P., "Properties of Steel-fiber Reinforced Concrete Subjected to Impact Loading," ACI Journal, Vol. 83, No. 1, January-February 1986, pp. 117-126.

8. Gopalaratnam, V.S., Shah, S.P., Batson, G., Criswell, M., Ramakrishnan, V., and Wecharatana, M., "Fracture Toughness of Fiber Reinforced Concrete," ACI Materials Journal, Vol. 88, No. 4, July-August 1991, pp. 339-353.

9. Balaguru, P., Narahari, R., and Patel, M., "Flexural Toughness of Steel Fiber Reinforced Concrete", ACI Materials Journal, Vol. 89, No. 6, November-December 1992.

10. Japan Concrete Institute, "Method of Test for Flexural Strength and Flexural Toughness of Fiber Reinforced Concrete," Standard SF4, JCI Standards for Test Methods of Fiber Reinforced Concrete, 1983, pp. 45-51.

TABLE 1 — MECHANICAL PROPERTIES OF FIBERS

Tensile Strength	130 ksi (8.96 MPa)
Young's Modulus	750 ksi (5,171 MPa)
Water Absorption	4.5%
Specific Gravity	1.16
Melting Point	460°F
Toughness	15 k-in/in^3 (103 MN-m/m^3)
Ultimate Elongation	20%

TABLE 2 — MIX PROPORTIONS

	Quantity ,lb/yd^3 (kg/m^3)	
Constituent Material	Normal Weight	Light Weight
ASTM Type I Cement	517 (305)	560 (330)
Natural Sand	1,370 (808)	1,250 (738)
Crushed Stone	1,800 (1,062)	1,000 (590)
Water	283 (167)	280 (165)
Water Reducing Admixture	3 oz/100 lb of cement	-
Air-Entraining Admixture	2 oz	1 oz

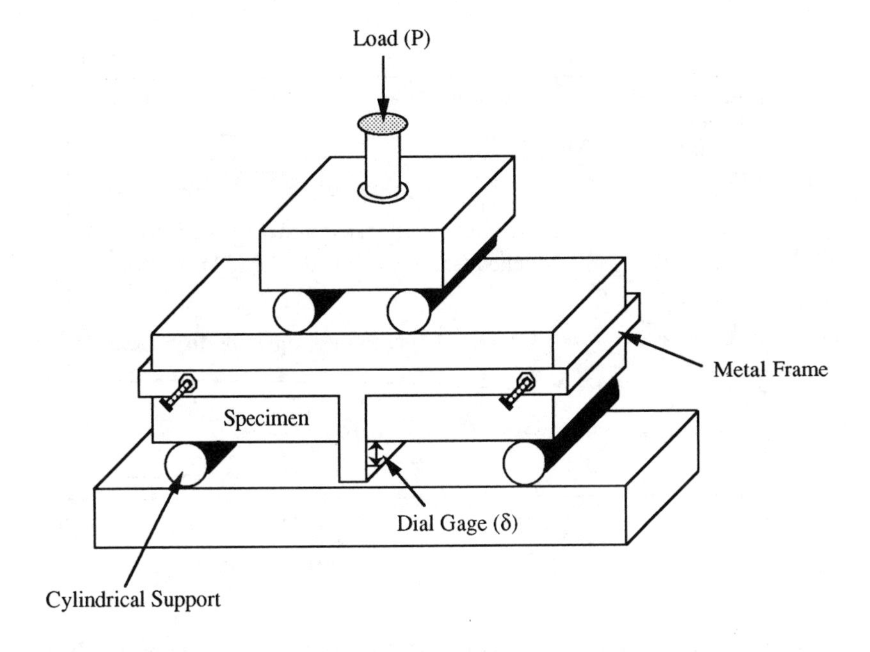

Fig. 1—Schematic of the flexural test set-up used at Rutgers University

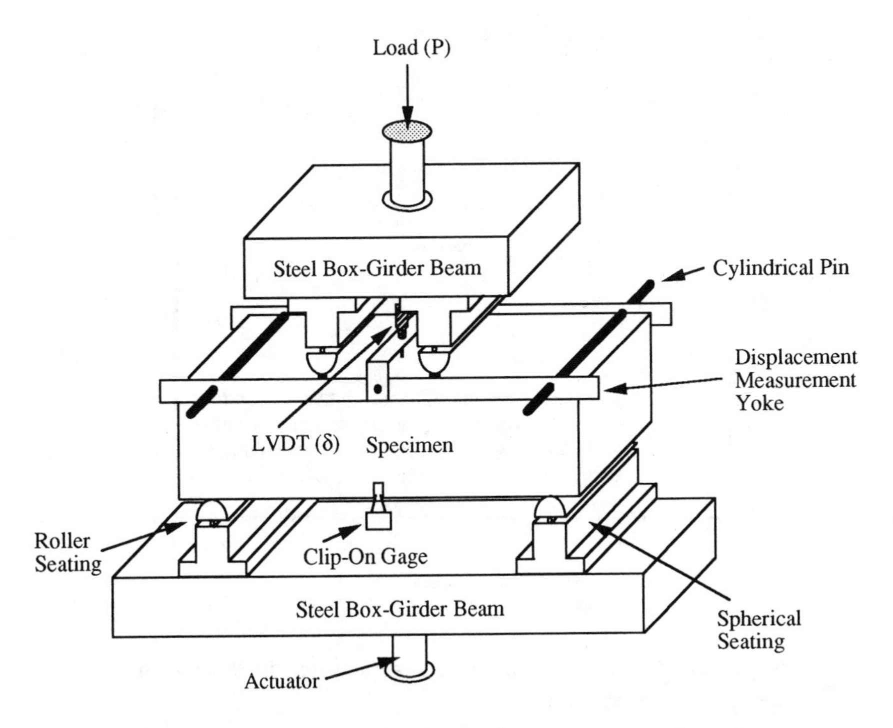

Fig. 2—Schematic of the flexural test set-up used at the University of Missouri-Columbia

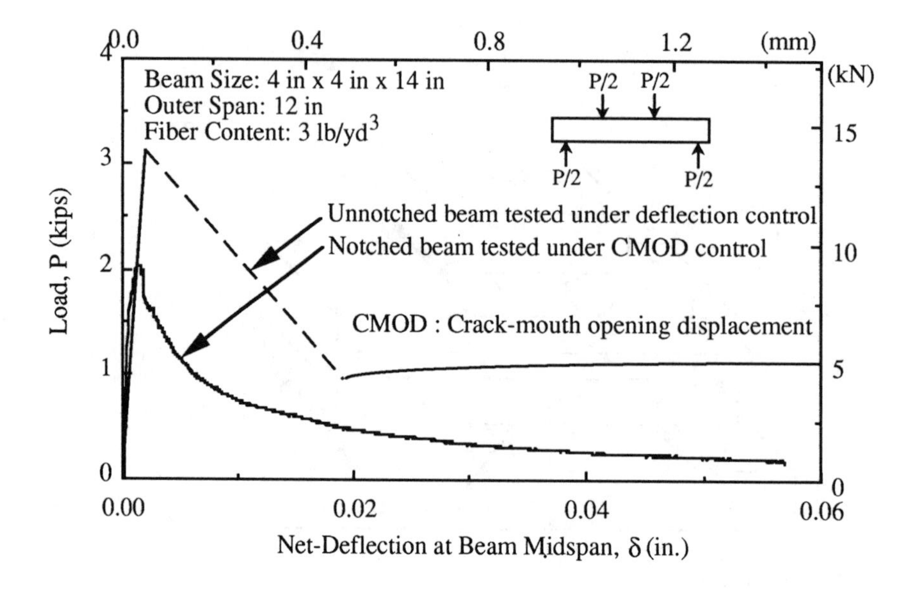

Fig. 3—Typical load-deflection curves for normal weight concrete beams tested under deflection and crack-mouth opening displacement control

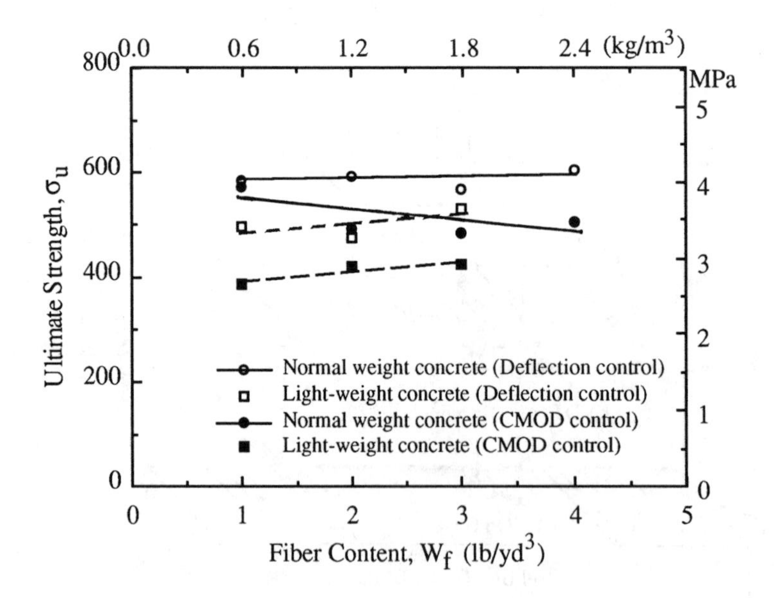

Fig. 4—Influence of the mixture composition on the ultimate strength of the specimen

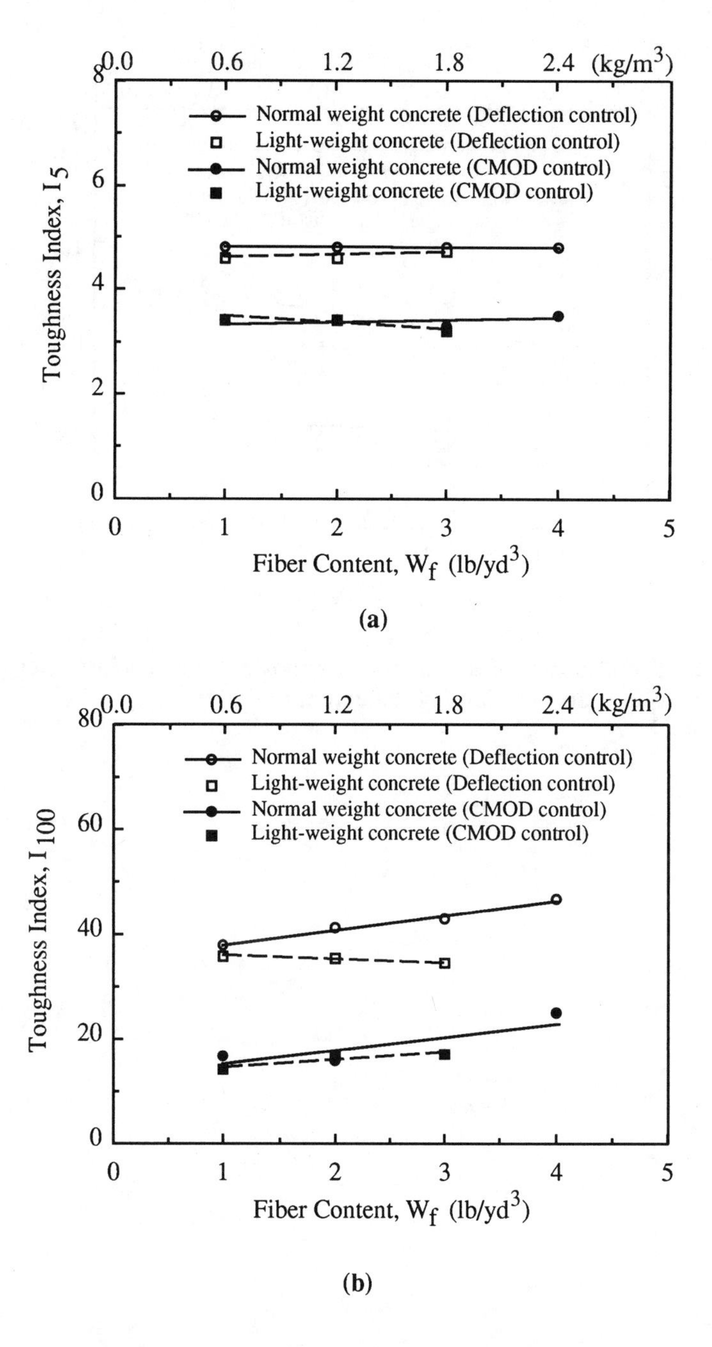

Fig. 5—Influence of the mixture composition on ASTM toughness indices (a) I_5 and (b) I_{100}

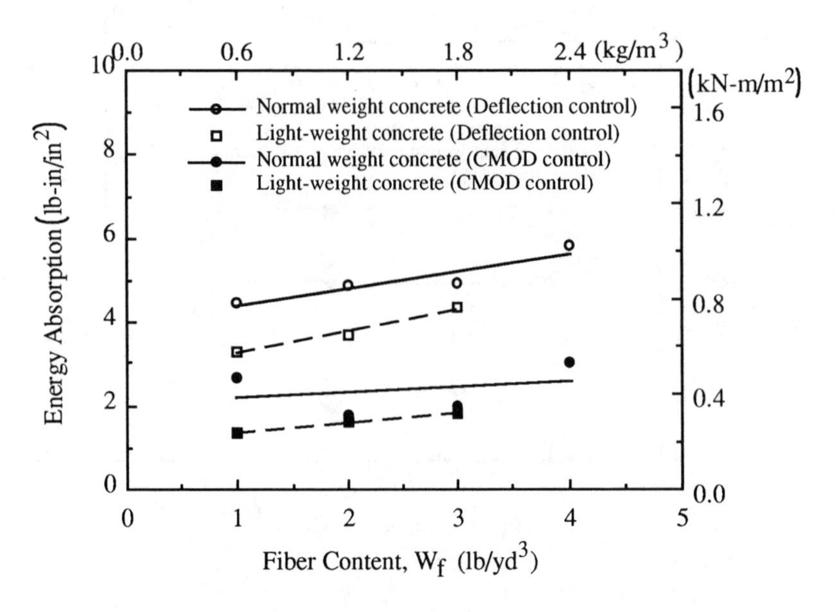

Fig. 6—Influence of the mixture composition on absolute energy absorption up to a limiting deflection of 0.06 in.

SP 142-10

Shear Behavior of Laboratory-Sized High Strength Concrete Beams Reinforced with Bars and Steel Fibers

by S.W. Shin, J.G. Oh, and S.K. Ghosh

Synopsis: This paper reports on an investigation on the behavior of high-strength concrete beams (with concrete compression strength equal to 11,600 psi or 80 MPa) with and without steel fiber reinforcement, to determine their diagonal cracking strength as well as nominal shear strength. Experimental data on the shear strength of steel fiber reinforced high-strength concrete beams are currently scarce to non-existent.

Twenty-two beam specimens were tested under monotonically increasing loads applied at mid-span. The major test parameters included the volumetric ratio of steel fibers, the shear-span-to-depth ratio, the amount of longitudinal reinforcement, and the amount of shear reinforcement.

It was found that steel fiber reinforced high-strength concrete beams effectively resist abrupt shear failure. Such beams exhibit higher cracking loads and energy absorption capabilities than comparable high-strength concrete beams without fibers.

Empirical prediction equations are suggested for evaluating the diagonal cracking strength as well as nominal shear strength of steel fiber reinforced high-strength concrete beams.

Keywords: Beams (supports); cracking (fracturing); ductility; energy absorption; high strength concretes; loads (forces); metal fibers; reinforcing materials; shear properties; shear strength

ACI Member Sung-Woo Shin is Associate Professor, Department of Architecture and Architectural Engineering, Hanyang University, Seoul, Korea. He has a Ph.D. degree in structural engineering from the University of Illinois at Chicago. He is actively engaged in research on the behavior of structural members made of high-strength concrete.

Jung-Geun Oh is an Engineer with Samsung Engineering and Construction Co. Ltd., Seoul, Korea. He received his BS and MS degrees in 1989 and 1991 from Hanyang University, Seoul, Korea. He is interested in the field of high-strength concrete research and construction.

ACI Fellow S. K. Ghosh is Director, Engineered Structures and Codes, Portland Cement Association, Skokie, Illinois, and Adjunct Professor of Civil Engineering, University of Illinois at Chicago. He has a Ph.D. degree in structural engineering from the University of Waterloo, Waterloo, Ontario, Canada. His research interests include the seismic behavior of concrete structures, including those utilizing high-strength concrete.

OBJECTIVE AND SCOPE

The objective of this study was to investigate the shear behavior, including ductility, of high- strength concrete beams (with concrete compression strength equal to 11,600 psi or 80 MPa) with and without steel fiber reinforcement. Shear failure should preferably be avoided in structural members with high-strength concrete.

The scope of the present investigation was limited to a consideration of monotonically increasing loads. The principal test variables were fiber volume fraction, the shear-span-to-depth ratio, the amount of longitudinal reinforcement, and the amount of shear reinforcement. The effects of each test variable were studied separately. Twenty-two beam specimens were tested.

RESEARCH SIGNIFICANCE

Because of the abrupt nature of shear (diagonal tension) failure, such failure should be avoided, insofar as practicable, in all structural members, including high-strength concrete members. The shear strength of high-strength concrete may be different due to the increased bond strength between the concrete matrix and reinforcement and between the cement matrix and aggregate.

Research on concrete employing steel fibers to control brittle failure has been carried out in recent times (1-3). But study on the behavior of high-strength concrete members with fiber has been scarce to non-existent. This research should inspire more confidence in designers using high-strength concrete with or without fibers for structural applications. Empirical prediction equations are suggested for evaluating the diagonal cracking strength as well as the nominal shear strength of steel fiber reinforced high-strength concrete beams.

TEST SPECIMENS

Beam Specimen Design

All specimens were 4x8 in. (100x200 mm) in cross section, as shown in Fig. 1. Table 1 lists the properties of the test specimens. The shear-span-to-depth ratio (a/d) was 2.0, 3.0, 4.5, or 6.0. The concrete compressive strength was maintained approximately constant at 11,600 psi or 80 Mpa in each specimen. A total of 22 specimens were manufactured with or without steel fibers, the volumetric ratio of fibers being 0, 0.5, or 1%. The tensile reinforcement ratio was either 0.5 ρ_b (under-reinforced beams) or 1.0 ρ_b. The shear reinforcement in a beam equalled 0, 25, or 50% of that required by the ACI Code.

The principal test variables were:

1) Shear-span-to-depth ratio (a/d = 2.0, 3.0, 4.5, 6.0)
2) Tensile reinforcement ratio (ρ = 0.5 ρ_b, 1.0 ρ_b)
3) Amount of shear reinforcement ($A_v/A_{v(ACI)}$ = 0, 25, 50, 100%)
4) Volumetric ratio of fibers (V_f = 0, 0.5, 1.0%)

Materials Used

The cement used in this study was a Type 2 portland cement. Fine aggregate was Han river sand with a fineness modulus of 3.0. Coarse aggregate was crushed limestone with a maximum size of 1/2 in. (13 mm). A Napthalene based superplasticizer was used.

No. 6 (20 mm diameter) Grade 60 deformed steel bars were used for tension reinforcement and No. 3 (10 mm diameter) Grade 40 deformed steel bars were used for compression reinforcement (where needed). The shear reinforcement consisted of No. 3 (10 mm diameter) deformed closed stirrups of Grade 40 steel.

Steel fibers were round straight bars. Diameter (d_f) was 0.016 in. (0.4 mm), length (l_f) was 1.575 in. (40 mm), and aspect ratio (l_f/d_f) was 100. The steel fibers had the following physical properties: f_y = 196.7 ksi or 1355 MPa, f_u = 269.3 ksi or 1856 MPa, E_s = 33,619 ksi or 231,633 MPa, and unit weight = 487 pcf or 7800 kg/m^3.

Mix Design

The mixes were designed to have desired strength and desired plastic properties (workability, finishability, etc.). A drastic slump loss was often observed upon addition of steel fibers. Concrete with no slump before the addition of superplasticizers was designed for high-strength steel fiber reinforced concrete specimens.

Fiber reinforced concrete matrices had a water-cement ratio (w/c) of 0.3, 1000 lbs. per cu.yd. (600kg/m^3) of cement, a fine-to-coarse aggregate ratio of 0.3, and a superplasticizer-to-cement ratio of 0.01 by weight. The latter ratio was kept constant even while V_f was varied. Measured slumps were 8.5 in., 6.0 in., and 5.0 in. for V_f = 0%, 0.5%, and 1.0%, respectively. High-strength fibers were used to prevent break-down of the steel fibers when diagonal cracks formed within the shear span.

TEST PROGRAM

The members were tested in a Universal Testing Machine with a maximum capacity of 220 kips (992 kN) at the structural laboratories of Hanyang University in Seoul. The details of twenty two test specimens are shown in Table 2.

Measurement of Deflection

An electrical dial gauge was placed at the center of the span of each member to measure deflections. Two dial gauges with a displacement range of 4 in. (100 mm) and a least count of 0.001 in. (0.25 mm) were used on the top face for displacement measurements at both ends of each specimen. The details are shown in Fig. 1.

Measurement of Strains

Strains in tension steel were measured at midspan by electrical foil-type strain gages to check the yielding of the reinforcement. Foil-type strain gages were mounted to investigate the tensile strain of two pieces of shear reenforcement at and adjacent to one support at mid-height of each beam. The measured strain data are not presented here for the sake of conciseness.

Test Procedure

All the tests in this program were performed using a Universal Testing Machine. The load was applied through a single-ended actuator to the center of each beam specimen that was supported on two steel rollers covering the entire width of the beam. The application of each increment of load (later deflection) and the taking of all the measurements required about 5 to 10 min. The complete testing of one specimen required from 1 to 3 hours.

TEST RESULTS

Failure Mode

Each specimen underwent initial cracking at midspan at a load corresponding to the modulus of rupture. Flexural cracking, as the load was increased, developed into diagonal cracking within the shear span. The ultimate failure mode after diagonal cracking depended on the shear-span-to-depth ratio (a/d), the volumetric ratio of fibers (V_f), and the amount of shear reinforcement (A_v). There was little difference in failure mode between beams with $\rho = 0.5\rho_b$ and corresponding beams with $\rho = \rho_b$.

In specimens without shear reinforcement, the reserve strength after diagonal cracking increased as the volumetric ratio of steel fibers increased. Thus steel fiber in adequate amounts is effective in preventing abrupt shear failure, and in increasing nominal shear strength of beams without shear reinforcement.

In specimens with a quarter of the shear reinforcement required by the ACI Code and without steel fibers, diagonal shear cracking nearly coincided with the yielding of stirrups. As the amount of steel fibers increased, the failure mode began to combine the crushing of concrete in the compression zone and the yielding of stirrups in under-reinforced beams.

Deflection of Specimens without Shear Reinforcement

Figures 2 and 3 show the load deflection curves for beams having the same longitudinal reinforcement ratio ($\rho = 0.5\ \rho_b$) and the same shear-span-to-depth ratio (a/d = 2 or 3), but different volumetric ratios of fiber (V_f = 0, 0.5, 1%). Both figures show that as the volumetric ratio of fibers increased, higher maximum loads were attained, and the drop-off in load carrying capacity became more gradual beyond the maximum load.

Figure 4 shows the load-deflection curves of specimens without shear reinforcement, and with different shear-span-to-depth ratios (a/d = 4.5 or 6), different tension reinforcement ratios, and different volumetric ratios of fiber. The under-reinforced beam with the lower a/d ratio (4.5) and the highest volume of fibers (1%) showed the largest peak load level and the most gradual drop-off after maximum load, due to arrested shear failure.

Deflection of Specimens with Shear Reinforcement

Figures 5 and 6 show that specimens with shear reinforcement were able to sustain higher loads beyond the maximum load level, as the volumetric ratio of fibers increased.

Shear Strength of Specimens without Shear Reinforcement

Shear-span-to-depth ratio (a/d) - Figures 7 and 8 show the effects of shear-span-to-depth ratio on shear strength when the amount of steel fibers varies between 0 and 1%. Regardless of the volumetric ratio of fiber, the diagonal cracking strength as well as the nominal shear strength decreased as the shear-span-to-depth ratio increased from 2.0 to 3.0. The rate of decrease was slower as a/d increased further from 3.0 to 4.5. This was probably because the arch action of beams when a/d was 2.0 changed to beam action when a/d was 3.0.

It should be noted that, throughout this study, v_c is the nominal shear stress corresponding to the experimentally measured load at which the first diagonal crack formed in the shear span. v_n is the nominal stress corresponding to the measured maximum load carried by a specimen.

Volumetric Ratio of Fibers (V_f) - The diagonal cracking strength increased slightly with the addition of steel fibers (Fig. 9). In beams with a/d = 2.0, the diagonal cracking strength increased by 39% with the addition of 1% steel fiber. In beams with a/d = 3.0 and 4.5, it increased by 32% and 29%, respectively, with the addition of 1% steel fiber. The nominal shear strength increased by 18%, 62% and 51% for specimens with a/d equal to 2.0, 3.0 and 4.5, respectively (Fig. 10).

The results indicate that the addition of steel fibers was more effective in increasing nominal shear strength than in improving cracking strength through the entire range of steel fiber volume fractions studied.

Shear Strength of Specimens with Shear Reinforcement

Shear Reinforcement Ratio ($A_v/A_{v(ACI)}$) - Figures 11 and 12 show the effects of the amount of shear reinforcement on diagonal cracking strength and nominal shear strength, respectively. The diagonal cracking strength (V_c) increased slowly as the shear reinforcement ratio (ratio of shear reinforcement provided to the shear reinforcement required by ACI 318-89, $A_v/A_{v(ACI)}$) increased from 0% to 25%, but the nominal shear strength (V_n) increased sharply.

As shear reinforcement ratio changed from 25% to 50%, the diagonal cracking strength as well as the nominal shear strength no longer increased, regardless of the amount of steel fibers.

Fiber Volume Fraction (V_f) - Figures 13 and 14 show the effects of fiber volume fraction (V_f) on the diagonal cracking strength and the nominal shear strength, respectively.

In beams without shear reinforcement, the nominal shear strength increased by 43%, and the diagonal cracking strength increased by 32% with the addition of 1% steel fiber.

But in beams with shear reinforcement, the diagonal cracking strength and the nominal shear strength no longer increased by the addition of up to 1% steel fiber.

It appears that the addition of steel fibers in beams with adequate shear reinforcement does not increase diagonal cracking strength. Also the increases in nominal shear strength, that are normally associated with steel fibers, are not apparent in the test results.

Ductility of Members

Ductility represents the ability of a material, section, member or structure to sustain substantial inelastic deformations without losing its load carrying capacity.

In this investigation, member ductility was defined in terms of deflections as follows:

$$\mu = \Delta_f/\Delta_y \qquad (1)$$

where Δ_f is the final deflection corresponding to 80% of the maximum load along the descendingbranch of the load-deflection curve.

and Δ_y is deflection at yielding of the tensile reinforcement.

Shear Reinforcement Ratio ($A_v/A_{v(ACI)}$) - Figure 15 shows the relationship between ductility index and shear reinforcement ratio. In beams with 0 and 0.5% fiber volume fraction, the ductility index increased significantly as the shear reinforcement ratio changed from 25% to 50%. But in beams with 1% fiber volume fraction, there was no increase of ductility with increasing amounts of shear reinforcement. This indicates that a shear reinforcement ratio of over 50% is no longer effective in improving the ductility of fiber-reinforced high-strength concrete beams.

Fiber Volume Fraction (V_f)

Figure 16 shows the relationship between ductility index and fiber volume fraction when the ratio of the amount of shear reinforcement provided to that required by ACI 318-89 is 25 or 50%. In beams with a 25% shear reinforcement ratio, ductility improved dramatically as the fiber volume fraction increased. The ductility index increased by a factor of 3.5 as V_f increased from 0 to 1%. However, in beams with a 50% shear reinforcement ratio, the ductility index increased by a factor of 2 for the same amount of increase in the fiber volume fraction.

The nominal shear strength of steel fiber reinforced high-strength concrete beams can be expressed as follows:

For beams with $a/d < 3$

$$v_n = 0.22 \cdot f_{sp} + 31671 \cdot \rho \cdot (d/a) + 0.834 \cdot v_b \text{ (psi)} \quad (5)$$

$$= 0.22 \cdot f_{sp} + 217 \cdot \rho \cdot (d/a) + 0.834 \cdot v_b \text{ (N/mm}^2\text{)}$$

(Standard Deviation = 4.12)

For beams with $a/d \geq 3$

$$v_n = 0.19 \cdot f_{sp} + 13571 \cdot \rho \cdot (d/a) + 0.834 \cdot v_b \text{ (psi)} \quad (6)$$

$$= 0.19 \cdot f_{sp} + 93 \cdot \rho \cdot (d/a) + 0.834 \cdot v_b \text{ (N/mm}^2\text{)}$$

(Standard Deviation = 3.41)

Table 2 compares the nominal shear strength of beams without shear reinforcement and with varying amount of steel fibers, as predicted by Narayanan et al. (4) and by Eq. (5).

According to Narayanan et al., the nominal shear strength of a beam with 1.2% fiber volume fraction and without shear reinforcement is equal to that of a beam without fibers and with 25% of shear reinforcement required by ACI 318-89. However, according to Eq. (5), a beam without shear reinforcement would have to have 2% fiber volume fraction for its nominal strength to be equal to that of a beam without fibers and having 25% of the shear reinforcement required by the ACI Code. Thus, calculations based on the authors' tests on small-scale beams indicate that a higher volume of steel fibers may be required for the substitution of the shear reinforcement.

CONCLUSIONS

From the experimental observations and analyses reported in this paper, the following conclusions can be drawn.

1) In beams without web reinforcement, reserve strength after diagonal cracking increased as volumetric ratio of steel fibers increased. Thus, fiber reinforcement could prevent abrupt shear failure and increase nominal shear strength.

2) In beams with adequate web reinforcement, addition of steel fibers did not appear to provide an increase in nominal shear strength.

3) The nominal shear strength of a high-strength concrete beam with 2% fiber and no web reinforcement was the same as that of a similar beam with no fiber and 25% of the web reinforcement required by ACI 318-89. This was theoretically determined from equations developed in this investigation on the basis of small-scale tests.

4) The ductility index of a high-strength concrete beam with 25% of the web reinforcement required by ACI and 0.5% fiber was nearly the same as that of a similar beam with 50% of the ACI required web reinforcement and no fiber.

NOTATION

a = shear span

A_v = area of shear reinforcement provided

$A_{v(ACI)}$ = area of shear reinforcement required by ACI 318-89

d = effective depth

d_f = fiber diameter

E_s = modulus of elasticity of reinforcement or fiber

f_{sp} = split tensile strength of fiber reinforced concrete cylinders

f'_c = specified compressive strength of concrete

f_u = ultimate tensile strength of reinforcement or fiber

f_y = yield strength of reinforcement or fiber

l_f = fiber length

v_c = nominal stress corresponding to diagonal cracking strength of member

v_n = nominal stress corresponding to nominal shear strength of member

V_f = volumetric ratio of fibers

Δ_f = final deflection corresponding to 80% of maximum load along descending branch of load-deflection curve

Δ_y = member deflection at yielding of tension reinforcement

μ = member ductility index

ρ = tension reinforcement ratio

ρ_b = balanced reinforcement ratio

REFERENCES

1. Jindal, R.L., "Shear and Moment Capacities of Steel Fiber Reinforced Beams," Fiber-Reinforced Concrete-International Symposium, SP-81, American Concrete Institute, Detroit, 1984, pp. 1-16.

2. Romualdi, P., and Mandel, J.A., "Tensile Strength of Concrete Affected by Uniformly Distributed and Closely Spaced Short Lengths of Wire Reinforcement," ACI Journal, Proceedings V. 61, No. 6, June 1964, pp. 657-671.

3. Muhidin, N.A., and Regan, P.E., "Chopped Steel Fibers as Shear Reinforcement in Concrete Beams," Fiber Reinforced Materials, Institution of Civil Engineers, London, 1977, pp. 135-149.

4. Narayanan, R., and Darwish, I.Y., "Use of Steel Fibers as Shear Reinforcement," ACI Structural Journal, May-June 1987, pp. 216-227.

5. Narayanan, R., and Kareem-Palanjian, A.S., "Effect of Fiber Addition on Concrete Strengths," Indian Concrete Journal, Bombay, V. 58, No. 4, April 1984, pp. 100-103.

TABLE 1 — PROPERTIES, SHEAR STRENGTHS, AND DUCTILITIES OF TEST SPECIMENS

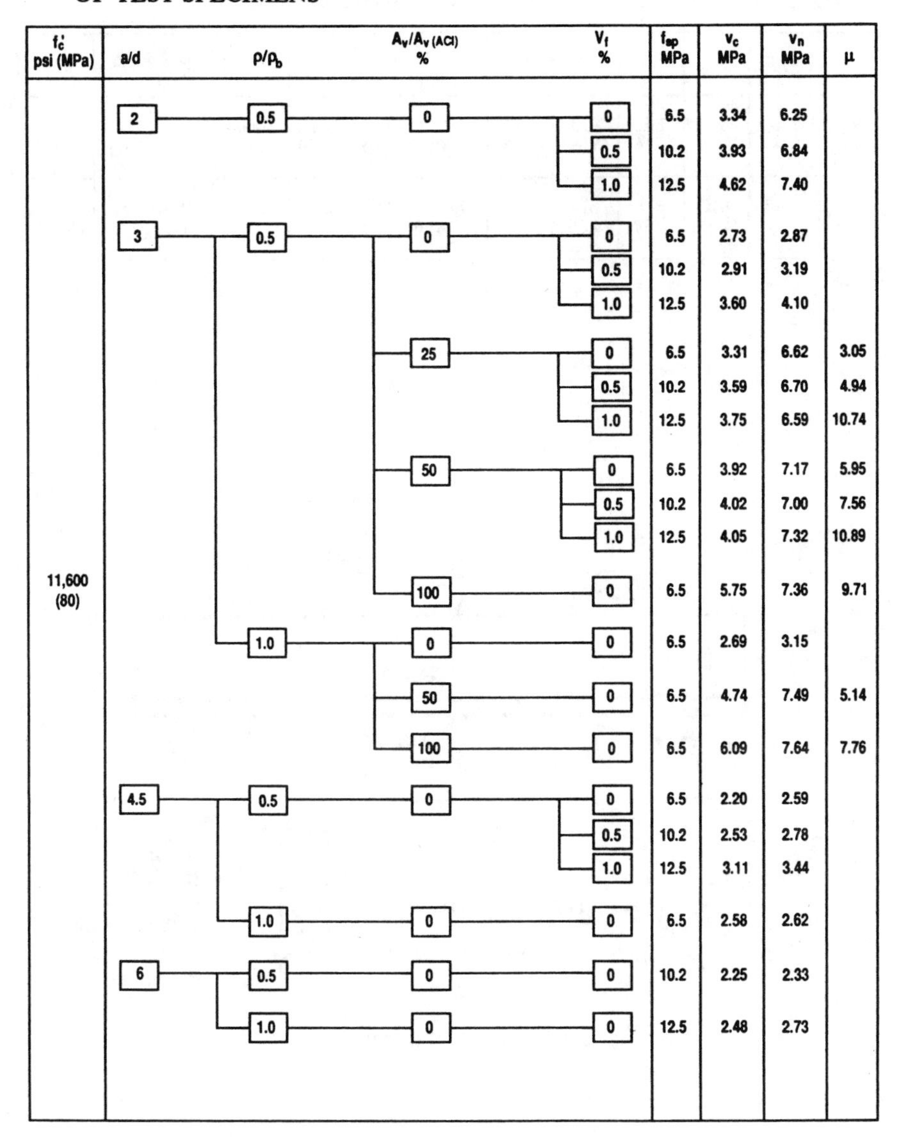

f'_c psi (MPa)	a/d	ρ/ρ_b	$A_v/A_{v\,(ACI)}$ %	V_f %	f_{sp} MPa	v_c MPa	v_n MPa	μ
11,600 (80)	2	0.5	0	0	6.5	3.34	6.25	
				0.5	10.2	3.93	6.84	
				1.0	12.5	4.62	7.40	
	3	0.5	0	0	6.5	2.73	2.87	
				0.5	10.2	2.91	3.19	
				1.0	12.5	3.60	4.10	
			25	0	6.5	3.31	6.62	3.05
				0.5	10.2	3.59	6.70	4.94
				1.0	12.5	3.75	6.59	10.74
			50	0	6.5	3.92	7.17	5.95
				0.5	10.2	4.02	7.00	7.56
				1.0	12.5	4.05	7.32	10.89
			100	0	6.5	5.75	7.36	9.71
		1.0	0	0	6.5	2.69	3.15	
			50	0	6.5	4.74	7.49	5.14
			100	0	6.5	6.09	7.64	7.76
	4.5	0.5	0	0	6.5	2.20	2.59	
				0.5	10.2	2.53	2.78	
				1.0	12.5	3.11	3.44	
		1.0	0	0	6.5	2.58	2.62	
	6	0.5	0	0	10.2	2.25	2.33	
		1.0	0	0	12.5	2.48	2.73	

TABLE 2 — COMPARISON OF SHEAR STRENGTH PREDICTIONS FROM PREVIOUS STUDIES AND THIS INVESTIGATION

V_f (%)	1.0	1.1	1.2	1.3	1.4	1.5	1.6	1.7	1.8	1.9	2.0
V_n, psi (Mpa) by Ref. 4	862 (5.94)	892 (6.15)	923 (6.37)	954 (6.58)	986 (6.80)	1016 (7.00)	1041 (7.18)	1068 (7.37)	1095 (7.55)	1115 (7.69)	1132 (7.81)
V_n, psi (Mpa) by Eq. (5)	617 (4.26)	646 (4.57)	673 (4.69)	698 (4.87)	731 (5.10)	760 (5.29)	788 (5.49)	814 (5.67)	846 (5.84)	885 (6.10)	912 (6.29)

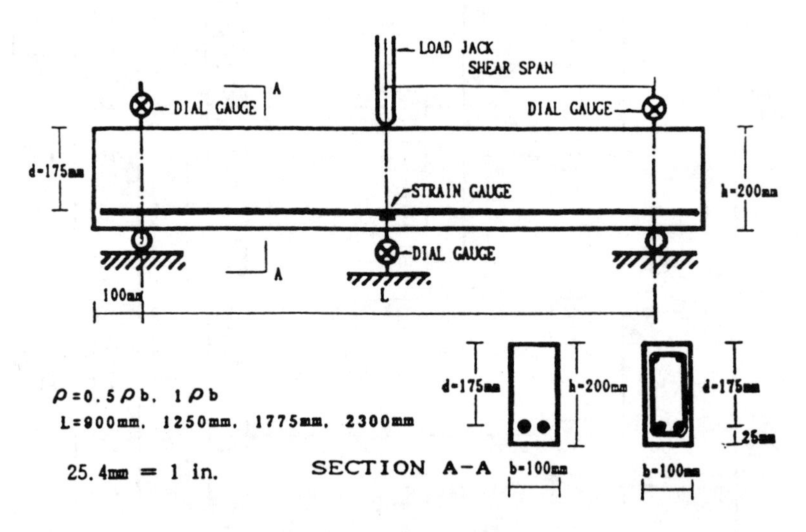

Fig. 1—Specimen and test set-up

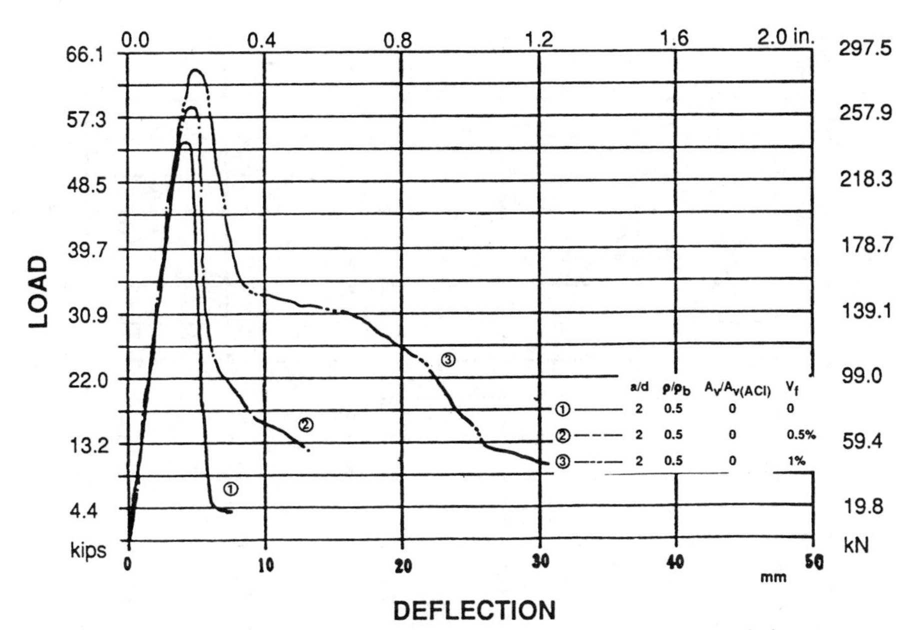

Fig. 2—Load-deflection curves of specimens without shear reinforcement; shear span to depth ratio = 2, fiber volume fraction varies

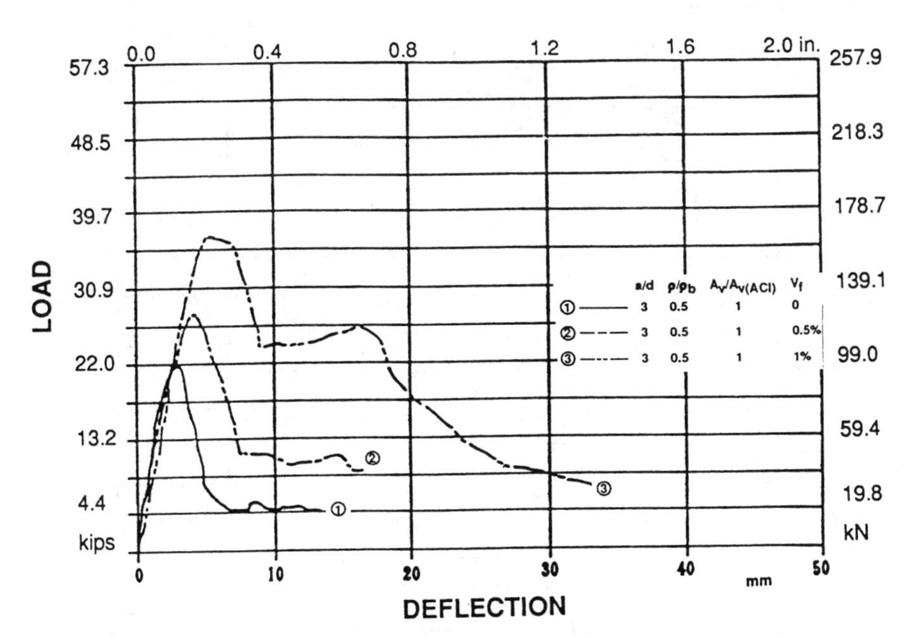

Fig. 3—Load-deflection curves of specimens without shear reinforcement; shear span to depth ratio = 3, fiber volume fraction varies

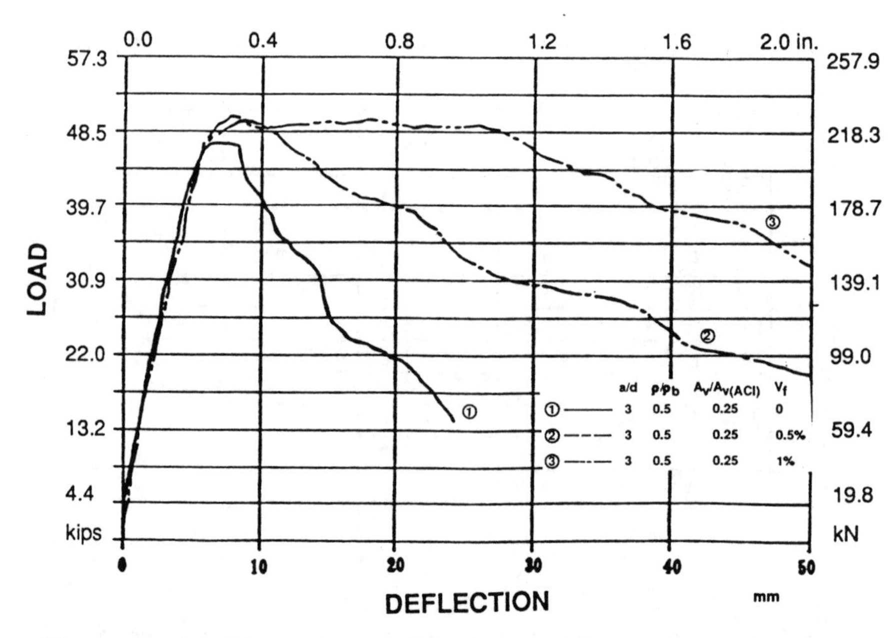

Fig. 4—Load-deflection curves of specimens without shear reinforcement; shear span to depth ratio, longitudinal reinforcement ratio and fiber volume fraction vary

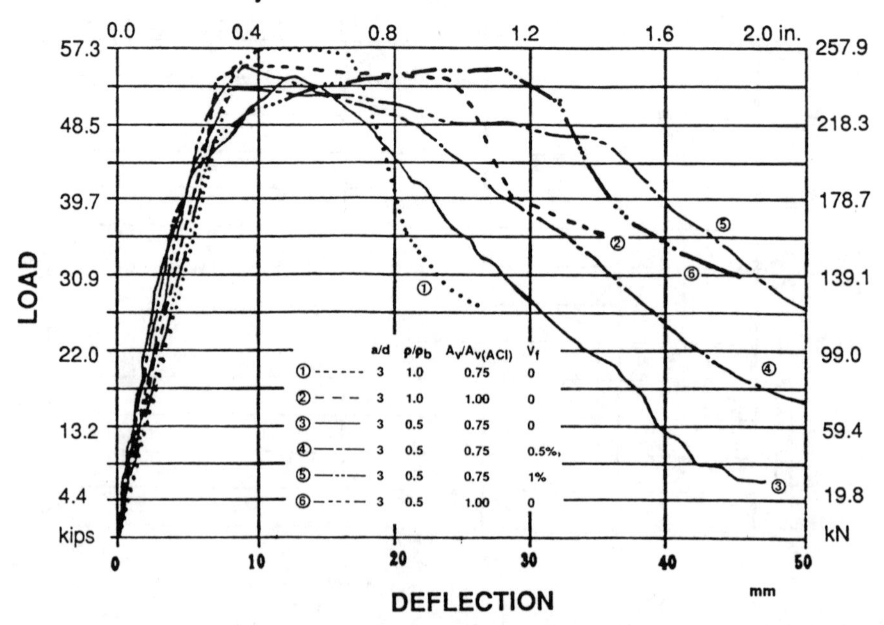

Fig. 5—Load-deflection curves of under reinforced specimens with 25 percent of the ACI required shear reinforcement; shear span to depth ratio = 3, fiber volume fraction varies

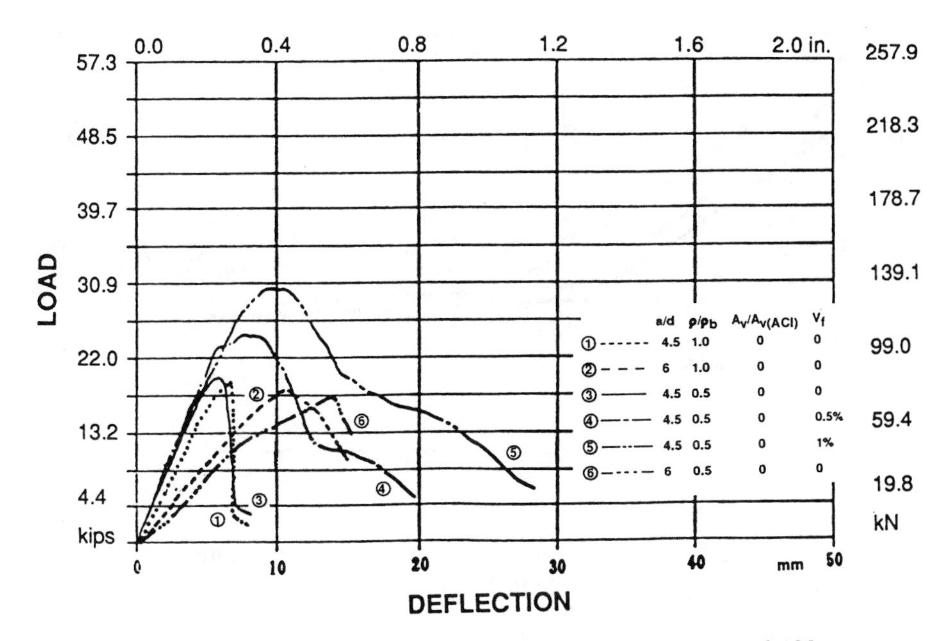

Fig. 6—Load-deflection curves of specimens with 50 percent and 100 percent of the ACI required shear reinforcement; shear span to depth ratio = 3, longitudinal reinforcement ratio and fiber volume fraction vary

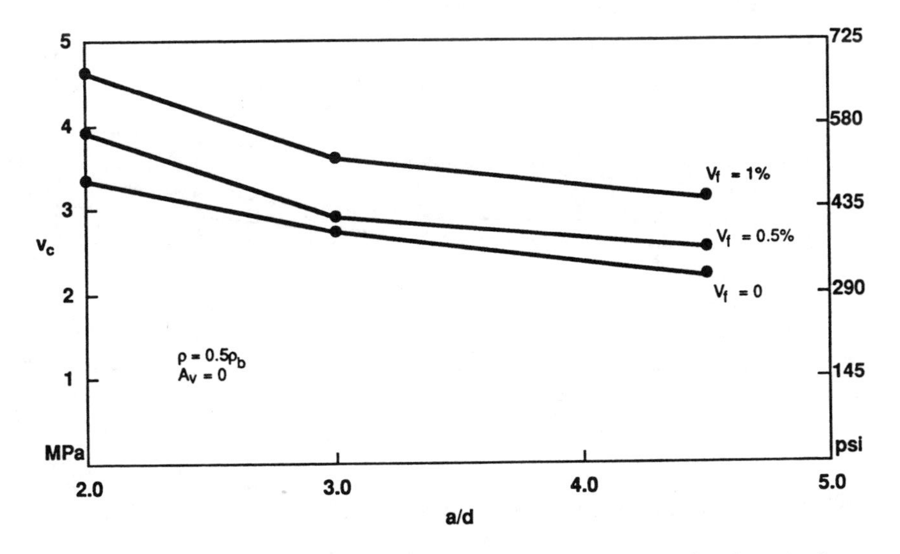

Fig. 7—Diagonal cracking strength versus shear span to depth ratio for different fiber volume fractions

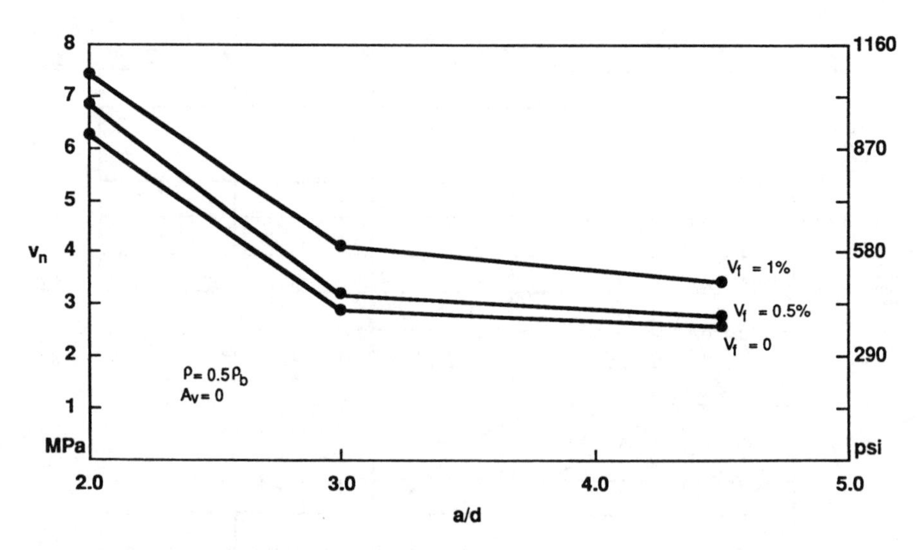

Fig. 8—Nominal shear strength versus shear span to depth ratio for different fiber volume fractions

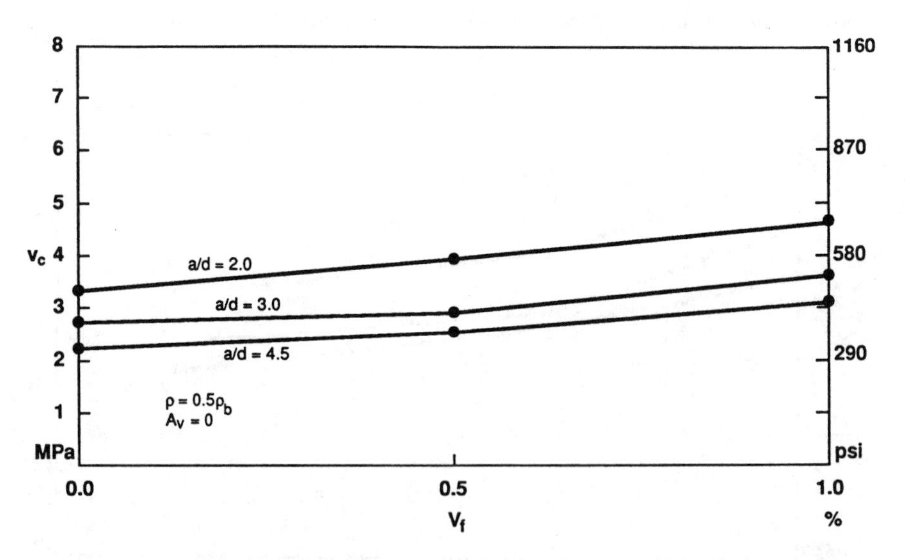

Fig. 9—Diagonal cracking strength versus fiber volume fraction for different shear span to depth ratios

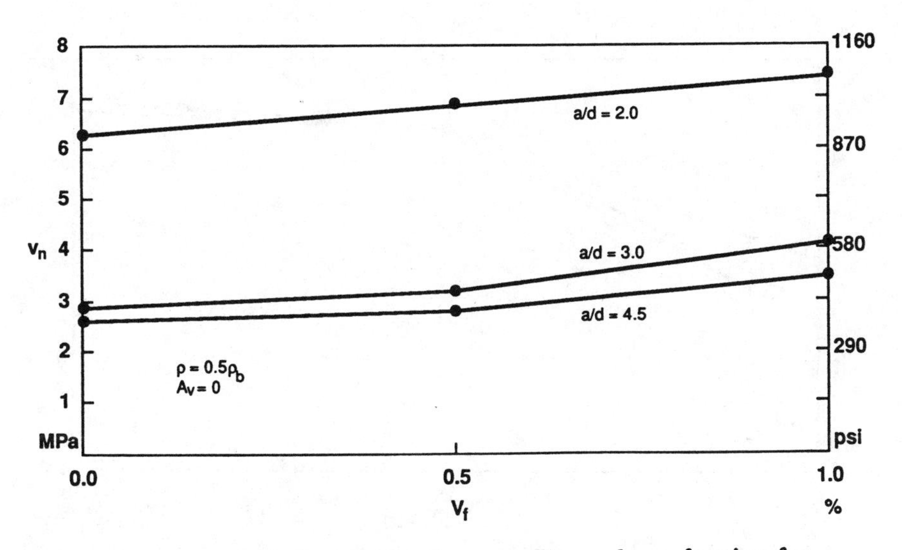

Fig. 10—Nominal shear strength versus fiber volume fraction for different shear span to depth ratios

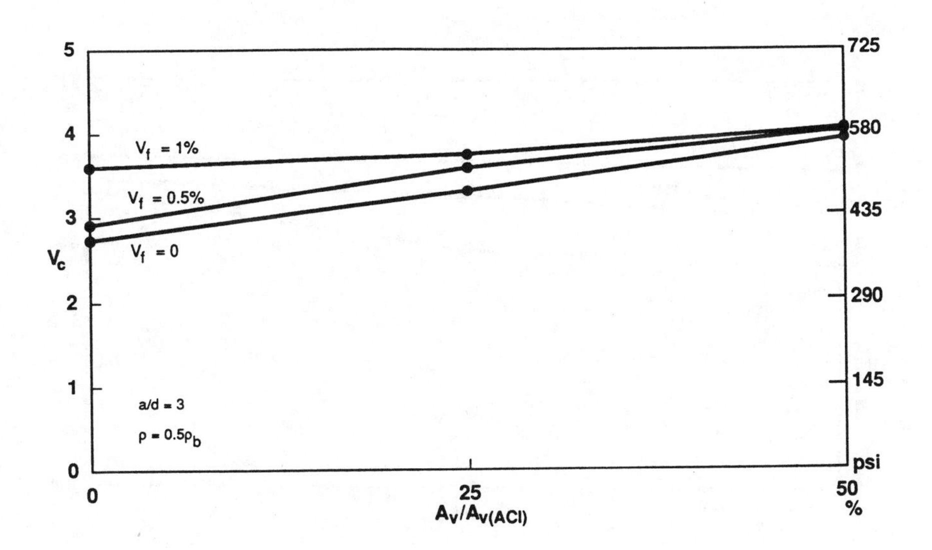

Fig. 11—Diagonal cracking strength versus shear reinforcement ratio for different fiber volume fractions

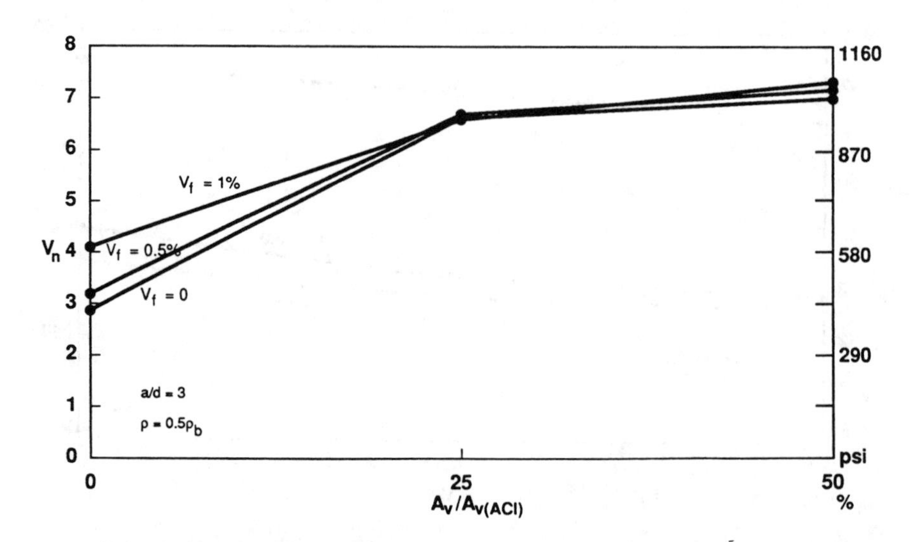

Fig. 12—Nominal shear strength versus shear reinforcement ratio for different fiber volume fractions

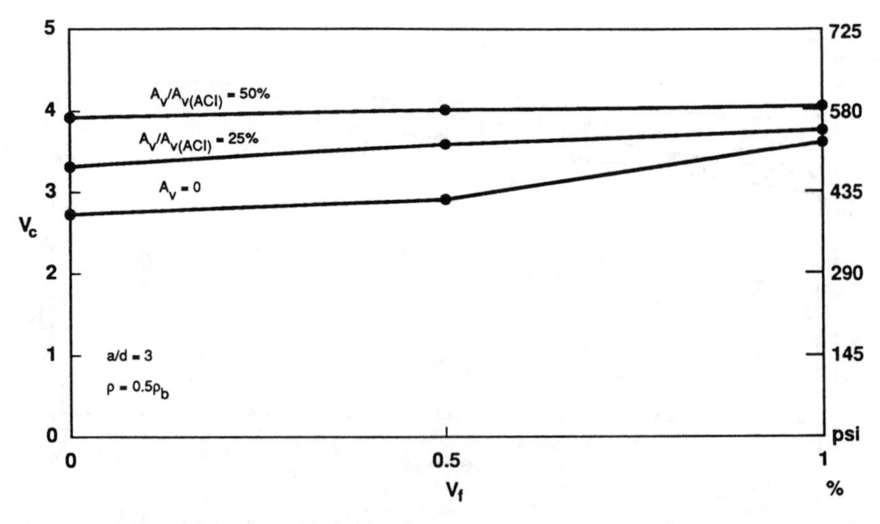

Fig. 13—Diagonal cracking strength versus fiber volume fraction for different shear reinforcement ratios

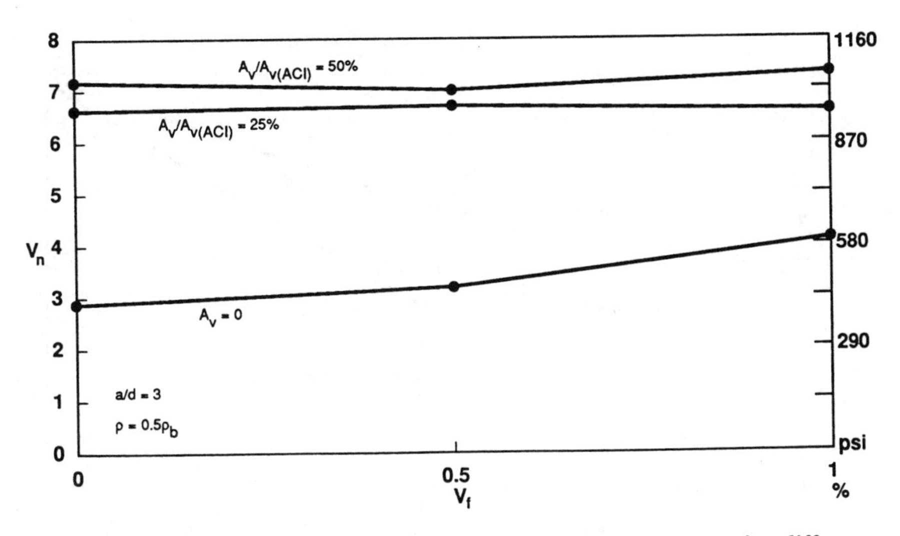

Fig. 14—Nominal shear strength versus fiber volume fraction for different shear reinforcement ratios

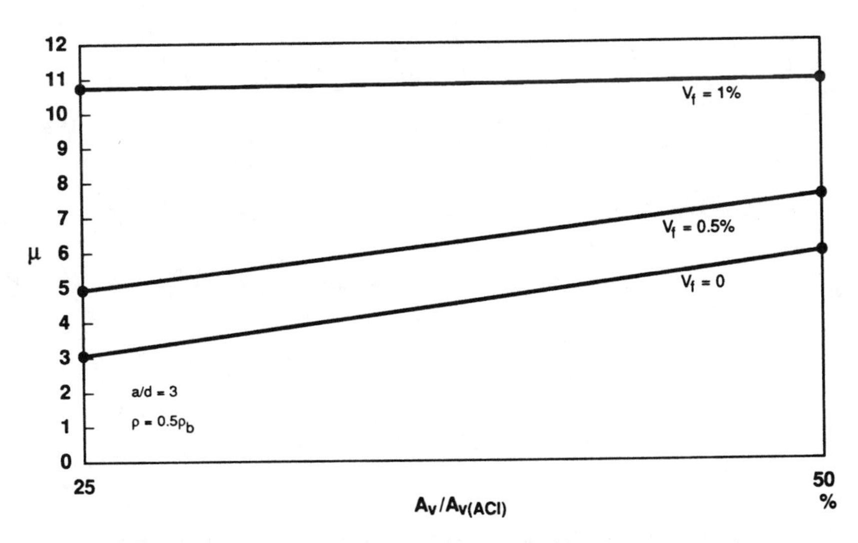

Fig. 15—Ductility index versus shear reinforcement ratio for different fiber volume fractions

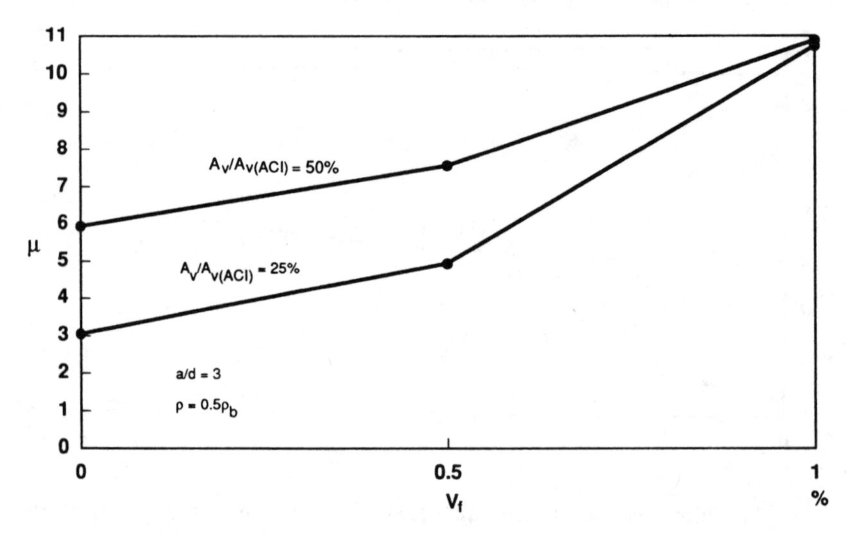

Fig. 16—Ductility index versus fiber volume fraction for different shear reinforcement ratios

SP 142-11

Behavior of Fiber Reinforced High Strength Concrete under Direct Shear

by M. Valle and O. Buyukozturk

Synopsis: This paper reports the results of an investigation on the strength and ductility of fiber reinforced high strength concrete under direct shear. Both experimental and modeling studies were performed. In the experimental study, fiber reinforced high strength concrete push-off specimens were tested. Two types of fibers, polypropylene and steel fibers, in conjunction with or without conventional stirrups were used. An existing model was further developed and used in the analytical prediction of the shear stress-strain relationships for these specimens.

In general, fibers proved to be more effective in high strength concrete than in normal strength concrete, increasing both ultimate load and overall ductility. This is attributed to the improved bond characteristics associated with the use of fibers in conjunction with high strength concrete. For the specimens with steel fibers, significant increases in ultimate load and ductility were observed. With polypropylene fibers, a lower increase in ultimate load was obtained when compared to the increase due to steel fibers. Ductility of the polypropylene fiber reinforced specimens was greater than that of the steel fiber reinforced specimens. In the tests involving the combination of fibers and conventional stirrups, slight increases in ultimate load while major improvements in ductility were observed in comparison to the values for plain concrete specimens with conventional stirrups. In general, good agreement between the model and the test results was found.

Keywords: Ductility; fiber reinforced concretes; high strength concretes; loads (forces); metal fibers; models; polypropylene fibers; shear properties; stirrups; strength; tests

Mariano A. Valle is a civil/structural engineer with Greiner, Inc. in Miami, Florida. He holds a bachelor in Civil Engineering, from the Catholic University of America, Washington, D.C., and a Master of Science in Civil Engineering from the Massachusetts Institute of Technology, Cambridge, MA.

ACI member, Oral Buyukozturk is a professor in the Department of Civil Engineering at the Massachusetts Institute of Technology, Cambridge, MA. He is a member of ACI Committee 446, Fracture of Concrete, a member of Joint ASCE-ACI Committee 447, Finite Element Analysis of Concrete Structures, and a member of ACI Committee 126, Data Development of Concrete Materials.

INTRODUCTION

With the production of high strength concrete enhanced material properties such as increased compressive and tensile strengths and elastic modulus can be achieved. However, high strength concrete is known to manifest a more brittle behavior than normal strength concrete representing a significant limitation for its wide-range application in innovative structural design. When shear stresses are involved, in addition to the low toughness (brittle) characteristics, a relatively low shear strength behavior may also be observed for concrete with high compressive strength. Shear failure can be sudden and catastrophic. This is especially true for critical sections where, due to construction constraints, little or no reinforcing steel may be placed. For a broader use of high strength concrete in innovative structural solutions there is a need for the development of a fundamental understanding of the shear behavior and ductility of this material. Furthermore, basic knowledge is needed on the effects of the addition of short, high strength and ductile randomly oriented fibers on the toughness and shear strength of high strength concrete.

For more than thirty years, fiber reinforced concrete (FRC) has been the object of numerous investigations. Research has been performed on the behavior of fiber reinforced concrete subjected to various load conditions, including flexural and tensile loadings. The addition of ductile high strength fibers to concrete generally produces improved ultimate tensile strength and toughness (ductility) properties, and provides a good crack control mechanism. The use of fibers to improve the shear behavior of concrete is also promising. However, reported research efforts on the shear behavior of FRC are limited[1,2].

Tests performed to study the shear behavior of FRC can be categorized into two general groups: direct shear tests, and tests on beams and corbels. The direct shear tests are required in order to understand the basic shear transfer behavior of concrete, while the tests on beams and corbels are necessary to understand the behavior of FRC structures. Several investigations have been reported on the direct shear behavior of FRC using push-off specimens[3,4,5,6,7]. Tan and Mansur[8], studied the interaction of steel fibers with stirrups in the shear transfer of push-off specimens with initially uncracked shear plane. Shear tests involving corbels have been reported by Fattuhi[9] and Hara and Kitada[10]. A number of researchers have reported combined shear and flexural tests on beams to investigate the mechanical improvements provided by the use of steel fibers in the specimens SFRC[11,12,13,14].

From the review of these reported tests it can be stated that the addition of fibers generally improves the shear strength and ductility of concrete. It has been reported that the stirrups as shear reinforcement in concrete would be partially or totally replaced by the use of steel fibers[15,16,17]. These reported tests on the shear behavior of FRC generally address the effects of limited parameters, and thus, the results may be regarded as interim. The lack of research in this area is even greater for FRC involving high strength concrete, probably due to the relative short history of this material. More experimental research, both experimental and analytical, is needed in this respect. The research reported in this paper is intended to provide a basic understanding of the shear behavior of high strength concrete reinforced with fibers.

RESEARCH SIGNIFICANCE

This research provides a fundamental understanding of the deformation and failure behavior of plain and fiber reinforced high strength concrete under direct shear. The emphasis of the research is on shear strength and ductility improvements obtained by the addition of steel and polypropylene fibers to the concrete mixture. In that respect, the effectiveness of fiber addition to high strength concrete as compared to the normal strength concrete is studied. Also, the combined effects of fiber reinforcement and conventional steel stirrups on the shear behavior are investigated. Analytical modeling and testing methodologies adopted in this research are described. The reported research results have important implications with respect to the use of fiber reinforced high strength concrete for innovative solutions in shear critical structural situations.

TEST PROGRAM

Test Specimen and Materials

The direct shear transfer behavior of fiber reinforced high strength concrete was investigated through testing of initially uncracked push-off specimens shown in Fig. 1. The specimens had dimensions of 21x10x3 in (533x254x76 mm), with a shear plane area of 30 sq. in (19,355 mm^2). These dimensions were determined on the basis established through a previous research[18].

The three parameters of the investigation were: (1) concrete type: high strength vs. normal strength concrete, (2) type of fiber: steel vs. polypropylene fibers, and (3) the presence of steel stirrups crossing the shear plane. By combining these three variables, twelve types of specimens, classified by the type of concrete and shear reinforcement used, were obtained, as outlined in Table 1. In this table the concrete types are identified as: normal strength concrete (NC), steel fiber reinforced normal strength concrete (SNC), polypropylene fiber reinforced normal strength concrete (PNC), high strength concrete (HC), steel fiber reinforced high strength concrete (SHC), and polypropylene fiber reinforced high strength concrete (PHC). The specimens with steel stirrups are identified by an "S" at the end of each notation (i.e., NCS stands for normal strength concrete with steel stirrups). The test program included 2 specimens for each type of specimen used, plus an additional one, adding to a total of 25 specimens.

In manufacturing the test specimens the following materials were used: type I portland cement, pea gravel with a maximum aggregate size of 3/8 inch (9.52 mm), sand, silica fume in slurry form (to obtain high strength concrete), high range water reducer superplasticizer) (ASTM C-494 Type A&F), mild steel deformed bars (#3 and #5) with a yield strength of 60 ksi (414 MPa), polypropylene fibrillated fibers with a length of 3/4 in (19.05 mm), and crimped-end steel fibers with a length of 1.2 in (30.48 mm) and diameter of 0.019 in (0.5 mm) (aspect ratio=60). The yield strength of the steel fibers was 150 ksi (1034 MPa). Elastic moduli of the steel and the polypropylene fibers were 29,000 ksi (200 GPa) and 100 ksi (690 MPa), respectively.

The mix proportions for the normal and high strength concrete are listed in Table 2. The high strength mix was designed to produce a 9,000 to 10,000 psi (62 to 69 MPa) compressive strength in 28 days, while the normal strength mix was designed to develop a 4,000 psi (27 MPa) compressive strength in 7 days. Fibers were added to the fresh mix by volume, taking into account the volume of all components in the mix.

The specimen was then placed in a MTS machine loading frame. A data acquisition system was used to record the two displacement signals from the LVDTs as well as the applied load signal from the MTS machine. The push-off specimens were tested in a stroke controlled configuration with a displacement rate of 1/19,000 in/sec (1/750 mm/sec).

The test setup was altered for the last tested high strength concrete specimen with steel stirrups (HCS). In order to investigate the relation between the shear displacement (vertical) at the top and the center of the shear plane the two LVDTs with similar orientation were placed in the specimen (Fig. 3a). Also, with the purpose of monitoring the strain in the steel stirrups crossing the shear plane, two strain gages were placed on the steel bars as shown in Fig. 3b. The output of the strain gages was read using a portable digital strain indicator.

TEST RESULTS AND DISCUSSION

Strength and Deformation Behavior

The results obtained from the first 24 tests are summarized in Table 3 and Table 4 for HC and NC mixes, respectively. Both the maximum shear stress, τ_{max}, and the cracking shear stress, τ_{cr}, are given for each specimen tested. The shear stress was obtained by dividing the applied load by the area of the shear plane. In these tables both the obtained maximum shear stresses and their normalized values with respect to $\sqrt{f'_c}$ are provided. The results obtained from the two tests of each specimen type were found to be consistent.

The normalized shear stress vs. vertical displacement relationships of the tested NC, SNC, and PNC specimens are shown in Fig. 4. For the NC specimen, the shear stress vs. vertical deformation behavior was linear up to failure which occurred immediately following the first apparent cracking. For the specimens reinforced with fibers, SNC and PNC, the behavior up to first cracking was similar to that of the NC specimens. After cracking, the SNC specimen carried a higher load due to the steel fibers in the concrete mix, resulting in a strength increase up to 36% compared to the NC specimen. After reaching the maximum shear stress level, the SNC specimen failed in a ductile manner showing a softening behavior due to the pull-out of the steel fibers from the matrix. The PNC specimen did not show any increase in maximum load as observed with the SNC specimen. After the first cracking, the shear stress decreased with increasing vertical deformation indicating the pull-out of the polypropylene fibers at the cracking load level.

In Fig. 5, normalized shear stress vs. vertical displacement relationships for the normal strength concrete specimen reinforced with stirrups (NCS) and those reinforced with stirrups plus fibers (SNCS and PNCS) are shown. The shear stress vs. vertical displacement behavior for the NCS specimen was linear up to cracking, after which the steel reinforcement enabled the specimen to carry higher loads of up to 62% over the plain NC specimen. Beyond the maximum load level, this specimen showed a softening behavior. After failure of the concrete in the NCS specimen, the shear stress vs. vertical deformation showed an unloading behavior of the vertical displacement. For the specimens with both steel stirrups and fibers, SNCS and PNCS, the shear stress vs. vertical deformation behavior was similar to that of the NCS specimens up to cracking. After cracking, these specimens were not able to develop significantly higher shear stress levels when compared to the NCS specimens, but they showed a greater ductility at the maximum load level. After the concrete failed SNCS and PNCS specimens manifested an unloading phenomenon similar to that observed with the NCS specimens.

The shear stress vs. vertical deformation for the specimens involving high strength concrete with or without fiber reinforcement, that is HC, SHC and PHC specimens, are shown in Fig. 6. The behavior of the HC specimen was almost identical to that of the NC specimen, being linear up to failure, with the difference that the HC specimen carried a higher load at failure. For the SHC and PHC specimens, the shear stress vs. vertical deformation relationship was also linear up to first cracking. With the SHC specimen, after cracking, considerably higher shear stresses of up to approximately 60% were developed compared to that with the HC specimen. After the maximum shear stress was reached the SHC specimen manifested a softening behavior. This softening behavior and subsequent drop in loading were affected by the yielding and braking of the steel fibers rather than their pulling-out as observed with the normal strength concrete. With the PHC specimen, after the first cracking occurred, a higher shear stress level of approximately 17% compared to the HC specimens was developed. This increase was not observed for the specimens with normal strength concrete with polypropylene fibers. After reaching the maximum shear stress level, the PHC specimens showed a softening behavior which is attributed to the pull-out of the polypropylene fibers from the high strength concrete matrix.

Fig. 7 shows the normalized shear stress vs. vertical displacement relationship for the specimen involving high strength concrete reinforced with stirrups alone and for those reinforced with stirrups plus fibers, i.e., specimens HCS, SHCS and PHCS.

Manufacturing of Specimens

The first step in this process was to prepare the steel bar reinforcement of the specimens. The steel reinforcement configuration is shown in Fig. 1. The vertical reinforcement, #5 bars in Fig. 1, were included in all push-off specimens to eliminate any possible failure modes other than that along the shear plane. This vertical reinforcement was tied using #3 bars. For the specimens with steel stirrups #3 bars crossing the shear plane were placed in hoops. The assembled steel bars were then placed in their molds. For mixing, an Omni mixer, which had the capability to pressurize the mixing chamber was used to improve the homogeneity of the concrete mixture. The mixing procedure was as follows:

a) mix dry components (cement, sand and gravel) for 2-3 minutes.

b) add water to the mix. In the case of high strength concrete the superplasticizer and silica fume were added to water before pouring it into the mixer.

c) the mixing chamber was then closed and pressurized to approximately 40 cmHg. The fresh concrete was then mixed for 5 minutes.

d) if the mixture required fibers, these were added by slowly sprinkling them into the mixer to avoid balling. After all the fibers were added, the mixer was closed and pressurized again to 40 cmHg. Then, the fresh concrete with fibers was mixed for 3 minutes.

The fresh concrete was then poured into the molds, and the molds were externally vibrated for 3 minutes to ensure proper placing of the concrete. Also, control cylinders of 3 in (76.2 mm) diameter with 6 in (152.4 mm) height were made for the compressive strength tests. The specimens were then covered with plastic. After 24 hours, the push-off specimens and the cylinders were removed from their molds and placed in water until testing. High strength concrete specimens were tested at 28 days, and normal strength concrete specimens were tested at 7 days.

Test Setup

The test setup was identical for the first 24 specimens cast. In order to measure the horizontal and vertical displacements at the shear plane, two LVDTs were attached on the specimen. The horizontal measurement was made to establish the cracking load as well as to measure the crack width across the shear plane. The loading condition and the position of the LVDTs are shown in Fig. 2.

Specimen HCS showed a linear behavior up to cracking, followed by a significantly higher shear strength value (up to 112%) compared to that with the plain HC specimen. After the maximum shear stress was reached, HCS specimen showed a softening behavior followed by the failure of the concrete and an unloading behavior as observed with the NCS specimens, but this time to a permanent deformation. For the specimens SHCS and PHCS, the behavior was also linear up to the first cracking. In the case of SHCS specimen, an increase in the maximum shear stress of approximately 24% over the HCS specimens was observed. Also, the SHCS specimen developed a plateau after the maximum shear stress was reached, manifesting a plastic deformation. This is followed by a softening behavior, and eventually by failure of the concrete with an unloading to a permanent deformation. The behavior of the PHCS specimen after first cracking was characterized as a more ductile behavior than that of the HCS specimen, developing maximum shear stress levels at larger vertical displacement values. Also, the PHCS specimen showed an unloading behavior of the vertical displacement to a permanent deformation.

In general, both types of fibers, steel and polypropylene, proved to be more effective in HC mixes than in NC mixes producing higher maximum shear stress as well as ductility of the specimens. This is attributed to the improved bond characteristics between the fibers and the matrix with the HC mixes. Steel stirrups alone proved to be more effective than fibers alone as shear reinforcement, although for the case of high strength concrete with steel fibers alone higher maximum shear stresses were obtained compared to normal strength concrete reinforced with steel stirrups only. Normal strength concrete with steel stirrups and fibers did not manifest any significant increase in maximum shear stress compared to the specimens with steel stirrups alone; the steel fiber inclusion increased the shear strength of the high strength concrete specimens with stirrups. Reinforcement with the combination of steel stirrups and fibers resulted, in all instances, in more ductile characteristics of the specimens than that with just steel stirrups.

Failure Modes

The observed failure mode of the concrete specimens without fiber or steel stirrup reinforcement (NC and HC), was very brittle, with no warning before collapse. These specimens lost their integrity, breaking into several pieces. Specimens reinforced with fibers alone developed several small diagonal cracks as shown in Fig. 8a. With the specimens SNC, PNC, and PHC, ultimate failure occurred when these series of diagonal cracks joined together forming a crack band along the shear plane and the fibers were obtained for specimens involving high strength concrete reinforced with steel stirrups and steel fibers over the high strength concrete reinforced with steel stirrups alone. The increase in the value of I_{30} index was approximately 100% for normal strength concrete specimens reinforced with steel fibers and stirrups when compared to normal strength concrete specimens with stirrups only.

SHEAR TRANSFER MODEL

For the analysis, a shear transfer model is used for predicting the shear stress-shear strain behavior of the plain and fiber reinforced concrete. The model is based on a truss model theory[20] considering the softening of concrete in compression due to the propagation and interaction of cracks. Further development of the model has been made for improved predictions. A brief description of the model follows. The objective is to predict the average shear stress vs. shear strain relationship for the element shown in Fig. 11. In this orthogonally reinforced concrete element the stress state can be represented by in-plane shear, τ_{lt} and normal stresses,σ_t and σ_l, as shown in Fig. 12a. The stress state of the reinforced concrete element can be resolved into the components contributed by the concrete element, σ_{tc}, σ_{lc}, and τ_{ltc}, and those by the reinforcing steel,σ_{ts}, σ_{ls} (Figs.12b and 12c). Furthermore, the stresses in the concrete, σ_{tc}, σ_{lc}, and τ_{ltc}, can be resolved into the d-r axes, σ_r, σ_d, coinciding with the principal stress axes for the concrete element (Fig. 12d and 12e). Here, α is defined as the angle between the l-t axes and the d-r axes. The reinforced concrete element is assumed to behave as a truss system in which the concrete is subjected to biaxial stress state, compression in the d-direction and tension in the r-direction (Fig. 12e); the steel reinforcement only carries normal stresses. This truss action must satisfy (a) equilibrium, (b) compatibility, and (c) material laws.

For the precracking stage, the reinforced concrete element is assumed to behave as a linear elastic material that satisfies the three requirements listed above. The present study accounts for the softening of concrete in tension before cracking, due to the existence of compressive stresses in the orthogonal direction. For this, empirical constants, by which the tensile stiffness of concrete is multiplied, were assessed experimentally. They were determined to be 0.35 for the normal and 0.40 for the high strength concrete. Also, for the precracking behavior, a parabolic shear strain distribution along the shear plane is assumed (Fig. 13). This distribution was obtained by measuring the vertical displacements at two points along the shear plane of the push-off specimen. The corresponding shear stress distribution along the shear plane is adopted as proposed by Cholewicki[21]. After cracking, both the shear strains and the shear stresses are assumed to be uniformly distributed along the shear plane (Fig. 13). This assumption was also confirmed with the experimental results.

Material Law for Steel Reinforcement

For the transverse and longitudinal steel bars, the steel is assumed to behave as an elastic-perfectly plastic material represented by the following equations:

$$\text{for} \quad \varepsilon_i < \varepsilon_y \quad f_i = E_s \varepsilon_i \qquad \text{Eq. 1a}$$

$$\text{for} \quad \varepsilon_i \geq \varepsilon_y \quad f_i = f_y \qquad \text{Eq. 1b}$$

where, ε_i=normal strain, f_i=stress in the steel, i denotes l and t for their respective axes, E_s=modulus of elasticity of steel, and f_y and ε_y are the yield stress and strain for steel, respectively.

Material Law for Concrete

Since the testing program involved six different types of materials, namely, NC, SNC, PNC, HC, SHC, and PHC, in the model different stress-strain behaviors for tension and for compression were adopted for these materials. The following is a brief description of the relationships used for each type of concrete.

(1) Compressive Behavior of Concrete

For the compressive behavior, all concrete types considered were assumed to behave basically in the same manner as shown in Fig. 14, but with different parameters. These parameters are the strain values corresponding to the peak strain and the ultimate strain value[22,23,24]. The numerical values of these strains for the specific concrete types considered are given in Table 5.

For the ascending branch of the compressive stress-strain curve, the following relationship was used[24]:

$$\text{for} \ |\varepsilon_d| \leq |\varepsilon_p| \quad \sigma_d = f'_c \left[2\left(\frac{\varepsilon_d}{\varepsilon_o}\right) - \lambda\left(\frac{\varepsilon_d}{\varepsilon_o}\right)^2 \right] \qquad \text{Eq. 2}$$

$$\lambda = \sqrt{0.7 - \frac{\varepsilon_r}{\varepsilon_d}} \qquad \text{Eq. 3}$$

where, ε_d=compressive strain of concrete, ε_o=peak strain for uniaxial compression, $\varepsilon_p = \varepsilon_o/\lambda$, f'_c=cylinder compressive strength, ε_r=tensile strain of concrete, and λ is the coefficient that incorporates the softening of concrete due to biaxiality (tensile stress in the orthogonal direction).

For the descending branch of the compressive stress-strain curve, the following relationship was assumed for all mixes involving NC or NC with fibers[24]:

$$\text{for } |\varepsilon_d|>|\varepsilon_p| \quad \sigma_d = \frac{f'_c}{\lambda}\left[1-\left(\frac{\frac{\varepsilon_d}{\varepsilon_o}-\frac{1}{\lambda}}{2-\frac{1}{\lambda}}\right)^2\right] \qquad \text{Eq. 4a}$$

For the mixes involving HC or HC with fibers, the following relationship was assumed:

$$\text{for } |\varepsilon_d|>|\varepsilon_p| \quad \sigma_d = \frac{f'_c}{\lambda} - 0.15f'_c\frac{(\varepsilon_d-\varepsilon_p)}{(\varepsilon_u-\varepsilon_o)} \qquad \text{Eq. 4b}$$

Different values for ε_o and ε_u were used according to the type of concrete being analyzed (Table 5).

(2) Tensile Behavior of Concrete

For all types of concrete used, a similar behavior was assumed for the precracking stage in the stress-strain tensile curve. However, for the behavior after cracking, differences were adopted corresponding to each concrete type as to whether or not the mix contained fibers (Fig. 15).

The initial tension stiffness of the concrete (E_{ct}) was obtained by using a modified law of mixtures that take into account the addition of randomly oriented fibers to the concrete mixture[25]. Further, as mentioned before, this initial stiffness was lowered by means of an empirical constant, C, in order to account for the biaxiality effects. The equation used was:

$$E_{ct} = C\,(E_{mt}V_{mt} + E_fV_f\,\eta_l\,\eta_o) \qquad \text{Eq. 5a}$$

where, E_{ct}=modulus of the composite in tension (psi), C= empirical constant equal to 0.35 or 0.40 for NC and HC, respectively, E_{mt} = modulus of the concrete $\left(E_{mt} = 40{,}000\sqrt{f'_c} + 1{,}000{,}000 \text{ psi}\right)^{26}$, V_m=volume percent of the concrete in the mix, E_f=modulus of the fibers, V_f=volume percent of fibers in the mix, η_o=orientation factor (=0.14)[25], and η_l=length efficiency factor[25]. For the case with no fibers, Eq. 5a becomes:

$$E_{ct} = CE_{mt} \qquad \text{Eq. 5b}$$

Using the above described equations, the pre-cracking behavior of concrete in tension, can be defined as:

$$\text{for } \varepsilon_r \le \varepsilon_{cr} \quad \sigma_r = E_{ct}\varepsilon_r \qquad \text{Eq. 6}$$

where, ε_{cr}=cracking strain=f_{cr}/E_{ct}, and f_{cr}, cracking stress, is assumed equal to $7.5\sqrt{f'_c}$ for NC and PNC and $6\sqrt{f'_c}$ for HC and PHC.

For SNC and SHC specimens due to the cracking strain, ε_{cr}, was calculated using the following formula[25]:

$$\varepsilon_{cr} = \eta_l \eta'_o V_f\left(\varepsilon_{fp} - \varepsilon_{mp}\right) + \varepsilon_{mp} \qquad \text{Eq. 7}$$

where, ε_{cr}=cracking strain of the composite, η'_o=orientation factor at cracking (=0.405)[25], ε_{fp} and ε_{mp} are the strains at the proportionality limit for the fiber and matrix, respectively.

The postcracking behavior is dependent on the type of fibers, if they are present, in the mix. For the case of NC or HC, similar relationships for the postcracking behavior were used (Fig. 15a)[24]:

$$\text{for } \varepsilon_r > \varepsilon_{cr} \quad \sigma_r = \frac{f_{cr}}{1 + \sqrt{\dfrac{\varepsilon_r - \varepsilon_{cr}}{0.005}}} \qquad \text{Eq. 8a}$$

For concrete reinforced with steel fibers (SNC and SHC), the postcracking behavior was assumed to be bilinear (Fig. 15b) as expressed by the following equations:

$$\text{for } \varepsilon_{cr} < \varepsilon_r < \varepsilon_{cr2} \qquad \sigma_r = f_{cr} + E_f V_f \eta_l \eta_o (\varepsilon_r - \varepsilon_{cr}) \qquad \text{Eq. 8b.1}$$

bridging the cracks pulled out. The fibers were able to preserve the integrity of the specimen. In the case of SHC specimens, the above was also true, with the difference that soon after the maximum load was reached, a softening behavior with a rapid drop in load occurred. This phenomenon is attributed to that some steel fibers bridging the crack along the shear plane may have yielded in tension, followed by a rupture upon increase of the deformation. It is interpreted that this yielding and breaking behavior of the fibers resulted primarily due to the improved bond provided by the HC.

For specimens involving steel stirrups crossing the shear plane (NCS, SNCS, PNCS, HCS, SHCS, and PHCS), the failure was with the formation of discrete diagonal cracks (Fig. 8b). As these cracks extended at an angle of 50 to 75 degrees with respect to the horizontal direction, they created well defined compressive struts in the concrete, which in combination with the tensile force carried by the steel stirrups, formed a truss like action. Ultimate failure occurred when the concrete struts crushed in compression. After this, since the truss action was no longer present, an unloading behavior was observed. In the specimens involving normal strength concrete (NCS, SNCS, and PNCS) the vertical displacements reduced to a zero value (Fig. 5) while the specimens with high strength concrete(HCS, SHCS, PHCS) showed a similar unloading behavior but to a finite permanent deformation (Fig. 7). The preceding discussion suggested that the steel stirrups in the specimens with NC did not reach their yielding strength since the vertical displacement was elastically recovered, while in the case of the specimens involving HC, the steel stirrups developed their yield strength, causing a permanent deformation. This behavior was later confirmed by performing an additional test on an HCS specimen, where the strain in the steel stirrups was monitored. The test results confirmed yielding of the steel stirrups as shown in Fig. 9.

Toughness

In order to evaluate the relative toughness associated with each type of specimen, the toughness indices proposed by ACI committee 544 were used[19]. In general, the addition of fibers resulted in an improvement of ductility for all cases. For example, the addition of polypropylene fibers resulted in an I_{30} index 14 times greater than the toughness obtained with the plain high strength concrete specimens, and the addition of steel fibers resulted in an I_{30} index equal to approximately 5. Also, the specimens reinforced with both steel stirrups and fibers, manifested a very ductile behavior. Fig. 10 shows a bar graph comparing the average toughness index, I_{30}, for all six high strength concrete specimens. Here, improvements of up to 265%

for $\varepsilon_r > \varepsilon_{cr2}$ $\qquad \sigma_r = f_u - E_f V_f \eta_l \eta_o (\varepsilon_r - \varepsilon_{cr2})$ Eq. 8b.2

where, ε_{cr2}= strain at peak tensile load= $\varepsilon_{cr}+\sigma_{sfu}/E_{sf}$, $f_u=f_{cr}+\eta_l\eta'_o V_{sf}E_{sf}$, and, σ_{sfu}, E_{sf} are the ultimate steel fiber strength and modulus, respectively. For concrete reinforced with polypropylene fibers (PNC and PHC) a linear decrease in stress was assumed up to a strain equal to 28 times the strain at cracking, where the stress was 0.3 times f_{cr} (Fig. 15c). The equation used was:

for $\varepsilon_r > \varepsilon_{cr}$ $\qquad \sigma_r = f_{cr} - \frac{0.7f_{cr}}{28\varepsilon_{cr}}(\varepsilon_r - \varepsilon_{cr})$ Eq. 8c

Application of Model to Shear Transfer Problem and Solution

By combining the equations of equilibrium and compatibility with those of material laws, a system of 11 non-linear equations, involving 14 unknowns ($\sigma_l,\sigma_t,\tau_{lt},\sigma_d,\sigma_r,f_l,f_t,\varepsilon_l,\varepsilon_t,\gamma_{lt},\varepsilon_d,\varepsilon_r,\alpha$ and λ) can be defined. These variables, as adopted in the model, represent the average values for the element being studied. For the shear transfer problem being investigated (Figs. 11a and 11b), the stresses acting on an element located at the shear plane are shown in Fig. 11c. Here, τ_{lt} is defined as the average shear stress acting on the shear plane, and is equal to

$$\tau_{lt} = \frac{P_t}{LH} \qquad \text{Eq. 9}$$

where, P_t=externally applied load, L and H are defined in Fig. 11a and 11b.

Further, Hsu, et al.[20] have demonstrated that σ_t and τ_{lt} can be related by

$$\sigma_t = K\tau_{lt} \qquad \text{Eq. 10}$$

and

$$\sigma_l = 0 \qquad \text{Eq. 11}$$

where, K=L/B, with L and B defined in Fig. 11.

By substituting Eqs.9-11 into the previously described system of equations, a solution for shear stress, τ_{lt}, and shear strain , γ_{lt}, can be found for a given value of ε_d. A detailed description of the solution procedure is contained in Ref. 27.

Comparison of Model and Experimental Results

In order to compare the test results with the model predictions, the measured shear strains had to be calibrated to account for the non-uniformity of the shear strain and shear stress distribution along the shear plane before cracking. Shear strains were obtained by dividing the vertical displacement measured in the tests by the gage length of the LVDT along the shear plane. Since the model predicts the average shear strain along the plane, and the measured shear strain in the tests corresponded to the top location in the plane, a correction was needed. To obtain a correction factor an additional test was performed in which the shear deformations at two points, the center and the top, in the shear plane were measured. Fig. 16 shows the measured deformation at these two locations of the shear plane. It is clear from this figure that before cracking the vertical deformations at the two points are quite different, being almost zero at the center and increasing with the applied stress at the top. After cracking, the vertical deformations of the two points follow an identical path, with an offset equal to the difference of the displacements at the cracking stress level. This is interpreted as that the strain distribution along the shear plane after cracking is almost uniform. Using this information, and the stress distribution along the shear plane proposed by Cholewicki[19], the shear strain and shear stress distributions shown in Fig. 13a and 13b, were assumed.

In general, good agreement between the test results and the model predictions were found for both before and after cracking. Figs. 17-19 show the test results and the prediction for the shear stress vs. shear strain curves for specimens HC, SHC and PHC. Fig. 20 shows the comparison between the test results and the model prediction for the cracking and maximum shear stresses for the specimens. Figs. 21 and 22 show a comparison of the test results for the cracking shear strains and shear strain values corresponding to the maximum shear stress. For the specimens containing steel stirrups and fibers as shear reinforcement, the model over-estimated the maximum shear stress by 15 to 20%. This is attributed to the interaction of the fibers and the steel stirrups, which is not considered in the model. Another factor would be related to the compaction problems in preparing the test specimens, since in this case the presence of steel stirrups made the placing of the fiber reinforced concrete difficult.

CONCLUSIONS

In this paper, strength and ductility properties of fiber reinforced high strength concrete under direct shear are studied. Experimental and analytical studies performed on steel and polypropylene fiber reinforced specimens with or without conventional stirrups are described. In what follows the main results and conclusions are given:

1. Greater shear strength increases were found with fiber reinforced high strength concrete specimens (60% with steel and 17% with polypropylene fibers) than with fiber reinforced normal strength concrete specimens (36% with steel fibers and no increase with polypropylene), compared to the strength of their respective unreinforced plain concrete specimens. Higher shear strength values were obtained with the high strength concrete specimens reinforced with steel fibers alone (18%) compared to the normal strength concrete specimens reinforced with stirrups only. The enhanced performance of fibers in high strength concrete is attributed to the improved bond characteristics between the fiber and the matrix associated with the high strength concrete with silica fume.

2. In all cases, fibers improved the shear deformation and ductility characteristics of concrete. Addition of steel fibers to high strength concrete produced a relative toughness which was greater (approximately 5 times) than that for the plain high strength concrete specimens. This improvement in shear deformation and ductility was even greater (up to 14 times), for the specimens reinforced with polypropylene fibers compared to plain high strength concrete specimens. Comparable improvements in toughness were obtained in normal strength concrete reinforced with fibers alone.

3. For the specimens reinforced with fibers alone, failure occurred by the formation of numerous small cracks diagonal to the shear plane, which ultimately joined and formed a crack band along the plane. Both steel and polypropylene fibers in normal strength concrete appeared to pull out of the matrix. High strength concrete specimens reinforced with polypropylene fibers also failed with fiber pull-out, but, after the development of some plastic deformation in the polypropylene fibers. In high strength concrete with steel fibers, due to the improved bond between the fiber and the matrix, some of the steel fibers bridging the cracks yielded and eventually broke.

4. For the normal strength concrete specimen with steel stirrups the measured shear strengths did not vary significantly with the addition of steel or polypropylene fibers, compared to the

specimens with steel stirrups alone. However, for the high strength concrete specimens containing both stirrups and steel fibers, an increase in the shear strength was observed over the shear strength of high strength concrete reinforced with stirrups alone. The combination of fibers and steel stirrups proved to significantly increase the overall ductility when compared to concrete reinforced with steel stirrups alone.

5. The obtained model predictions for the shear behavior of the tested specimens correlate well with the experimental results. Both shear stresses and shear strains are predicted with good accuracy. Thus, the model represents a good basis for a parametric study of the variables involved in the shear transfer of fiber reinforced concrete.

6. In view of the results obtained in this investigation it is concluded that the use of fibers alone or in combination with steel stirrups as shear reinforcement in concrete appears to have a promising future. This is especially true for high strength concrete, where fiber reinforcement was observed to be more effective. The research reported in this paper represents an initial investigation. Further studies, both experimental and analytical, are needed to assess various effects such as the interaction between fiber and stirrups. Future work should include an optimization study of the combined use of stirrups and fibers as shear reinforcement, to obtain economic solutions with higher shear capacities and ductility.

ACKNOWLEDGEMENT

The authors acknowledge the support provided by W. R. Grace Co., in Cambridge, MA., which provided the polypropylene fibers, silica fume and superplasticizer used in this study. The authors would like to thank Kwang M. Lee, a graduate student at M.I.T., for his valuable comments and for his efforts that made possible finalizing this paper.

REFERENCES

1. Zahar, G.J., "Flexural Behavior of Mortar Reinforced with Carbon Fibers", M.S. Thesis, Department of Civil Engineering, Massachusetts Institute of Technology, 1987.
2. Ward, R., "Steel and Synthetic Fibers as Shear Reinforcement," M.S. Thesis, Department of Civil Engineering, Massachusetts Institute of Technology, 1989.
3. Kohno, K., Horii, K., Yukitomo, K., and Gotoh, Y., "Shearing Strength of Steel Fiber Reinforced Concrete," *Transactions of the Japan Concrete Institute*, Vol. 5, No. 4, 1983, pp. 231-238.

4. Hara, T., "Effects of Steel Fibers on Shear Transfer," *Transactions of the Japan Concrete Institute*, Vol. 6, 1984, pp. 425-432.
5. Van de Loock, L., "Influence of Steel Fibers on the Shear Transfer in Cracks", *Proceedings of the International Symposium on Fiber Reinforced Concrete*, Madras, India, 1987, pp. 1.101-1.112.
6. Swamy, R.N., Jones, R., and Chiam, T., "Shear Transfer in Steel Fiber Reinforced Concrete," Fiber Reinforced Concrete Properties and Applications, ACI SP-105, 1987, pp. 565-592.
7. Barr, B., "The Fracture Characteristics of FRC Materials in Shear," Fiber Reinforced Concrete Properties and Applications, ACI SP-105, 1987, pp. 27-53.
8. Tan, K.H., and Mansur, M.A., "Shear Transfer in Reinforced Fiber Concrete," *Journal of Materials in Civil Engineering*, Vol. 2, No. 4, Nov. 1990, pp. 202-214.
9. Fattuhi, H.I.,"SFRC Corbel Tests," *ACI Structural Journal*, Vol. 84, No. 2, 1987, pp. 119-123.
10. Hara, T., and Kitada, Y., "Shear Strength of Reinforced Concrete Corbels and Steel Fibers as Reinforcement,"*Transactions of the Japan Concrete Institute*, Vol. 2, 1980, pp. 279-286.
11. Narayan, R., and Darwish, I.Y.S., "Use of Steel Fibers as Shear Reinforcement," *ACI Structural Journal*, Vol. 39, No. 138, March 1987, pp. 42-50.
12. Shanmugam, N.E., and Swaddiwndhipong, S., "The Ultimate Load Behavior of Fiber Reinforced Concrete Deep Beams," *Indian Concrete Journal*, Vol. 58, No. 8, 1988, pp. 211-218.
13. Swamy, R.N., and Bahia, M.H., "The Effectiveness of Steel Fibers as Shear Reinforcement," *Concrete International*, Vol. 7, No. 3, March 1985, pp. 35-40.
14.Ward, R. J. and Li, V. C., "Dependance of Flexural Behavior of Fiber Reinforced Mortar on Material Fracture Resistance and Beam Size," *ACI Materials Journal*, Vol. 87, No. 6, Nov.-Dec. 1990, pp. 627-637.
15. Batson, G.B., Jenkins, E., and Spatney, R., "Steel Fibers as Shear Reinforcement in Beams", *ACI Journal*, Vol. 69, No. 10, 1972, pp. 640-644.
16. Lim, T.Y., Paramassiram, and Lee, S.L., "Shear and Moment Capacity of Reinforced Steel-Fiber-Concrete Beams", *Magazine of Concrete Research*, Vol. 39, No. 140, 1987, pp. 148-160.
17. Mansur, M.A., Ong, C.G., and Paramasivam, P., "Shear Strength of Fibrous Concrete Beams without Stirrups," *Journal of Structural Engineering*, Vol. 112, No. 9, 1986, pp. 2066-2079.
18. Buyukozturk, O. Bakhoum, M. M., and Beattie, S.M., , "Shear Behavior of Joints in Precast Concrete Segmental Bridges," *Journal of Structural Engineering*, ASCE, Vol. 116, No. 12, December 1990, pp. 3380-3401.

19. ACI Committee 544, "Measurement of Properties of Fiber Reinforced Concrete," *ACI Materials Journal*, Vol. 85, No. 6, November-December 1988, pp. 583-593.
20. Hsu, T.T., Mau, S.T., and Chen B., "Theory of Shear Transfer Strength of Reinforced Concrete," *ACI Structural Journal*, Vol. 84, No. 2, 1987, pp. 149-160.
21. Cholewicki, A., "Loadbearing Capacity and Deformability of Vertical Joints in Structural Walls of Large Panels," *Building Science*, Vol. 6, Pergamon Press, 1971, pp. 163-184.
22. Green, E. C., " Behavior of High Strength Fiber Reinforced Concrete," M.S. Thesis, Department of Civil Engineering, Massachusetts Institute of Technology, 1989.
23.Fanella, D. A. and Naaman, A. E., "Stress-Strain Properties of Fiber Reinforced Mortar in Compression," *ACI Journal*, Vol. 82, No. 4, July-August 1985, pp. 475-483.
24. Vecchio, F. and Collins, M.P.,"Stress-Strain Characteristics of Reinforced Concrete in Pure Shear," Final Report, IABSE Colloquium on Advanced Mechanics of Reinforced Concrete (Delft, 1981), International Association for Bridge and Structural Engineering, Zurich, pp. 211-225.
25. Lim,T.Y., Paramasivam, P., and Lee, S.L., "Analytical Model for Tensile Behavior of Steel-Fiber Concrete," *ACI Material Journal*, Vol. 84, No. 2, 1987, pp. 286-298.
26. ACI Committee 363, "State-of-the-art-Report on High Strength Concrete," *ACI Journal*, Vol. 81, No. 4, July-August 1984, pp. 364-406.
27. Valle, M., "Shear Transfer in Fiber Reinforced Concrete," M.S. Thesis, Department of Civil Engineering, Massachusetts Institute of Technology, February 1991.

TABLE 1 — TEST SPECIMEN CLASSIFICATION BY TYPE OF CONCRETE AND SHEAR REINFORCEMENT

Specimen identification	Concrete Type	Vol. fraction steel fibers V_{sf} %	Vol. fraction polypropylene fibers V_{pf} %	Steel stirrup reinforcing ratio ρ_l
NC	NC	-	-	-
SNC	SNC	1.0%	-	-
PNC	PNC	-	1.0%	-
NCS	NC	-	-	1.47%
SNCS	SNC	1.0%	-	1.47%
PNCS	PNC	-	1.0%	1.47%
HC	HC	-	-	-
SHC	SHC	1.0%	-	-
PHC	PHC	-	1.0%	-
HCS	HC	-	-	1.47%
SHCS	SHC	1.0%	-	1.47%
PHCS	PHC	-	1.0%	1.47%

TABLE 2 — CONCRETE MIX PROPORTIONS BY WEIGHT

MIX	cement (C)	sand/ C	aggre./ C	SF/C	steel fibers/ total	poly. fibers/ total	super plast./C	W/C
HC	1	2.0	2.0	5%	-	-	1%	0.35
PHC	1	2.0	2.0	5%	-	0.3%	1%	0.35
SHC	1	2.0	2.0	5%	3.27%	-	1%	0.35
NC	1	1.7	2.0	-	-	-	0.5%	0.40
PNC	1	1.7	2.0	-	-	0.3%	1%	0.40
SNC	1	1.7	2.0	-	3.27%	-	1%	0.40

TABLE 3 — TEST RESULTS FOR NORMAL STRENGTH CONCRETE SPECIMENS

specimen	f'c (psi)	max. load, P_t (lbs)	τ_{max} (psi)	$\tau_{max}/\sqrt{f'c}$	% incr. avg. τ_{max}	τ_{cr} (psi)
NC-1	4,500	23,251.8	775.06	11.55	-	775.06
NC-2	4,500	22,323.9	744.13	11.09		744.13
SNC-1	4,200	30,303.0	1,010.10	15.6	36.00	618.26
SNC-2	4,200	29,552.1	985.07	15.2		593.44
PNC-1	4,010	23,651.7	788.39	12.45	9.76	788.39
PNC-2	4,010	23,556.6	785.22	12.4		785.22
NCS-1	4,950	39,258.9	1,308.63	18.6	62.10	823.87
NCS-2	4,950	38,203.5	1,273.45	18.1		805.58
SNCS-1	3,800	36,024.9	1,200.83	19.48	68.20	669.46
SNCS-2	3,800	34,397.4	1,146.58	18.6		621.99
PNCS-1	4,900	38,535.0	1,284.50	18.35	62.32	747.6
PNCS-2	4,900	38,640.0	1,288.00	18.4		755.3

(1 psi = 6.895 kPa, 1 lb = 4.448 N)

TABLE 4 — TEST RESULTS FOR HIGH STRENGTH CONCRETE SPECIMENS

specimen	f'c (psi)	max. load, P_t (lbs)	τ_{max} (psi)	$\tau_{max}/\sqrt{f'c}$	% incr. avg. τ_{max}	τ_{cr} (psi)
HC-1	9,000	24,843.3	828.11	8.73		827.90
HC-2	9,000	26,927.1	897.57	9.16		869.07
SHC-1	11,600	45,493.8	1516.46	14.08	58.58	1151.35
SHC-2	11,600	46,172.4	1539.08	14.29		1129.81
PHC-1	9,100	29,763.0	992.10	10.4	17.16	884.30
PHC-2	9,100	30,220.8	1007.36	10.56		903.38
HCS-1	9,680	52,155.0	1738.50	17.67	112.69	1024.21
HCS-2	9,680	60,153.9	2005.13	20.38		1054.71
SHCS-1	10,930	67557.9	2251.93	21.54	139.68	1259.79
SHCS-2	10,930	66,930.9	2231.03	21.34		1323.55
PHCS-1	9,020	49,377	1645.90	17.33	92.45	1009.57
PHCS-2	9,020	48,721.5	1624.05	17.1		1001.67

(1 psi= 6.895 kPa, 1 lb= 4.448 N)

TABLE 5 — PEAK AND ULTIMATE STRAINS USED FOR THE DIFFERENT TYPES OF CONCRETE

CONCRETE TYPE	PEAK STRAIN(ε_o)	ULTIMATE STRAIN(ε_u)
NC	0.002	0.0035
SNC	0.0035	0.005
PNC	0.002	0.0035
HC	0.0025	0.003
SHC	0.003	0.0045
PHC	0.0025	0.0035

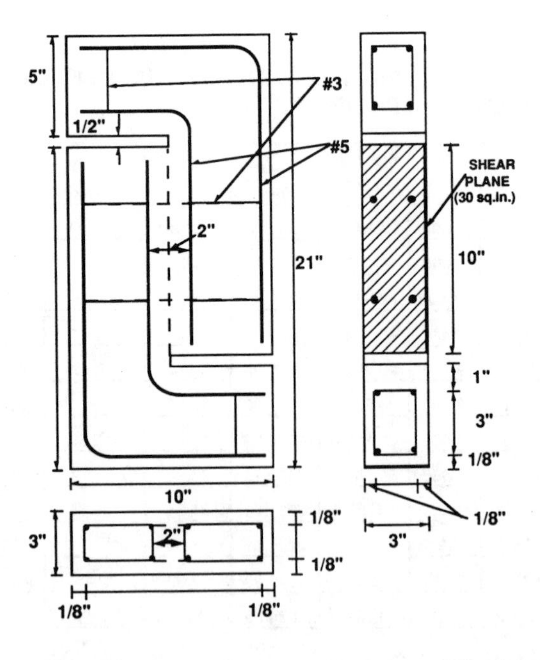

Fig. 1—Geometry and steel bar reinforcement distribution for push-off specimen (1 in. = 25.4 mm)

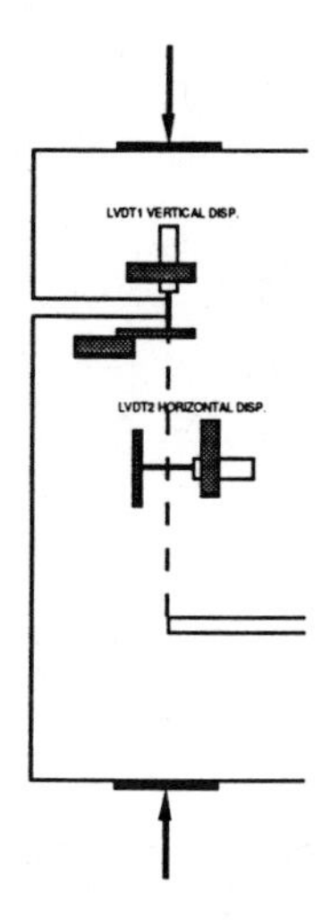

Fig. 2—Loading configuration and position of LVDTs

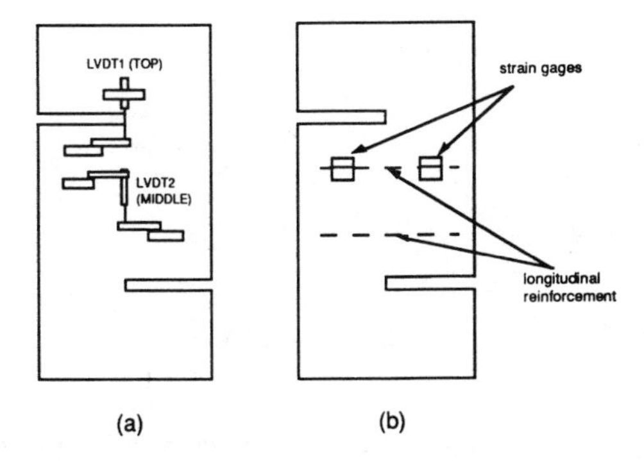

Fig. 3—Experimental set-up for test: (a) position of LVDTs to measure shear deformations along shear plane, (b) position of strain gages to monitor strain in longitudinal steel bars

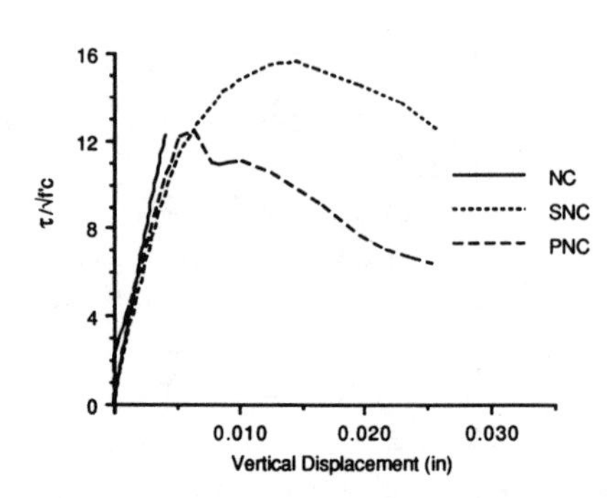

Fig. 4—Normalized shear stress versus vertical displacement for NC, SNC, and PNC specimens (1 in. = 25.4 mm)

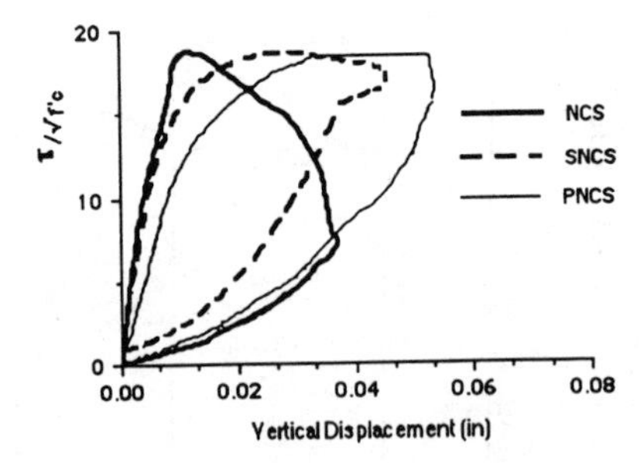

Fig. 5—Normalized shear stress versus vertical displacement for NCS, SNCS, and PNCS specimens (1 in. = 25.4 mm)

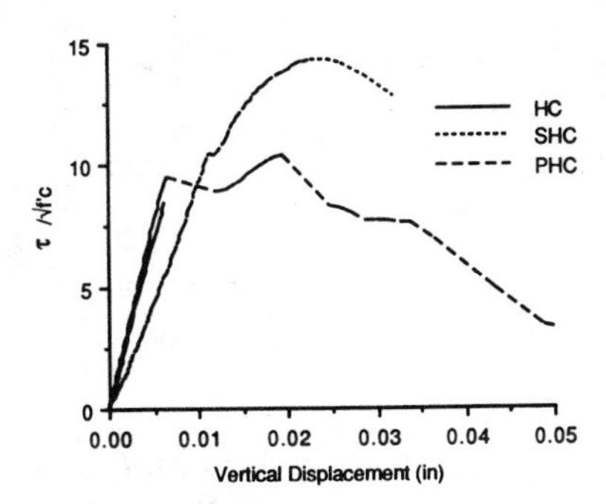

Fig. 6—Normalized shear stress versus vertical displacement for HC, SHC, and PHC specimens (1 in. = 25.4 mm)

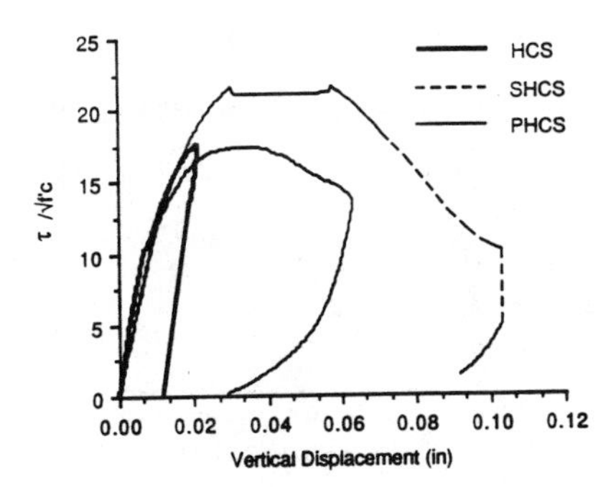

Fig. 7—Normalized shear stress versus vertical displacement for HCS, SHCS, and PHCS specimens (1 in. = 25.4 mm)

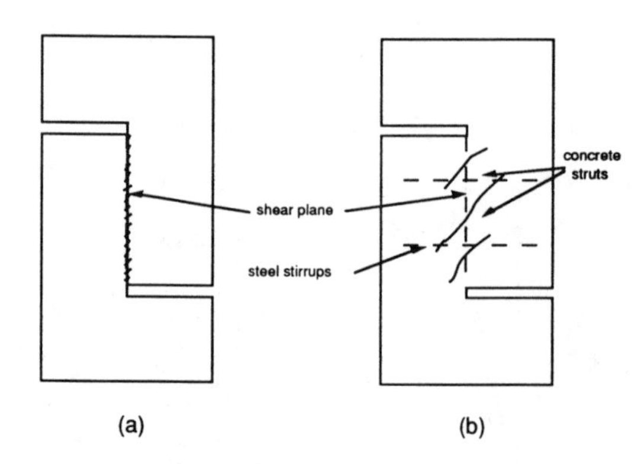

Fig. 8—Cracking patterns for push-off specimens: (a) with no steel stirrups crossing the shear plane; (b) with steel stirrups crossing the shear plane

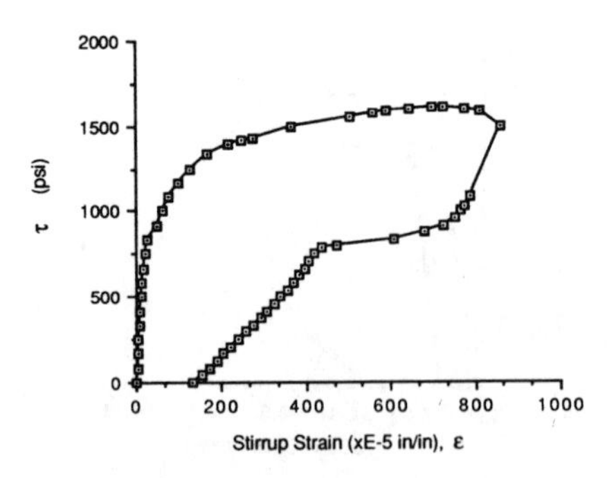

Fig. 9—Shear stress versus stirrup strain for HCS specimen (1 psi = 6.895 kPa)

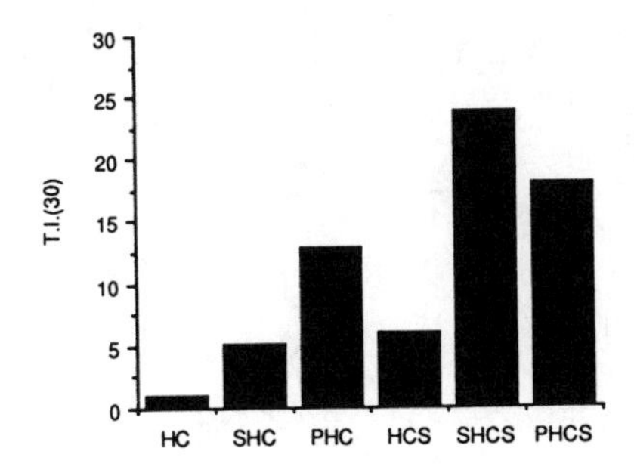

Fig. 10—Toughness index values, T.I. (30), for high strength concrete specimens

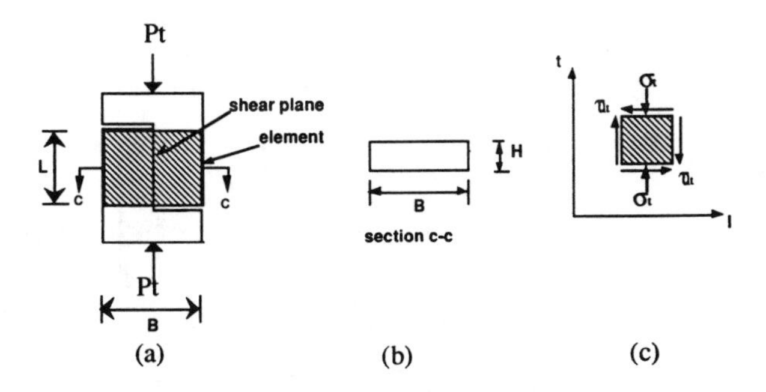

Fig. 11—Shear transfer problem: (a) and (b) push-off specimen, (c) stress state of element at shear plane

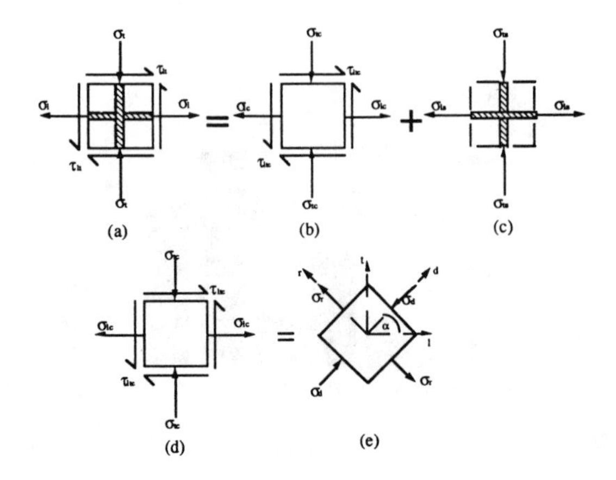

Fig. 12—Shear transfer model: (a) Reinforced concrete element, (b) stresses in the concrete element, (c) stresses in the steel, (d) stresses in the concrete in l-t axes, (e) stresses in the concrete in principal axes d-r

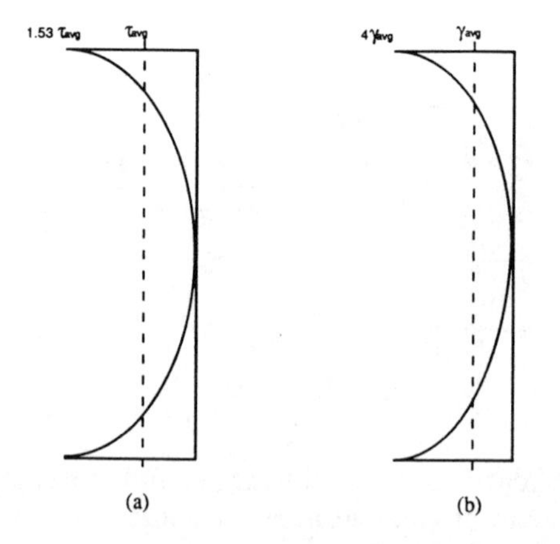

Fig. 13—Shear stress and shear strain distribution before cracking: (a) shear stress distribution, (b) assumed shear strain distribution

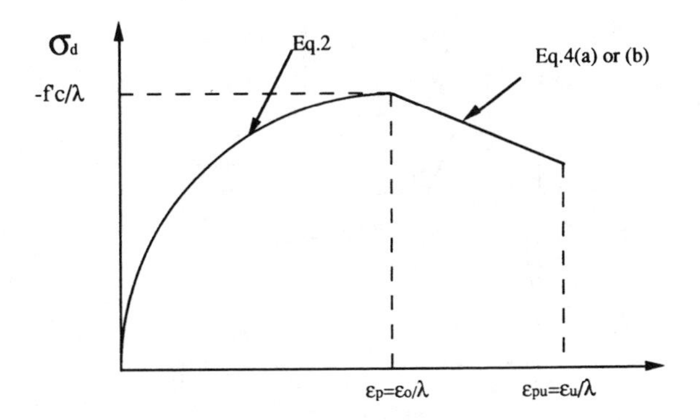

Fig. 14—Idealized stress-strain curve for concrete in compression

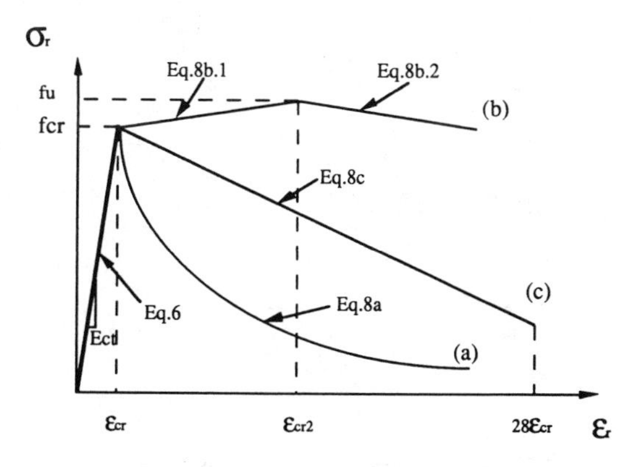

Fig. 15—Idealized tension stress-strain curve for: (a) plain concrete, (b) steel fiber reinforced concrete, and (c) polypropylene fiber reinforced concrete

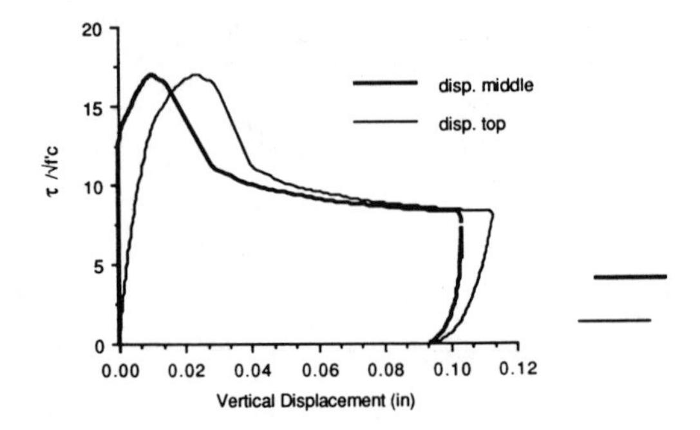

Fig. 16—Vertical displacement at the top and middle of the shear plane for HCS specimen (1 in. = 25.4 mm)

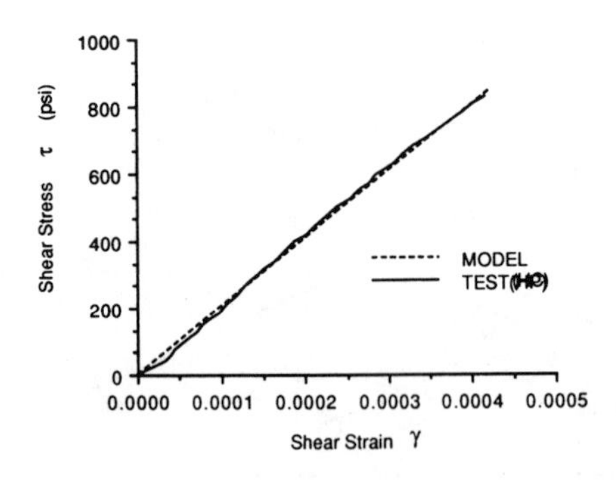

Fig. 17—Shear stress versus shear strain curve for HC specimen (1 psi = 6.895 kPa)

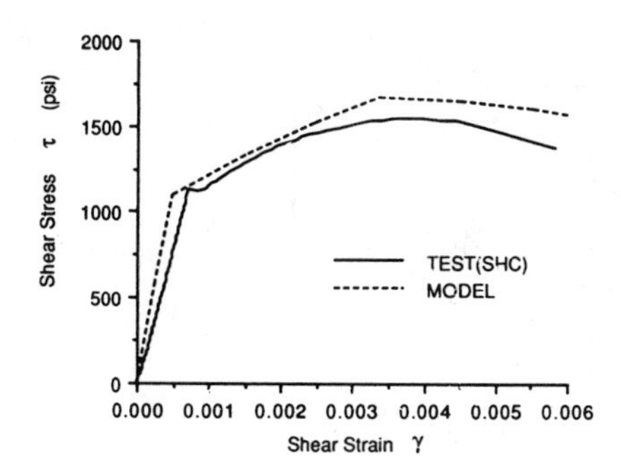

Fig. 18—Shear stress versus shear strain curve for SHC specimen (1 psi = 6.895 kPa)

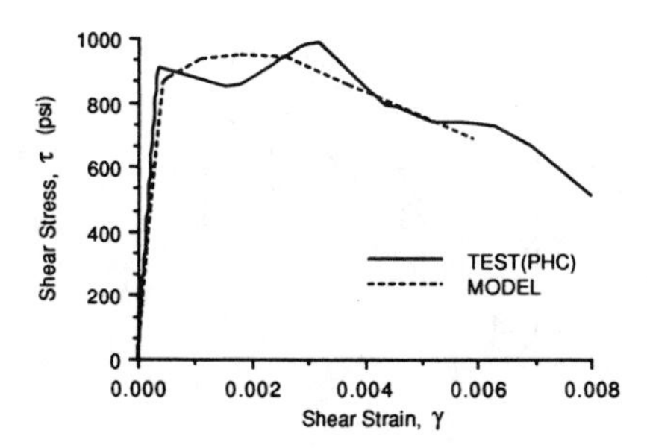

Fig. 19—Shear stress versus shear strain curve for PHC specimen (1 psi = 6.895 kPa)

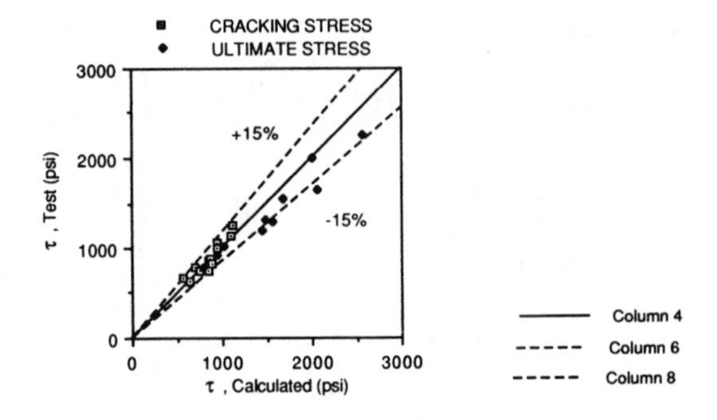

Fig. 20—Comparison of predicted and test values of cracking and maximum shear stresses (1 psi = 6.895 kPa)

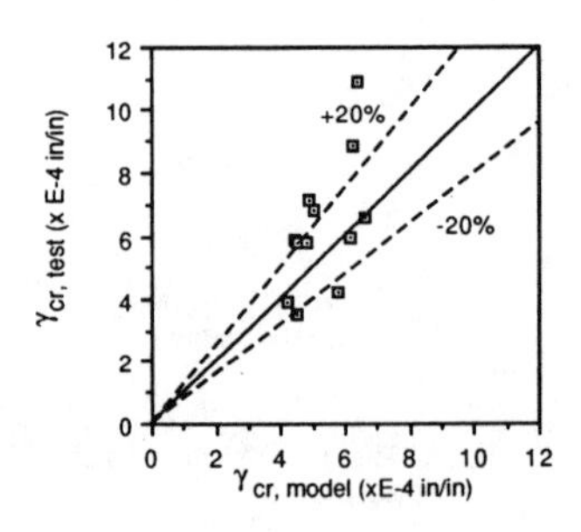

Fig. 21—Comparison of predicted and test values of cracking shear strain

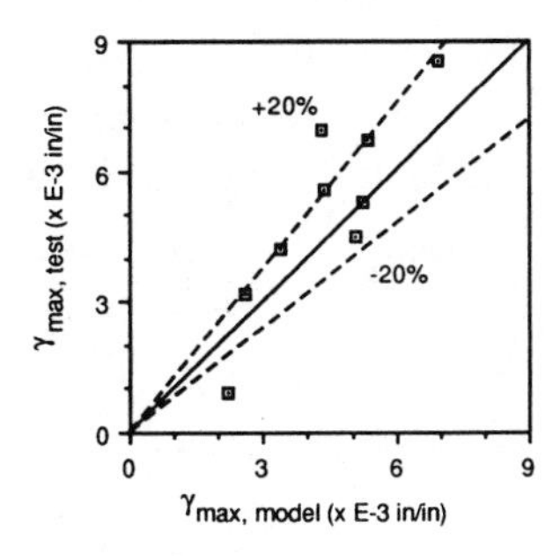

Fig. 22—Comparison of predicted and test values of shear strain at maximum shear stress

SP 142-12

Ultra High Performance Reinforced Concrete

by L.E. Hackman, M.B. Farrell, and O.O. Dunham

Synopsis: An innovative technique for reinforcing concrete to achieve extremely high flexural strengths has been developed. This technique utilizes a **steel fiber mat** instead of short, discrete steel fibers. The mat configuration is preplaced for infiltration with a concrete slurry to yield a composite with flexural strengths approaching ten times that of conventional concrete.

Applications include high performance bridge decks, earthquake resistant structures, nuclear waste containment, military applications and other innovative uses where flexural strength is at a premium. Stainless steel mats or other advanced alloys can be provided where corrosion resistance or high temperature strength are required.

Keywords: Corrosion resistance; energy absorption; fibers; flexural strength; reinforced concretes; slurries; steel fiber mat; strength; temperature

ACI member Lloyd E. Hackman is President, Ribbon Technology Corporation, Gahanna, Ohio. He is a member of ACI Committees 544, Fiber Reinforced Concrete; and 549, Ferrocement and other thin reinforced products.

Mark B. Farrell is Manager, New Market Development, Ribbon Technology Corporation, Gahanna, Ohio. He has served as carbon steel sales manager and is responsible for the application of new products produced by the melt overflow process.

Orville O. Dunham, Jr. is Product Manager, Ribbon Technology Corporation, Gahanna, Ohio. He was responsible for the design and manufacture of a unique air laying machine that conveys metallic fibers into a continuous, integrated mat.

Introduction

The addition of steel to concrete has greatly enlarged the capability of concrete as a useful building material. Although rebar and wire mesh provide the bulk of this reinforcement, steel fiber has gained an increasing share of this market. One promising new approach involves placement of steel fiber mat in the concrete matrix. This new approach, called SIMCON (slurry infiltrated mat concrete), results in a composite concrete with extremely high flexural strength.

The advantage over the current practice of using a large volume of discrete steel fibers is that the mat configuration provides inherent strength and can utilize steel fibers with much higher aspect ratios. The fiber volume is less than half that required for ultra high performance SIFCON (slurry infiltrated fiber concrete), while achieving similar flexural strength and energy absorbing toughness.

Both the SIMCON and SIFCON techniques are approaches where the reinforcement is preplaced prior to infiltration with a concrete slurry. These approaches allow for very high volume percentages of steel fiber in concrete that are not achievable when the fiber is added during mixing and not preplaced. SIFCON was developed as a high cost, premium performance concrete by Lankard Material Labs in the early eighties.

The current market for SIFCON has been limited to military and specialized industrial applications, due to the high volume of discrete fibers required for its vastly improved performance and SIFCON's subsequent high cost of materials and labor. These applications include military shelters, refractory concretes, loading docks, high traffic airport pavements, and other concrete pavements and precast shapes where standard modes of reinforcement are ineffective. SIMCON broadens these market applications by cutting the fiber quantity in half and substantially reducing the product cost.

SIMCON Properties

SIMCON is a non-woven steel fiber mat that is infiltrated with a concrete slurry. The steel fiber is directly cast from molten metal using a rapidly spinning chilled wheel, then interlayed into a 1/2" to 2" (12-51mm) thick mat. This mat is then rolled and coiled into weights and sizes convenient to a customer's application, but can range up to 48"

(1.2m) wide and 500lb per mat if required.

There are a variety of factors which infuence the performance of SIMCON. These are consistent with work reported over the last twenty years on discrete steel fiber reinforced concrete, but also include the added benefit of the interlayed mat, which is a new concept in concrete reinforcement.

High Aspect Ratio

Aspect ratio is defined as the length/diameter of the individual fiber. Higher fiber aspect ratios are critical to obtaining increased flexural strength in the concrete composite. Steel fiber manufacturers attempt to achieve the highest aspect ratios without causing handling or balling problems while the concrete is being placed. Typical aspect ratios range from 40 up to 100, although special handling procedures may be required as the aspect ratio approaches 100. SIMCON utilizes fibers with aspect ratios exceeding 500. Since the mat is already in a preformed shape, handling problems are minimized and balling does not become a factor.

The fibers prepared for testing were of a manganese carbon steel, approximately 9.5" (.24m) long with an equivalent diameter of .010- .021" (.25-.53mm). Stainless steel mats were also produced using a 9.5" (.24m) long fiber with an equivalent diameter of .010-.020" (.25-.51mm).

Fiber Volume

There is an upward limit that steel fiber volume cannot exceed when using conventional stell fibers in concrete. It has been found that this practical upper limit for the volume fraction of steel fiber is around 2 percent, with the average being just under 1 volume percent. Since there are applications where greater flexural and compressive strength are required, a technique was developed by Lankard Material Labs and Wahl Refractories called SIFCON, where fiber volume percent from 5 to 18 percent could be achieved.

The SIFCON approach can rightly be thought of as preplaced fiber concrete, where the placement of steel fibers in a form or mold preceeds the slurry infiltration. A fine grained cement based slurry is used instead of conventional concrete because the larger aggregate would prevent proper infiltration into the highly packed fiber.

SIMCON can also be considered a preplaced fiber

concrete, with the only difference being that the fiber is placed in the form of a mat rather than discrete fibers. This provides a significant time savings since the steel fiber mat can be easily rolled into place.

A special technique called Melt Overflow Rapid Solidification Technology (MORST) has been developed and used for SIMCON fiber production. This technique is adaptable to handle other metals or fiber geometries.

Two different alloys were chosen to evaluate performance and ease of processing. Four manganese carbon steel fiber mats ranging from densities of 1.2 to 3.6 percent were tested, while a stainless steel mat was packed to a maximum density of 5.7 percent. These fiber mats can be made more or less dense by changing the fiber geometry and the strength of the compression roll.

SIMCON Preparation

Each steel fiber mat was enclosed in a 20" x 40" x 2" (.51m x 1.02m x .05m) wooden mold with the open face (filling port) being the 2" x 40" (.05m x .51m) dimension (see Figure 1). A calcium aluminate cement-based slurry was used to infiltrate these panels as shown in Figure 2. Once infiltration was achieved, the panels were cured one day in the mold and then placed in a 74F/100RH environment for three days until two individual specimens at each density, roughly 2" x 4" x 20" (.05m x .1m x .51m) were sawcut from each panel. A total of ten samples were evaluated.

For comparison purposes, three SIFCON 2" x 4" x 14" (.05m x .10m x .36m) beam specimens were also prepared with SIFCA slurry containing 14 volume percent 1" (25mm) long 304 stainless steel fibers. These specimens were also cured at 74F/100RH for three days prior to sawcutting.

Flexural Strength Testing

Flexural strength testing was done on the two 2" x 4" x 20" (.05m x .1m x .51m) beams prepared from the various composites. In accordance with ASTM C1018, the Standard Method for Flexural Toughness and First-Crack Strength of Fiber Reinforced Concrete, testing was done using third-point loading and a 12" (.3m) span. Load-deflection data was recorded during the flexural strength testing of the composites.

Evaluation Procedure

The average ultimate flexural strengths of the composites are shown in Figure 3. The table in Figure 3 also compares the ultimate flexural strength and a measure of the flexural toughness for the various test specimens. The inability to determine the proportional limit of the load-deflection curves precludes the calculation of a standard I5 and I10 as described in the ASTM C1018 procedure. To permit a comparison between the composites evaluated here, a total area under the load-deflection curve, to a maximum deflection of 0.35" (9mm) was calculated.

Flexural Strength Results

The average ultimate flexural strength of the conventional SIFCON composite (14 volume percent 1" (25mm) discrete fibers) is 6440 psi (44MPa). The SIMCON composites at fiber mat loadings of only 3.3 and 3.6 volume percent provided an ultimate flexural strength exceeding 4800 psi (33MPa). This is roughly 75 percent of the flexural strength of conventional SIFCON at only 25 percent of the fiber volume used in the SIFCON. At a 5.7 volume percent loading of stainless steel fiber mat, the resulting SIMCON composite tests out with an average ultimate flexural strength of 5470 psi (38MPa). This is 85 percent of the flexural strength of SIFCON at 41 percent of the SIFCON fiber volume.

At the lower fiber volume loadings, the results for SIMCON are still impressive. Nearly 50 percent of SIFCON's ultimate flexural strength is achieved at only a 1.7 percent fiber mat loading for the SIMCON. For comparison purposes, conventional unreinforced concrete starts at 550 to 600 psi (3-4MPa) in flexural strength. The significant increases in flexural strength for these high fiber volume concrete composites creates a new category of building materials.

Fiber Efficiency

Steel fiber is utilized more efficiently in the concrete specimen with the interlayed mat concept. An arbitrary designation of fiber efficiency was defined to compare the flexural strength and flexural energy absorption capacity versus the fiber volume. In Figures 3 and 4, fiber efficiency is the ultimate flexural strength (psi) divided by the fiber volume (percent). A second fiber efficiency value is defined as the flexural energy absorption capacity versus the fiber volume. As can be seen in Figure 3, the fiber efficiency for SIMCON is higher in all cases than SIFCON or conventional steel fiber reinforced concrete (SFRC).

A comparison of the concrete test specimen containing Mat F and the SIFCON test specimen in Figure 3 further highlights the improved fiber efficiency using the fiber mat concept. A reinforcement level in SIMCON of only 25 percent that of conventional SIFCON provides 75 percent of its ultimate flexural strength. At only a 12 percent SIMCON loading, you still achieve 50 percent that of conventional SIFCON in flexural strength.

In Figure 4, Mat B at a 5.7% fiber volume achieved an ultimate flexural strength of 5470 psi (38MPa), but had a somewhat lower fiber efficiency than the conventional SFRC sample. This suggests that there there is an optimum fiber volume that needs to be balanced against the desired ultimate flexural strength.

Energy Absorption Capacity

The energy absorption capability or toughness of the concrete material can become the key design criteria particularly where there is any load cycling. SIMCON shows its greatest potential in this area. As can be seen in Figure 3, a fiber mat loading in SIMCON of only 25 percent that of conventional SIFCON actually shows a 15 percent higher capacity for energy absorption. Figures 5,6 and 7 graphically illustrate load deflection curves of various SIFCON and SIMCON composites.

The improved performance of the mat reinforcement over the discrete fiber approach is related to the bonding of the mat fibers in the composite. In the standard SIFCON, the relatively short embedment length of the 1" (25mm) fibers results in fiber pullout as the primary failure mode (see Figure 8). Once a crack forms in the standard SIFCON specimen under flexural load, the energy absorption capacity of the specimen reflects the energy required to propogate and enlarge this single crack. Energy absorption is dictated by fiber pullout resistance.

In the composites reinforced with steel fiber mats, the mode of failure is unique. As shown in Figure 9, multiple cracking occurs in the composites. Ultimate failure occurs through fiber breakage in the high tensile stress zones of one or more of these crack planes. The energy absorption capacity of the mat reinforced composites reflects the total energy required to initiate, enlarge, and propogate all of the cracks and to break a portion of the manganese steel fibers in one or more of the cracks. In the mat reinforced composites, the yield strength of the steel is fully utilized.

Effect of Fiber Diameter

A comparison of the energy absorption capacity of the composites reinforced with 0.013" (0.33mm) and 0.021" (0.53mm) equivalent diameter fiber illustrate the impact on performance that fiber geometry has. The 0.013" (0.33mm) fiber mat had a loading roughly half that of the 0.021" (0.53mm) fiber mat, yet provided an equivalent energy absorption capacity in the composite. Since the fiber lengths for both mats are equivalent, the effect of aspect ratio is again seen as the determining factor.

Mats E and F have densities that are roughly equivalent, but the energy absorption capacity is 35 percent greater for Mat F, which has the finer fiber diameter and higher aspect ratio. Although the ultimate flexural strengths for both specimens are equal at 4800 psi (33MPa), the load deflection curves in Figure 6 show the improved performance of Mat F.

The limit to using even finer diameter fiber in the mat is that densities above 4 percent volume in the SIMCON composite were difficult to achieve with our current process. Higher densities could be achieved by increasing the compressive strength of compaction.

Conclusion

The results of the testing establish that the SIMCON or "mat" concept of reinforcement represents a significant improvement in the reinforcement efficiency in high density, high strength fiber reinforced composites. Comparable levels of flexural strength and flexural energy absorption capacity can be achieved at greatly reduced fiber loadings relative to the short, discrete fiber reinforcement approach.

Earthquake resistant structures could benefit greatly by using the SIMCON concept or in some cases a combination of the SIMCON concept and structural rebar. Nuclear waste containment structures have both a requirement for strength and shielding, making SIMCON an ideal new material for consideration as a cost effective alternative.

Other applications such as military structures or

industrial applications with high strength requirements would also be well served by SIMCON where the standard modes of reinforcement are not sufficient. SIMCON offers the designer a premium building material to meet these specialized niche applications.

References

1. Lankard, D.R., "Investigation of Manganese Steel Fiber Mats Used in the Fabrication of SIFCON Panels," Progress Report # I-1100-126-2, Aug 21, 1991, 15 pp.

2. Lankard, D.R., "Investigation of 304 Stainless Steel Fiber Mats as Reinforcement in a Refractory Concrete Composite," Progress Report # I-1100-128-1, Aug 16, 1991, 16 pp.

3. Lankard, D.R., "Slurry Infiltrated Fiber Concrete (SIFCON)," Concrete International, Dec 1984, pp. 44-47.

Fig. 1—Placement of the SIMCON mat in a plywood form designed to compress the mat to a final thickness of 2 in.

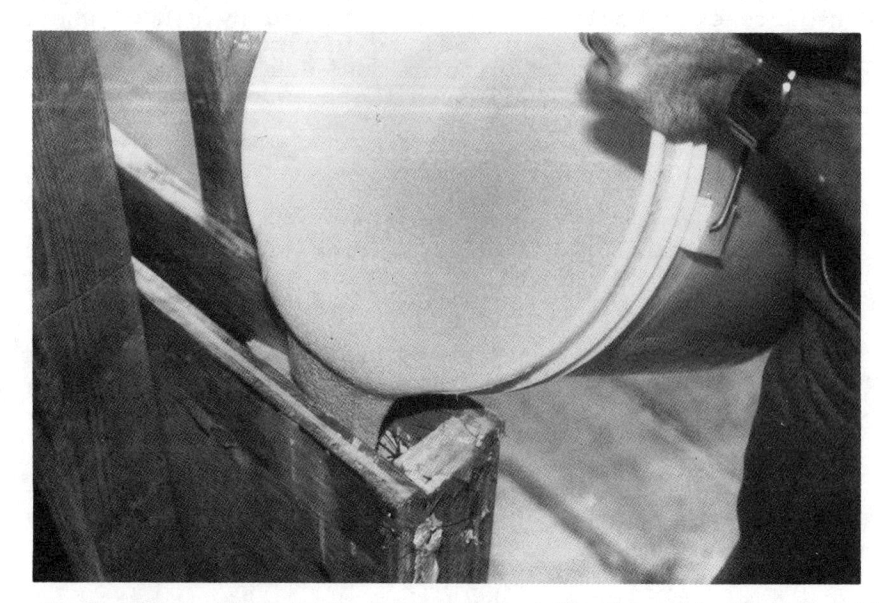

Fig. 2—Plywood form is vibrated during the infiltration of the fiber mat with a fine grained refractory slurry (Wahl Refractories SIFCA Composition)

Composite Type	Fiber Volume %	Ultimate Flexural Strength		Flexural Energy Absorption Capacity		Number of Fibers per pound
		psi	efficiency	L-D area*	efficiency	
Mat C .010"	1.2	1950	1625	204	170	3740
Mat D .013"	1.7	3205	1885	712	419	2220
Mat E .021"	3.3	4805	1456	718	218	1145
Mat F .013"	3.6	4865	1351	1091	303	2220
SIFCON 1" .031"	14.0	6440	460	926	66	8790
SFRC 2" .042"	0.75	870	1160	75**	100	1470

* Area under L-D curve was measured to a deflection of 0.35".
** Area under L-D curve per C 1018 calculation of I10.

Fig. 3—SIMCON manganese steel fiber mat performance

Composite Type	Fiber Volume %	Ultimate Flexural Strength		Flexural Energy Absorption Capacity		Number of Fibers per pound
		psi	efficiency	L-D area*	efficiency	
Mat B .024"	5.7	5470	960	1326	233	1250
SIFCON 1" .031"	14.0	6440	460	926	66	8790
SFRC 2" .042"	0.75	870	1160	75**	100	1470

* Area under L-D curve was measured to a deflection of 0.35".
** Area under L-D curve per C 1018 calculation of I10.

Fig. 4—SIMCON stainless steel fiber mat performance

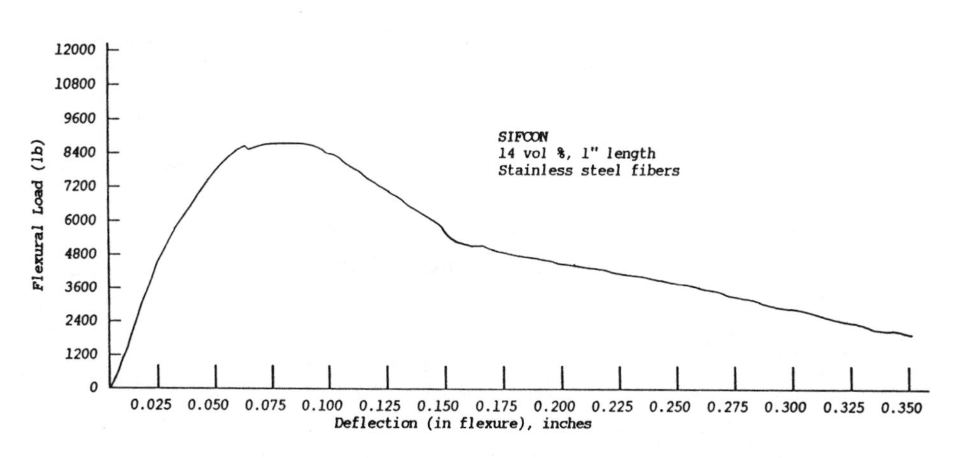

Fig. 5—Load-deflection behavior of stainless steel SIFCON composite. Third point loading, 12 in. span. Cross sections are approximately 4 in. x 2 in.

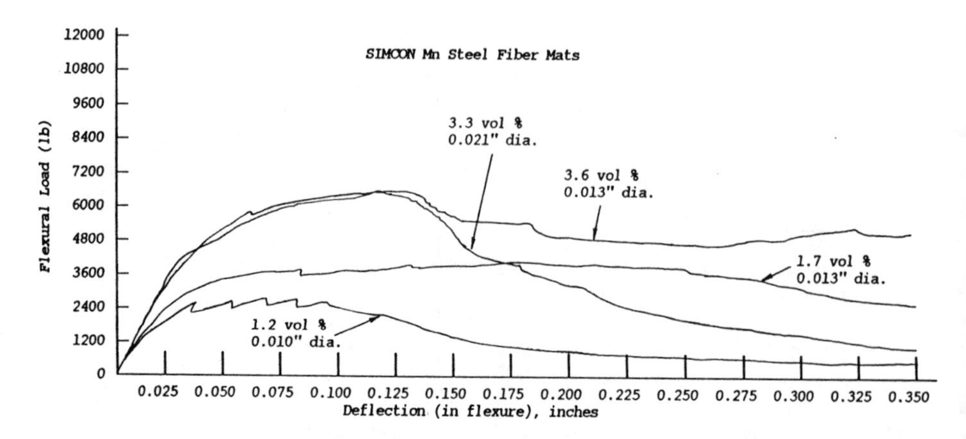

Fig. 6—Load-deflection behavior of *Mn* steel fiber mat SIMCON composite. Third point loading, 12 in. span. Cross sections are approximately 4 in. x 2 in.

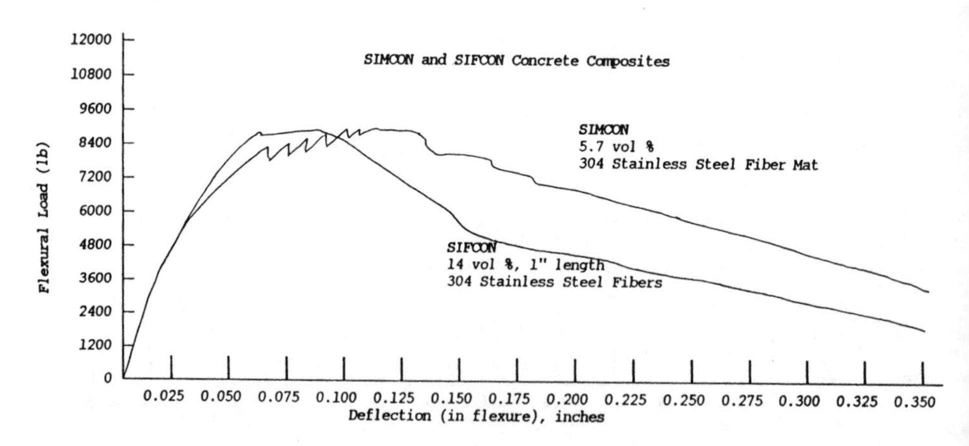

Fig. 7—Load-deflection behavior of stainless steel SIFCON composite. Third point loading, 12 in. span. Cross sections are approximately 4 in. x 2 in.

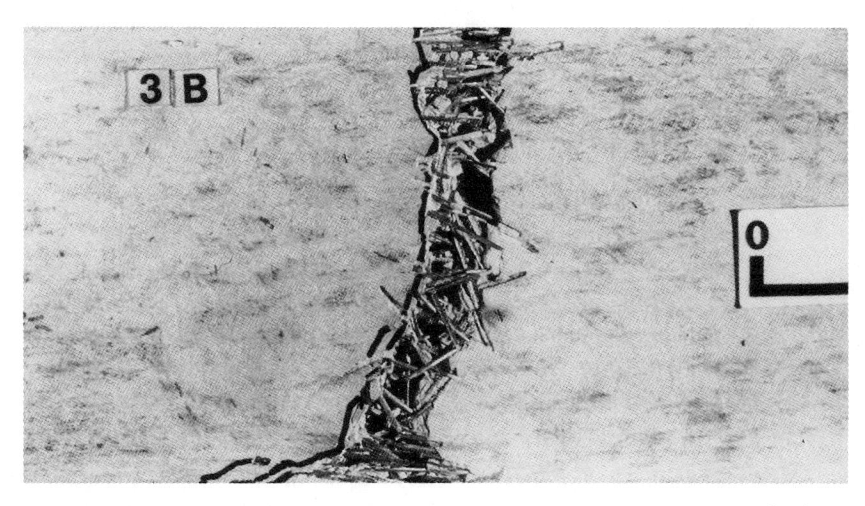

Fig. 8—High tensile stress surface of stainless steel SIFCON composite beam (14 volume percent, 1 in. fiber) following flexural loading. Specimen failed through the formation of a single crack

Fig. 9—High tensile stress surface of SIMCON composite beam (5.7 volume percent steel fiber mat) following flexural loading. Multiple small cracks have been inked to facilitate viewing, and indicate that the steel fiber mat is more fully bonded to the concrete matrix

SP 142-13

Constitutive Modeling of Fiber Reinforced Concrete

by D.J. Stevens and D. Liu

Synopsis: As is well recognized, Fiber Reinforced Concrete (FRC) exhibits a number of superior properties relative to plain concrete, such as improved strength, ductility, impact resistance, and failure toughness. These advantageous features of FRC can lead to novel structural applications, for which standard design and analysis procedures must be supplemented by numerical modeling (e.g., the Finite Element Method). This, in turn, makes necessary the development of satisfactory constitutive models that can predict the behavior of FRC under different load conditions, both monotonic and cyclic.

In this paper, a constitutive model for FRC is developed loosely within the theory of mixtures. For plain concrete, an anisotropic, strain-based, continuum damage/plasticity model with kinematic and isotropic damage surfaces is developed. To represent the effect of the fibers, a simplified model that accounts for the tensile resistance of the fibers and the enhanced tensile resistance of the plain concrete is proposed. The predictions of the FRC constitutive model are compared to data from laboratory tests of Steel Fiber Reinforced Concrete (SFRC) specimens under uniaxial and biaxial loadings.

Keywords: Ductility; failure; fiber reinforced concretes; finite element method; impact strength; loads (forces); models; strength; toughness

David J. Stevens is currently a Senior Research Engineer at Southwest Research Institute, San Antonio, Texas; at the time of this work, he was an Assistant Professor of Civil Engineering at Clarkson University. He received his PhD from the University of Minnesota in 1988. Dr. Stevens is secretary of Committee 370, Short Duration Dynamics and Vibratory Load Effects, and is a member of Committee 544, Fiber Reinforced Concrete, and Committee 444, Experimental Analysis for Concrete Structures.

Dajin Liu is currently a Principal Design Engineer at Wong and Associates, King of Prussia, Pennsylvania; at the time of this work, he was a Research Assistant in the Department of Civil Engineering at Clarkson University. He received his PhD from Clarkson University in 1992.

INTRODUCTION

Fiber Reinforced Concrete (FRC) is generally superior to plain concrete in strength, ductility, failure toughness, and impact resistance (1). These characteristics of FRC can be put to advantage in conventional reinforced concrete structures as well as in special applications. In the design and analysis of standard and unique FRC structures, the typical approaches must often be supplemented with numerical modeling (e.g., the Finite Element Method). Since numerical analyses are only as good as the material models that are used, adequate constitutive models, which can predict the behavior of FRC under different load conditions, both monotonic and cyclic, must be developed and implemented. However, currently, an adequate constitutive model for the rate-independent, triaxial response of FRC is not available.

A number of distinct approaches for modeling FRC have been attempted in the past, including: fracture mechanics approaches, mixture models, fictitious crack models, micromechanics models, and continuum damage mechanics. Some of these models were discussed in recent review articles (2, 3), from which a portion of the following is excerpted.

In the past, a majority of FRC models have taken either fracture mechanics or law of mixture approaches. The emphasis on fracture approaches is due, in no small part, to the pioneering work of Romualdi and Batson (4), who recognized that the fibers would strongly affect the crack growth. However, it is difficult to translate fracture mechanics concepts directly into constitutive models for the multiaxial compressive and tensile behavior of FRC.

Typically, mixture models have been developed to predict the tensile behavior of FRC; a volume weighted sum of the concrete and fiber response is used to predict the composite behavior. The physical interaction between the two materials, which is a function of the spacing, orientation, and geometry of the fibers, as well as the interface properties between the fiber and concrete, is usually accommodated through "efficiency" or "orientation" constants that multiply the fiber's contribution to the overall sum.

Other examples of composite models include Naaman et al. (5), who combined a statistical composite model with fracture mechanics criteria to model ductile and brittle modes of tensile failure, and, Fanella and Krajcinovic (6) who used a parallel bar model and the theory of continuum damage mechanics to model the uniaxial response of FRC.

The fictitious crack model, originally developed for plain concrete (7), was later applied to the modeling of FRC (8, 9). In this approach, a stress-strain curve is used for the tensile response up to peak stress; thereafter, in the strain softening region, a stress-crack width curve is used to model the material. Combined with the Finite Element Method, this model was successfully applied to problems involving localized fracture, but there is some question of objectivity since the crack must follow the mesh's topology (unless an adaptive mesh technique is used) and also, the results can depend on the element size (10).

Micromechanical approaches have also been used to examine the behavior of FRC; these approaches are often based on Eshelby's equivalent inclusion concept (11, 12, 13). Further examinations of the micromechanics of FRC, using the Finite Element Method, have also been made (14, 15, 16).

Previous mixture models have focused on the uniaxial tensile behavior of FRC. However, it is well known that the inclusion of fibers can greatly increase the strength, toughness, and ductility of concrete and mortar in compressive loadings (1). In this paper, the classic mixture approach is loosely applied for the development of a multi-axial model, by combining a continuum damage/plasticity model for plain concrete with a simplified *effective* fiber model. The concrete and fiber models are phenomenological, although the concrete model is based, in an averaged way, on the underlying micromechanics of microcrack growth, coalescence, opening and closure.

MECHANICAL BEHAVIOR

Laboratory tests show that randomly distributed fibers in plain concrete act as crack arrestors, greatly improving the ductility, failure toughness, tensile strength, compressive strength, flexural strength, shear and torsional strength, postcracking strength, impact resistance, and fatigue strength, while reducing the number of cracks and the mean crack width (1, 17, 18, 19, 20, 21, 22).

Of direct interest in this paper are the biaxial testing programs of Yin et al. (22) and Mansour (19). Yin et al. found that the biaxial strength of FRC plate specimens (6" x 6" x 1.5") with steel fiber (1% and 2% volume ratios) was greatly increased over the plain material. For equal biaxial loading, the strength of the SFRC (2% volume fiber) was 35% greater than the plain concrete strength. For uniaxial loading, little increase in strength was seen. In addition, they found that under axial and biaxial load conditions, plain concrete specimens failed by cracking in a direction parallel to the plane of loading (or alternatively, perpendicular to the tensile strain direction). In contrast, the SFRC specimens responded in a shearing or "faulting" manner, with the failure occurring along multiple inclined fault lines. The tests were run under load control, so the strain-softening region was not recorded. Yin et al. hypothesized that the increased SFRC ultimate strength due to the fibers is analogous to the effects of a small amount of confining pressure in the out-of-plane direction.

Mansour (19) reported the results of load controlled, biaxial testing of 3 inch cube specimens with plain and SFRC. In his test program, normal and high strength concretes were reinforced with different volume fractions of two different fiber types. Mansour found that the strength of SFRC strongly depends upon the type of fiber and, that for 1.5% volume of hooked fibers, the biaxial strength increased by 75%. The failure modes of the specimens were similar to that found by Yin et al.

Lastly, of importance for the material model developed herein, Shah and coworkers at Northwestern (see, e.g., 23, 24) have investigated the contribution of the matrix to the tensile resistance of specimens with high percentages (in the range of 5% to 15%) of continuous, aligned polypropylene fibers. They found that the fibers inhibited the growth of the matrix microcracks and suppressed localization of the deformation. This, in turn, greatly increased the contribution of the **matrix** to the resistance of the tensile stress. Extrapolating to other fiber types and volume percentages, the total tensile resistance of fiber reinforced cementitious materials can be taken as a combination of the fiber resistance and the fiber-enhanced tensile resistance of the plain matrix.

APPROACH

While FRC is composed of a number of distinct phases (the three materials and their interfaces), only two phases are considered in this model: the plain concrete and fibers. Additionally, it is assumed that, when viewed on a sufficiently large scale, the strain in the concrete ε^c and the randomly distributed fibers ε^f are equal to the overall strain ε (a Voigt estimate). It is further assumed that the main effect of the fibers is to create additional tensile resistance to opening of the microcracks. The additional tensile resistance is a combination of the tensile stress in the fibers and the improved tensile properties of the plain concrete, as discussed above.

In the classic theory of mixtures, the stress σ of a composite, such as FRC, is given by the volume weighted sum of the stresses in the constituents:

$$\sigma = V^c\sigma^c + V^f\sigma^f \tag{1}$$

where V^c and V^f are the volume fractions of the concrete and fiber, and σ^c and σ^f are the stresses in the concrete and fiber, respectively (second order tensors are denoted by bold symbols, unless otherwise noted). Note that it is implied in the classic mixture approach that the stresses of the constituents are independent of each other, which is certainly not true for FRC in the pre- or post-peak regions. As discussed above, the tensile contribution of the plain concrete is **enhanced** by the presence of fibers. Therefore, to remove the implicit dependence that Eqn. (1) requires, a modified mixture approach is taken:

$$\sigma = \sigma^c + \sigma^f \tag{2}$$

Again, unlike typical mixture approaches, the summation is not weighted by the volume percentage, since the fiber contribution reflects **both the fiber and (fiber-enhanced) concrete response**. A strain-based, continuum damage/plasticity model with isotropic and kinematic hardening is presented for the plain concrete, and an *effective* fiber model is developed in the following sections. A discussion of strain softening is also given.

Continuum Damage/Plasticity Model for Concrete

In this model, it is assumed that the majority of the large scale response of concrete is determined by two small scale phenomena: the initiation, growth and coalescence of microcracks and the pressure-dependent (frictional) tangential movement of the microcrack surfaces. An additional mechanism of smaller importance is the mechanical mismatch that occurs between the rough boundaries of the cracks when they are subjected to a closing stress. Damage is created by the growth and coalescence of the microcracks, while permanent deformations are created through frictional slip across the microcracks; thus, a combination of plasticity and continuum damage theories appears to be of advantage for modeling this behavior.

Due to the strong relationship between damage and tensile strain, the continuum damage model is set in strain space. More specifically, it is based upon the elastic strain, due to it's strong relationship to damage growth, stiffness recovery, permanent deformation, and the current stress level (25). To preserve consistency and retain simplicity, the plasticity approach is also elastic strain-based, and, in fact, the same "inelastic" surface in strain space is used to determine the onset of damage growth as well as plastic flow. In contrast to an earlier work by the authors (26), these surfaces incorporate both kinematic **and** isotropic hardening.

The stress is decomposed as

$$\sigma = \sigma^e - \sigma^p \tag{3}$$

where σ^p is the plastic stress of the concrete, $\sigma^e = \mathbf{C}:\varepsilon$ is the elastic stress, and the superscript c has been dropped. **C** is the 4th order anisotropic secant stiffness tensor of the concrete. **C** can be decomposed as (27):

$$C = C^o - C^+ - C^- \tag{4}$$

$\mathbf{C}^o$ is the original elastic stiffness, and, $\mathbf{C}^+$ and $\mathbf{C}^-$ are the changes in the positive (tensile) and negative (compressive) **effective** stiffness.

To accommodate the compressive mode of damage and deformation, an "inelastic", **isotropic hardening** compressive surface, g^- is used. To predict the tensile damaging behavior of concrete, a **kinematically hardening** tensile surface, g^+, is employed:

$$g^+(\varepsilon^e,\alpha^+) = \tau^+ - r_o^+ = 0, \qquad g^-(\varepsilon^e) = \tau^- - r^- = 0 \tag{5}$$

where

$$\tau^+ \equiv \sqrt{<\varepsilon^{e+} - \alpha^+>:C^o:<\varepsilon^{e+} - \alpha^+>}\,, \qquad \tau^- \equiv \sqrt{\varepsilon^{e-}:C^o:\varepsilon^{e-}} \tag{6}$$

$$\varepsilon^{e+} \equiv \sum_{a=1}^{3} <\varepsilon^e_{(a)}>\, \underline{e}^e_{(a)} \otimes \underline{e}^e_{(a)}, \qquad \varepsilon^{e-} = \varepsilon^e - \varepsilon^{e+} \tag{7}$$

$$<\varepsilon^{e+}-\alpha^+>_{ij} = <\varepsilon^{e+}_{ij}-\alpha^+_{ij}> \tag{8}$$

τ^- and τ^+ are the energy norms of the negative strain tensor and the shifted positive strain tensor, respectively. r_o^+ and r^- are the energy thresholds for further damage/permanent deformation; r_o^+ is a constant while r^- evolves with compressive damage from an initial value of r_o^-. α^+ is a kinematic "back strain" that defines the current origin of g^+. $\varepsilon_{(a)}^e$ and $\underline{e}_{(a)}^e$ are the eigenvalues and normalized eigenvectors of ε^e, respectively and <x> is the Macaulay bracket. Figure 1 shows these surfaces for a plane strain condition and an elastic stiffness, C, equal to the identity tensor for plotting purposes. The general form of the "inelastic" surface was suggested in (28), where an isotropic tensile "energy" surface for damage evolution and a separate yield surface for plastic flow were used; a damage criterion based on the (unshifted) positive elastic strain was later proposed (29).

The inelastic surfaces in Eq. 5 are combined with associated flow rules to define the rate equations of elastic degradation:

$$\dot{C}_t^+ = \dot{\mu}^+ \frac{\partial g^+}{\partial \varepsilon^e \otimes \varepsilon^e}, \qquad \dot{C}_t^- = \dot{\mu}^- \hat{H}(tr\varepsilon^{e+}) \frac{\partial g^-}{\partial \varepsilon^e \otimes \varepsilon^e} \tag{9}$$

where $\dot{C}_t^+$ and $\dot{C}_t^-$ are the positive and negative total stiffness rates, respectively, which will be related to the effective stiffnesses, C^+ and C^-, later. $\dot{\mu}^+$ and $\dot{\mu}^-$ are the consistency parameters. The use of the Heaviside function, $\hat{H}(*)$, accommodates pressure effects (30).

The kinematic hardening or translation of the tensile surface is governed by the following associated flow rule:

$$\dot{\alpha}^+ = \dot{\mu}^+ \frac{1}{H^+} \frac{\partial g^+}{\partial \varepsilon^e} \tag{10}$$

$$H^+ = \frac{1}{\tau^+ + \tau^-} \gamma_1 \hat{H}(\lambda_{min} - \varepsilon_{ii}^{e-}) + \gamma_2 \hat{H}(\varepsilon_{ii}^{e+} - \lambda_{max}) + \gamma_3 \hat{H}(\varepsilon_{ii}^{e}) \tag{11}$$

where $\varepsilon_{ii}^{e-} = tr(\varepsilon^{e-})$, $\varepsilon_{ii}^{e+} = tr(\varepsilon^{e+})$, and λ_{min} and λ_{max} are the minimum and maximum eigenvalue of ε^e. γ_1, γ_2, γ_3 are material constants. This tensile surface combined with an associated kinematic hardening rule allows elastic degradation (damage) to occur in one direction without degrading the strength in the orthogonal direction. An isotropic hardening law would result in unrealistically large tensile strengths in the direction orthogonal to the maximum tensile strain due to the uniform expansion of the surface.

The isotropic hardening relation for the compressive surface is taken as:

$$\dot{r}^- = \frac{\dot{\mu}^-}{2\tau^- H^-} \tag{12}$$

$$H^- = \frac{A^- - B^- \tau^-}{r_o^-} \alpha_c \tag{13}$$

where H^- is the hardening function. A^- and B^- are material constants, as is α_c which is used to account for confinement effects:

$$\alpha_c = \left\langle \begin{matrix} \gamma_4 & \textit{if } tr(\varepsilon^{e+}) = 0 \textit{ and } tr(E^{e-}) \neq 0; \\ 1 & \textit{otherwise} \end{matrix} \right\rangle \tag{14}$$

$$E^{e-} \equiv \varepsilon^{e-} - \frac{1}{3} \varepsilon_{kk}^{e-} \delta \tag{15}$$

E^{e-} is the deviatoric tensor of the compressive elastic strain tensor.

Kuhn-Tucker relations are used to define the loading/unloading conditions for the plastic stress and elastic degradation. By use of the consistency condition, the elastic degradation rates can be written:

$$\dot{C}_t^+ = \frac{H^+}{2} \frac{\langle \varepsilon^{e+} - \alpha^+ \rangle : C^o : d\varepsilon^{e+}}{\langle \varepsilon^{e+} - \alpha^+ \rangle : C^o : P^+ : C^o : \langle \varepsilon^{e+} - \alpha^+ \rangle} P^+ : C^o : P^+ \tag{16}$$

$$\dot{C}_t^- = \mathfrak{t}^- H^- P^- : C^o : P^- \hat{H}(tr\, \varepsilon^{e+}) \tag{17}$$

where

$$P^+ \equiv \sum_{a=1}^{3} \hat{H}(\varepsilon^e_{(a)}) \underset{\sim}{e}^e_{(a)} \otimes \underset{\sim}{e}^e_{(a)} \otimes \underset{\sim}{e}^e_{(a)} \otimes \underset{\sim}{e}^e_{(a)}, \qquad P^- = I - P^+ \tag{18}$$

$\mathbf{P}^+$ and $\mathbf{P}^-$ are the positive and negative orthogonal projection operators (27); $\mathbf{I}$ is the fourth order identity tensor.

In the development of the elastic degradation, it is assumed that all of the cracks are active; thus, the evolution equations are irreversible and define the change in the total elastic stiffness. To capture stiffness recovery under reversed loading, the effective stiffnesses, $\mathbf{C}^+$ and $\mathbf{C}^-$, are related to the total stiffnesses, $\mathbf{C}_t^+$ and $\mathbf{C}_t^-$ as follows (27):

$$C^+ = P^+ : C_t^+ : P^+, \qquad C^- = P^- : C_t^- : P^- \tag{19}$$

The development of permanent deformation is also signaled by the inelastic surfaces; associated flow rules are used with both surfaces to define the rate and direction of plastic stress evolution:

$$\dot{\sigma}^p = \mu^+ \frac{\partial g^+}{\partial \varepsilon^e} + \mu^- \frac{\partial g^-}{\partial \varepsilon^e} \tag{20}$$

The Kuhn-Tucker loading conditions and consistency condition lead to:

$$\dot{\sigma}^p = H^+ \frac{\langle \varepsilon^{e+} - \alpha^+ \rangle : C^o : d\varepsilon^{e+}}{\langle \varepsilon^{e+} - \alpha^+ \rangle : C^o : P^+ : C^o : \langle \varepsilon^{e+} - \alpha^+ \rangle} P^+ : C^o : \langle \varepsilon^{e+} - \alpha^+ \rangle + 2\mathfrak{t}^- H^- P^- : C^o : \varepsilon^{e-} \tag{21}$$

Effective Fiber Model

Fibers that develop sufficient bond with the concrete will resist crack opening (tensile and splitting) through debond, friction- and pressure-dependent pullout, mechanical interlock, yielding and dowel action. In addition, the fibers act as local stress reducers, lowering the stress concentrations in the vicinity of cracks or fields of cracks. All of these mechanisms contribute to the improved mechanical response of FRC relative to the plain material. In the proposed approach, a simple technique is used to account for both the crack-closing effects of the fibers across open or "active" cracks and the enhancement of the plain concrete tensile response when fibers are present.

In the *effective* fiber model, the fiber response is assumed to augment the resistance of FRC in the directions of elastic tensile strain only; the contribution of fibers in the direction of compressive strains is taken as zero. If the fiber distribution across the "active" cracks is sufficiently random, and, by extrapolating from experimental tensile stress-crack width data for Fiber Reinforced Materials (18), the relationship between normal tensile strain and the resulting effective fiber stress can be approximated as elastic/perfectly plastic/linear softening as shown in Figure 2. The pre-peak region reflects the elastic contribution of the fibers and the enhanced tensile response of the concrete. The plastic plateau reflects the pullout, debond, and yielding of the fibers, as well as a constant contribution from the concrete. The linear softening region represents the pullout and/or fracture of the fibers and final exhaustion of the concrete tensile resistance.

The "yield strain" ε_{yt} and "yield stress" σ_{yt} can be determined from the inflection point of the tensile stress-strain curve that occurs just as a crack localizes. The critical strain ε_c and final strain ε_f are of importance when a boundary value problem involving localization is solved; in this case, these values may be extracted from experimental stress-crack width curves through energy equivalence arguments, in which the energy dissipated in the model of the boundary value problem is matched via a characteristic material length to that observed experimentally (32). Two items deserve emphasis. First, the material constants (ε_{yt}, σ_{yt}, ε_c, ε_f) will be specific to each particular combination of fiber type, mortar mix, and aggregate size; thus, the data from a uniaxial tensile test on a particular FRC must be available to accurately determine these constants. Second, the *effective* fiber model is a very simplified representation of the actual complicated and inter-related mechanical processes that occur during deformation of FRC. As such, the effects of fiber length, fiber geometry, and interface properties are only represented in a gross way through the choice of the material constants (ε_{yt}, σ_{yt}, ε_c, ε_f), which, again, must be experimentally determined for each particular FRC.

The experimental results of Yin et al. (23) imply that increased confinement will increase the tensile resistance of the fiber. To incorporate this effect, the "yield stress" σ_{yt} is modified as:

$$\sigma_{yt} = \sigma_{yt}^{o}\left[1 + \gamma_5 \frac{|\varepsilon_{ii}^-| + \min(\varepsilon_{11},\varepsilon_{22},\varepsilon_{33})}{|\varepsilon_{ii}^-|} - \frac{\varepsilon_{ii}^+ - \max(\varepsilon_{11},\varepsilon_{22},\varepsilon_{33})}{\varepsilon_{ii}^+}\right] \tag{22}$$

where σ_{yt}^{o} is the "yield stress" under zero confinement; m is a constant.

Assuming that the fiber distribution is uniformly random, the magnitude of the fiber stress vector $\underline{\sigma}_N$ on the active tensile plane can be calculated and then converted to the stress tensor σ^f:

$$\sigma^f = \sum_{N=1}^{m} |\underline{\sigma}_N|\, \underline{e}^{(N)} \otimes \underline{e}^{(N)} \tag{23}$$

where m is the number of active cracks (maximum 3). If the fiber distribution is not uniformly random, then the principle of virtual work can be used to relate the fiber stress on the crack plane to the overall fiber stress tensor.

Strain-Softening of FRC

As with plain concrete, FRC exhibits strain-softening in tension and in compression. As reported in (21), the strain-softening portion of uniaxial compressive stress-strain curves of FRC is size dependent and brittleness increases with the slenderness of the specimen. Due to the heterogeneity created by coalesced microcracks, strain softening is a "structural" phenomenon, not a material characteristic (31). Since strain-softening is size dependent, the post-peak region must considered within the framework of boundary value problems, not just as one aspect of the material model. In the solution of strain-softening problems, the constitutive model or numerical technique must be modified to remove the mesh sensitivity and to predict the correct energy dissipation. Examples of such methods include nonlocal approaches (32) and fracture energy equivalence methods (33). Within the context of this model, strain-softening will be addressed in a later publication when a nonlocal approach to boundary value problem solutions is attempted.

It is important to emphasize that, in the post-peak region of the stress-strain curve of plain concrete and FRC, the response is completely determined by a localized crack (or cracks); in order to model the localized response, a boundary value problem approach must be used, as stated above. In the plots given later, any agreement in the post-peak range between the predicted (non-localized) response and the measured (localized) data should be viewed as strictly fortuitous. (However, if a nonlocal approach [32] is used in the boundary value problem solution, then some correspondence between the predicted post-peak response and the actual post-peak response is beneficial).

RESULTS

A successful constitutive model for FRC must also be effective in the case when the volume of fibers is zero, i.e., plain concrete. Thus, the first few applications of the model are compared to the results from plain concrete tests and then, later, the model is used for FRC. The numerical evaluation of the constitutive equations was performed with an explicit Forward Euler integration.

The values of the material constants for all applications of the model are shown in Table 1. The initial modulus of elasticity and Poisson's ratio are easily determined from laboratory data. The initial sizes of the two inelastic surfaces, r_o^+ and r_o^-, are determined from the elastic strain at which nonlinearity is first exhibited in the uniaxial tension and compression tests, respectively. Since the first occurrence of nonlinearity is difficult to determine, and, also, since uniaxial tensile tests are not often performed, these values can be chosen using a trial and error method or an optimization approach; the values shown in Table 1 were determined with the Powell optimization method. A^- and B^- are chosen using the nonlinear portion of the unconfined uniaxial compressive test; γ_4 is determined from confined compression tests or biaxial tests. The three material constants defining the evolution of tensile damage and deformation, γ_1, γ_2, and γ_3, are determined by a trial and error process from uniaxial tension and compressive test data under low confinement. First, γ_2 and γ_3 are selected to match the uniaxial tension test data, and, then, γ_1 is selected to match compressive test data.

The material constants for the *effective* fiber model can be determined from a uniaxial tension test on the FRC under consideration; unfortunately, for the two cases considered later, this data is not available and reasonable estimates for these values were determined from the results of other researchers, who tested similar fiber types and volume percentages of fibers. These constants are given in Table 1.

Figures 3, 4, and 5 show the response predicted by the constitutive model for plain concrete. Figure 3 shows very good agreement between the predicted and experimental values of Kupfer et al. (34) for both the stress-strain response and the volumetric response of plain concrete under uniaxial and biaxial compression. Good agreement is seen in Figure 4 where the confined compression, displacement-controlled results of Smith (35) are plotted with the model's results. The model predicts the increase in peak strength and strain with confinement. The post-peak strain softening response does not agree well but, again, this will be addressed when the model is implemented into a Finite Element analysis. Figure 5 shows the predicted response of plain concrete under tension followed by unloading and then reloading into the compression range. Shown for comparison is the model prediction for a monotonic compression loading. The figure indicates that the model predicts permanent deformations in tension, stiffness degradation upon unloading in tension, stiffness recovery under stress reversal, and a degrading stiffness upon unloading in compression. Upon further loading in tension, the remaining tensile strength is exhausted. The model does not predict compressive strength degradation after a tensile excursion. The authors have not been able to locate experimental data for this type of loading path, but, intuitively, it is expected that the compressive strength after tensile loading should be relatively close to the undamaged compressive strength. If isotropic hardening was used for the tensile surface, the compressive strength would be greatly increased after a tensile excursion, due to the uniform expansion of the surface (25).

Figures 6 thru 9 present the model's results for FRC. In Figure 6, the predicted uniaxial and biaxial compressive stress-strain curves for plain concrete and Steel Fiber Reinforced Concrete (SFRC) are compared with the experimental values of Mansour (19); in this comparison, the specimens consisted of plain concrete with 5830 psi uniaxial strength and a volume fraction of 1% of low carbon steel, hooked fibers with circular cross-section and an aspect ratio of 60. The tests by Mansour were run under load control. Figure 7 shows the predicted and measured surfaces of peak strength of the SFRC and plain concrete. Overall, the experimental and numerical results agree well.

In Figure 8, the predicted uniaxial compression curves for plain concrete and SFRC are compared with the experimental values of Yin et al. (22), whose specimens consisted of plain concrete with 6100 psi uniaxial strength and 1% by volume of 1 inch long, smooth, straight slit steel fibers. The tests by Yin et al. were run under load control and no post peak data is available. The model does predict a small increase in uniaxial strength, as seen experimentally by Yin et al. In Figure 9, the predicted and experimentally determined surfaces of peak strength for plain concrete and SFRC specimens are shown. Good agreement can be seen.

CONCLUSIONS

The proposed constitutive model for FRC satisfactorily reproduces the pre-peak stress-strain curves of biaxially loaded FRC specimens, and, the peak strength surfaces for FRC, tested in two separate laboratory projects, are predicted with good accuracy. In addition, the combination of continuum damage and plasticity approaches for plain concrete results in the evolution of stiffness degradation and permanent deformations. The *effective* fiber model appears to be a simple but efficient method for including the contribution of the fibers to the enhanced response of the composite. And, lastly, the combination of the concrete model with the *effective* fiber model yields a relatively simple approach for predicting the multi-axial response of FRC.

REFERENCES

1. ACI SP-81, "State of the art report on fiber reinforced concrete." ACI 544.1r-82, Int. Symp. of Fiber Reinforced Concrete, (G. Hoff, Ed.), 1984.

2. Gopalaratnam, V.S., and Shah, S.P., "Failure mechanisms and fracture of fiber reinforced concrete." Fiber Concrete Symp., ACI, Baltimore, 1986, pp. 1-25.

3. Ramakrishnan, V., and Kumar, M.S., "Constitutive relations and modelling for concrete fiber composites, a state-of-the-art report." Int. Symp. on Fibre Reinforced Concrete, Madras, India, Vol. I, 1987, pp. 1.21-1.56.

4. Romualdi, J.P., and Batson, G.B., "Behavior of reinforced concrete beams with closely spaced reinforcement." ACI J., 60(6), 1963, pp. 775-789.

5. Naaman, A.; Argon, A.; and Moavenzadeh, F., "A fracture model for fiber reinforced cementitious materials." Cem. and Con. Res, 3(4), 1973.

6. Fanella, D., and Krajcinovic, D., "Continuum damage mechanics of fiber reinforced concrete." J. Eng. Mech., ASCE, 111(8), 1985, pp. 995-1009.

7. Hillerborg, A., "A model for fracture analysis." Report TVBM-3005, Div. of Building Materials, Lund Inst. of Tech., 1978.

8. Hillerborg, A., "Analysis of fracture by means of the fictitious crack model, particularly for fiber reinforced concrete." Int. J. of Cem. Comp., 2, 1980, pp. 177-184.

9. Petersson, P.E., "Fracture mechanics calculations and tests for fiber reinforced cementitious materials." Advances in Cement Matrix Composites, Materials Research Society Symposium, Boston, 1980, pp. 95-106.

10. Bazant, Z.P., "Mechanics of distributed cracking." Appl. Mech. Rev., 39(5), 1986, pp. 675-705.

11. Taya, M., and Mura, T., "On stiffness and strength of an aligned short-fiber reinforced composite containing fiber-end cracks under uniaxial applied stress." J. Appl. Mech., ASME, 48, 1981, pp. 361-367.

12. Takao, Y.; Chou, T.W.; and Taya, M., "Effective longitudinal Young's modulus of misoriented short fiber composites." J. of Appl. Mech., ASME, 49, 1982, pp. 536-540.

13. Argon, A.S., and Shack, W.J., "Theories of fiber cement and fiber concrete." Fiber Reinforced Cement and Concrete, RILEM Symp., The Construction Press, 1975, pp. 39-53.

14. Paramasivam, P.; Curiskis, J.I.; and Valliappan, S., "Micromechanics analysis of fiber reinforced cement composites." Fiber Science and Technology, 1984, pp. 99-120.

15. Mandel, J.A., and Pack, S.C., "Crack growth in fiber reinforced materials." J. Eng. Mech., ASCE, 108(3), 1982, pp. 509-526.

16. Pack, S.C., and Mandel, J.A., "Micromechanical multiplane finite element modelling of crack growth in fiber reinforced materials." Eng. Frac. Mech., 20(2), 1984, pp. 335-349.

17. Gopalaratnam, V.S., and Shah, S.P., "Properties of steel fiber reinforced concrete subjected to impact loading." ACI, 83(1), 1986, pp. 117-126.

18. Gopalaratnam, V.S., and Shah, S.P., "Tensile failure of steel fiber-reinforced mortar", J. Eng. Mech., 113(5), 1987, pp. 635-652.

19. Mansour, S.A., "Static and fatigue behavior of low and high-strength plain and steel fiber reinforced concrete," Ph.D. Dissertation, New Mexico State University, Civil Engineering Department, 1989.

20. Shah, S.P., "Strength evaluation and failure mechanisms of fiber reinforced concrete." Int. Symp. on Fibre Reinforced Concrete, Madras, India, Vol. I, 1987, pp. 1.3-1.19.

21. Tanigawa, Y.; Yamada, K.; and Hatanaka, S., "Inelastic behavior of steel fiber reinforced concrete under compression." Int. Symp. Mat. Research Society: Advances in Cement-Matrix Composites, Boston, 1980, pp. 107-118.

22. Yin, W.S.; Su, E.C.M.; Mansur, M.A.; and Hsu, T.T.C., "Biaxial tests of plain and fiber concrete," ACI Materials J., 86(3), 1989, pp. 236-243.

23. Mobasher, B.; Ouyang, C.; and Shah, S.P., "High performance fiber-reinforced cement," Proceedings, First Materials Engineering Congress, ASCE, Ed. by B.A. Suprenant, 1990, pp. 725-734.

24. ACBM (NSF Center for Advanced Cement-Based Materials), "What is the upper limit of the fracture strength of cement-based materials?," Spring Issue, Northwestern University, 1990, pp. 1-5.

25. Stevens, D.J., and Liu, D., "Strain-based constitutive model with mixed evolution rules for concrete," J. Eng. Mech., ASCE, 118(6), 1992, pp. 1184-1200.

26. Stevens, D.J., and Liu, D., "An extended mixture approach for modeling of fiber reinforced cementitious materials," Proceedings, First Materials Engineering Congress, ASCE, Ed. by B.A. Suprenant, 1990, pp. 715-724.

27. Ortiz, M., "A constitutive theory for the inelastic behavior of concrete." Mech. of Mat. 4, 1985, pp. 67-93.

28. Simo, J.C., and Ju, J.W., "Strain- and stress-based continuum damage models-I. Formulation." Sol. Struct., 23(7), 1987, pp. 821-840.

29. Ju, J.W., "On energy-based coupled elastoplastic damage theories: constitutive modeling and computational aspects," Int. J. Solids Structures, 25(7), 1989, pp. 803-833.

30. Yazdani, S., and Schreyer, H. L., "Combined plasticity and damage mechanics model for plain concrete." J. of Eng. Mech., 116(7), 1990, pp. 1435-1450.

31. Read, H.E., and Hegemier, G.A., "Strain softening of rock, soil, and concrete-a review article." Mech. of Mat., 3, 1984, pp. 271-294.

32. Pijaudier-Cabot, G., and Bazant, Z.P., "Nonlocal damage theory." J. Eng. Mech., 113(10), 1987, pp. 1512-1533.

33. Pramono, E., and Willam, K., "Fracture energy-based plasticity formulation of plain concrete." J. of Eng. Mech., 115(6), 1989, pp. 1183-1204.

34. Kupfer, H.; Hilsdorf, H.K.; and Rusch, H., "Behavior of concrete under biaxial stresses", J. ACI, 66(8), 1969, pp. 656-666.

35. Smith, S.E., "On fundamental aspects of concrete behavior." SRS Rpt. 87-12, Dept. of Civil, Env., and Arch. Eng., U. of Colorado, Boulder, 1987.

TABLE 1 — MATERIAL VALUES

	E (10^6 psi)	ν	r_o^+ $(psi)^{½}$	r_o^+ $(psi)^{½}$	A^- $(psi)^{-½}$	B^- $(psi)^{-1}$	γ_1 (10^6 psi)	
Kupfer et al. (34)	4.5	0.2	0.3	0.8	5.x10^{-2}	5.x10^{-3}	3.4	
Smith (35)	2.1	0.2	0.3	0.8	4.x10^{-2}	5.x10^{-3}	1.2	
Mansour (19)	4.9	0.2	0.3	1.0	3.x10^{-2}	5.x10^{-3}	5.4	
Yin et al. (22)	3.7	0.22	0.3	1.0	3.x10^{-2}	5.x10^{-3}	2.6	
	γ_2 (10^6 psi)	γ_3 (10^6 psi)	γ_4	m	σ_{yt}^o (psi)	ε_{yt}	ε_c	ε_f
Kupfer et al. (34)	2.4	90.0	6.0	NA	NA	NA	NA	NA
Smith (35)	0.5	90.0	6.0	NA	NA	NA	NA	NA
Mansour (19)	2.8	90.0	6.0	1.12	400.0	3.x10^{-4}	5.x10^{-3}	6.x10^{-3}
Yin et al. (22)	1.5	90.0	6.0	1.01	200.0	4.x10^{-4}	5.x10^{-3}	6.x10^{-3}

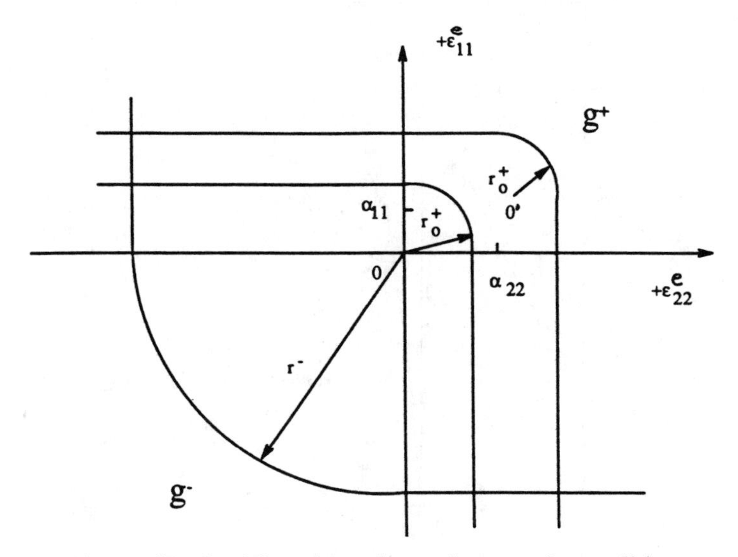

Fig. 1—"Inelastic" surfaces for a plane strain condition, with C = I (for plotting purposes)

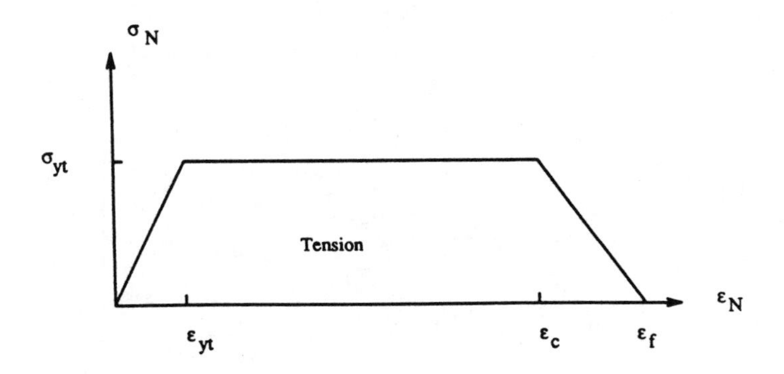

Fig. 2—Effective fiber stress-strain curve

a)

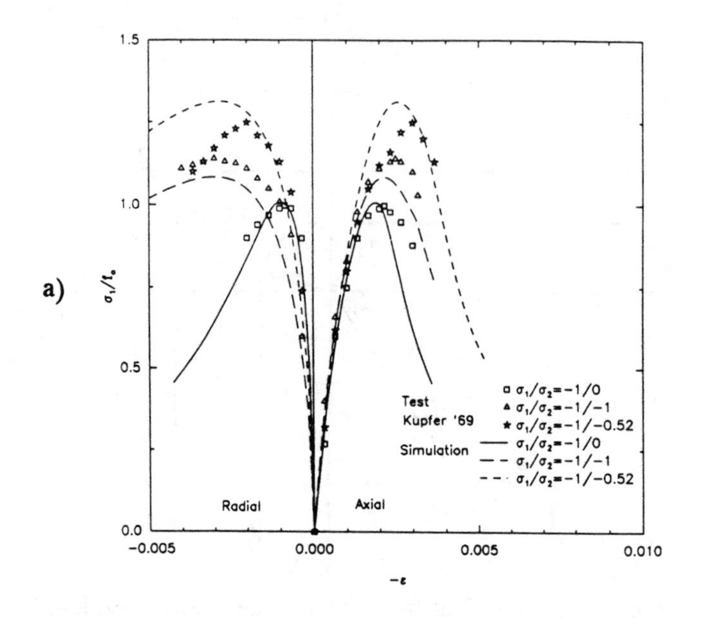

b)

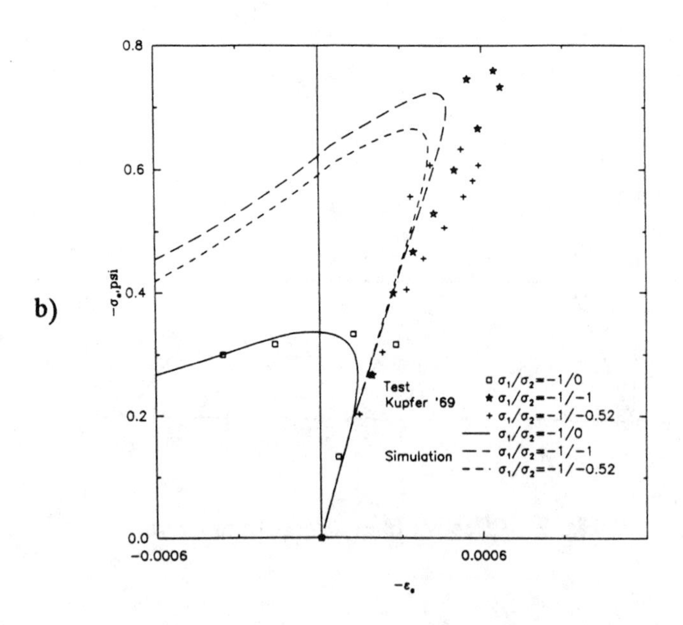

Fig. 3—(a) Axial and radial stress versus strain, and 9b) volumetric stress σ_o versus volumetric strain ϵ_o for the biaxially loaded plain concrete specimens of Kupfer et al, 1969 (f_c = uniaxial cylinder strength of the plain concrete)

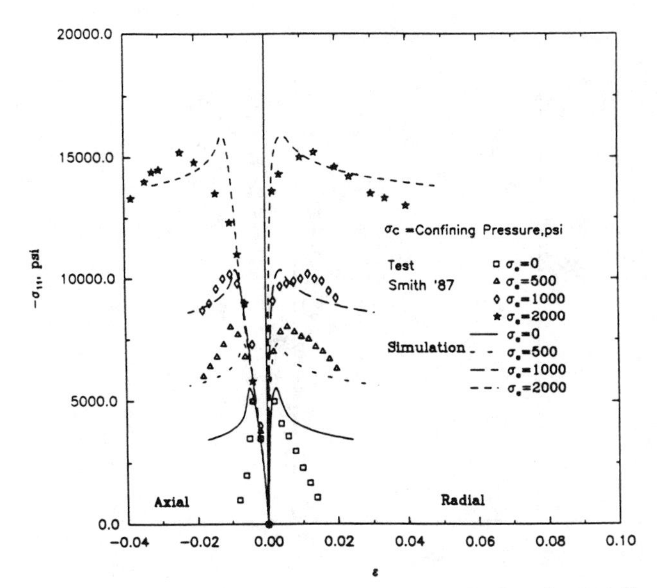

Fig. 4—Axial and radial stress versus strain for the confined compression tests of plain concrete, from Smith, 1987

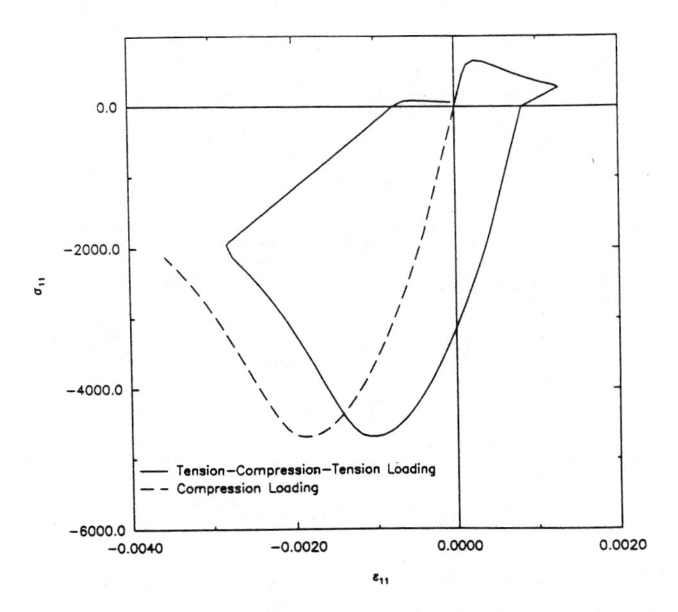

Fig. 5—Model predictions for uniaxial monotonic and reversed loadings of plain concrete

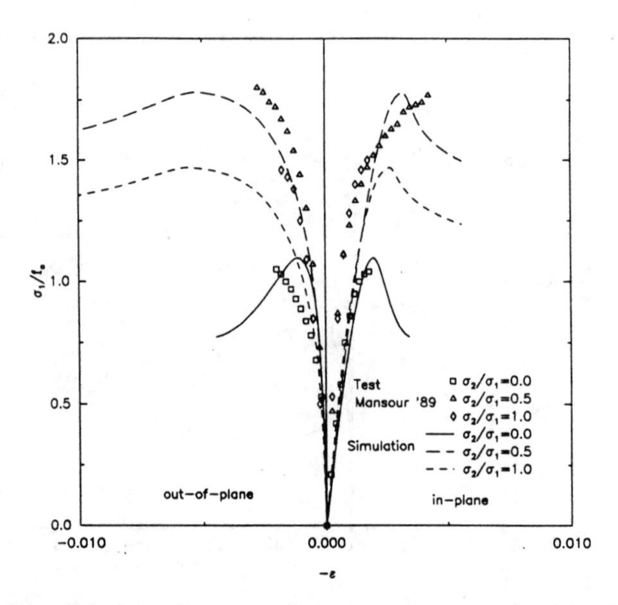

Fig. 6—In-plane and out-of-plane stress versus strain for the biaxially loaded steel fiber reinforced concrete specimens of Mansour, 1989

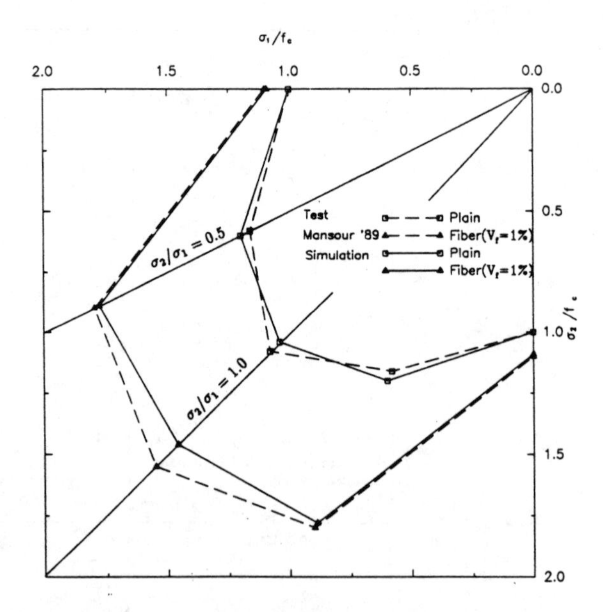

Fig. 7—Peak strength surfaces for the plain and fiber reinforced concrete specimens of Mansour, 1989

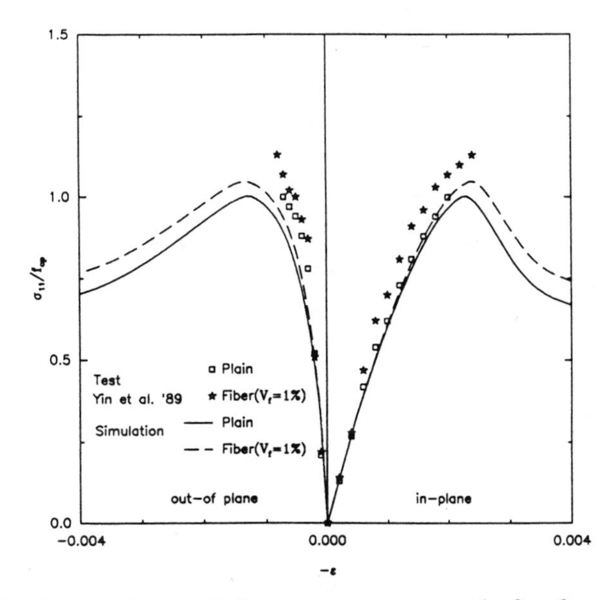

Fig. 8—In-plane and out-of-plane stress versus strain for the uniaxially loaded specimens of Yin et al, 1989 (f_{cp} = uniaxial compressive strength of plain concrete plate specimens)

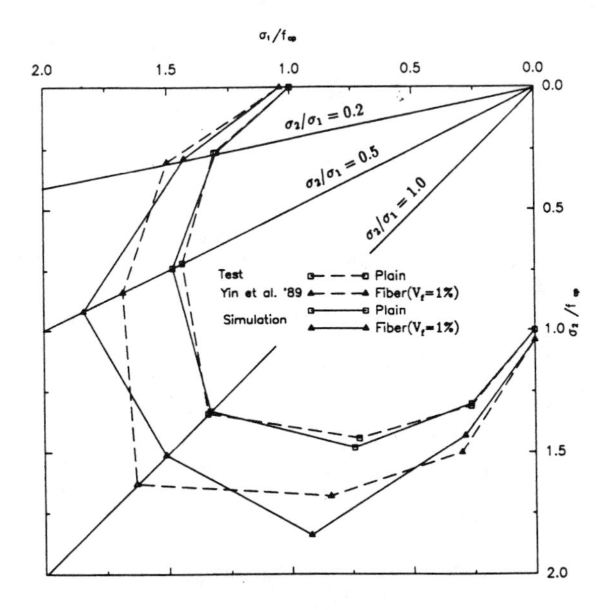

Fig. 9—Peak strength surfaces for the plain and fiber reinforced concrete specimens of Yin et al, 1989

SP 142-14

Analytical Deflection Evaluation of Partially Prestressed Fiber Reinforced Concrete Beams

by A.S. Ezeldin

Synopsis: Partially prestressed beams contain both prestressed and non-prestressed reinforcement . Addition of steel fibers results in an increase in first crack moment and flexural strength, and a decrease in deflection and reinforcement stresses.

This paper presents an analytical method to compute the deformation of partially prestressed beams made with fiber reinforced concrete. A computer program is developed to evaluate the theoretical moment-curvature and moment-deflection relationships. It uses the linear and nonlinear stress-strain relationships of the composite materials. Strain compatibility concept is incorporated to obtain the stresses in concrete, prestressed steel, and non-prestressed steel. The cracking moment and the nominal flexural strength are also computed.

The method can analyze prestressed sections of rectangular, T, I, and box shapes. The analytical predictions of the proposed method agree well with experimental results.

Keywords: Beams (supports); deflection; fiber reinforced concretes; flexural strength; metal fibers; microcomputers; moment-curvature relationship; prestressed concretes; stresses

ACI Member A.Samer Ezeldin is an assistant professor at Stevens Institute of Technology, New Jersey. His research interests include computer aided design of structural elements, development of new construction materials, and stabilization of contaminated wastes.

INTRODUCTION

Concrete with short discontinuous steel fibers is termed steel fiber concrete (SFC) . Recently, SFC has been used in many applications such as hydraulic structures, airport and highway paving, refractory concrete, and bridge decks [1-3]. Researchers are studying the possibility of using this material with conventional reinforcement [4-12] and prestressed reinforcement [13]. These studies indicate that addition of steel fibers results in an increase in first crack moment, flexural strength, and ductility, and yields a decrease in cracks width and deflection. The principal concern in most analytical studies of the behavior of steel fiber reinforced concrete members has been the prediction of the ultimate strength. Few studies have dealt with the deformation behavior [5-14-15]. This aspect is important, especially in applications where allowable deflection criteria is the limiting factor in design rather than strength. This paper presents an analytical algorithm that predicts moment-curvature and load-deflection responses of steel fiber concrete beams. The beams may be reinforced with prestressed reinforcement, non-prestressed reinforcement, or both (partial prestressing). The analytically obtained curves are compared with experimental results from the literature to check the algorithm validity.

Early in the development of prestressed concrete (1930), the philosophy of design was the complete elimination of concrete tensile stress at service service loads by a compressive prestressing force. Observations on early prestressed structures indicated the existence of extra strength and in some cases the occurrence of undesirable upward camber due to eccentric prestressing force aggravated by the creep in the concrete. In recent years, partial prestressing has emerged as a broader view of prestressing [16-17-18]. Since concrete tension and cracking are permitted in traditional reinforced concrete construction without detrimental effect, they could be allowed in prestressed concrete members. Required prestressing force may be reduced to avoid extra strength and undesirable deformation characteristics under working loads. Non-prestressed reinforcement may be added for concrete cracking control, higher ultimate strength, and ductility. Hence "Partial Prestressing" may define either or both of the following two conditions, although in the United States frequently it is employed to denote the first condition:

1- Prestressed and non prestressed reinforcements are employed in the member.
2- Tensile stresses are permitted in the concrete under working loads.

Partially prestressed beams are permitted by many specifications, including the ACI Code [19].

The overall behavior of simply supported partially prestressed beams subjected to a monotonically increasing load can be well described by its load-deflection curve [16]. Such a typical curve is shown in Figure 1 for an under-reinforced beam with bonded tendons. Point 1 corresponds to the camber of the beam assuming that all losses have occurred. Point 2 indicates the point of zero deflection where the section is subjected to a uniform compression stresses. Point 3 corresponds to cracking of concrete tension face. Point 4 represents the point of ultimate load. The post-ultimate behavior, similar to conventionally reinforced beams, can be improved by the addition of steel fibers, compression steel , or both (Point 5). Generally, the load-deflection curve for a beam has the same form as the moment-curvature curve from which it can be analytically derived.

RESEARCH SIGNIFICANCE

Since SFC is increasingly being used in conventional concrete and prestressed concrete applications, a method to predict the complete deformation and strength behavior is needed. An analytical algorithm based on basic material parameters is proposed to predict the moment-curvature and load-deflection responses of partially prestressed fiber reinforced concrete beams. The algorithm may be also applied to conventional reinforced concrete and fully prestressed beams. The algorithm can be used to study both the strength and deformation characteristics of steel fiber concrete beams in bending.

MATERIALS CONSTITUTIVE MODELS

Three basic assumptions are made in connection with this analysis.

1- Plane sections before bending remain plane after bending.
2- Perfect bond exists between concrete and reinforcement.
3- The stress-strain relationship for each used material is known.

Steel fiber concrete in compression

Typical experimental compressive stress-strain curves for plain and steel fiber concrete are shown in Figure 2. The complete stress-strain relation in compression for plain and fiber concrete can be described by using a simple non linear equation originally proposed by Carreira and Chu for plain concrete [20] and given as

$$f_c = f'_{cf} \left[\frac{\beta\ (\epsilon / \epsilon_0)}{\beta - 1 + (\epsilon / \epsilon_0)^{\beta}} \right] \qquad [1]$$

where f'_{cf} = compressive strength of fiber reinforced concrete
ϵ_0 = strain corresponding to the compressive strength
f_c, ϵ_c = stress and strain values on the curve
β = empirical material parameter.

For $\beta = 1$ a perfectly plastic postfailure behavior is obtained. For $\beta = \infty$, total loss of strength occurs after ultimate strength is reached.

Based on best fitting analysis of experimental data , Ezeldin and Balaguru [21] proposed the following equation relating β to steel fiber content and aspect ratio:

$$\beta = 1.093 + 0.7132\ (RI)^{-0.926} \text{ for hooked ends fiber} \qquad [2]$$

and

$$\beta = 1.093 + 7.4818 (RI)^{-1.387} \text{ for straight fibers} \qquad [3]$$

where RI is the reinforcing index by weight ($= W_f * \ell/\phi$). The idealized stress-strain compression curve is shown in Figure 3. In this study, the maximum usable strain was limited to 0.015 (five times the ultimate concrete strain of 0.003 adopted in the ACI Code [19]) .

Steel fiber concrete in tension

Many researchers have developed tensile stress-strain curves for steel fiber concrete [5-6-15]. The general shape for these curves is shown in Figure 4. Curve 1 is generally used for moderate fiber content (up to 1% by volume). Curve 2 represents the behavior for large fiber content (up to 3% by volume). Curves 3 can be used for very large fiber content as is the case in SIFCON. Generally, to avoid casting problems, steel fibers are added to structural beams with a volume content less than 1%. Figure 5 shows the idealized tensile stress-strain relationship of the composite used in this analysis. The curve is defined uniquely by the parameters E_c , f_{cr}, and f_{tu}. f_{cr} is usually obtained from experimental testing. The parameter f_{tu} can be taken as [22]:

$$f_{tu} = 1.12\, F_{be}\, (\ell/\phi)\, \rho_f \qquad [4]$$

where F_{be} = bond efficiency of fibers

ℓ = fiber length

ϕ = fiber diameter

ρ_f = percent of steel fibers by volume.

Non prestressed Reinforcement:

When steel fibers are added larger strains can be sustained by the concrete. Hence, the strains of the non-prestressed reinforcement steel will attain values higher than the yield stress. As a result, the effect of strain hardening must be considered. Figure 6 shows idealized relations adopted for non-prestressed reinforcement [23]. It consists of three parts corresponding to the elastic, yielding, and strain hardening ranges.

region AB: $\epsilon_s \leq \epsilon_y$

$$f_s = \epsilon_s E_s \qquad [5.a]$$

region BC: $\epsilon_y \leq \epsilon_s \leq \epsilon_{sh}$

$$f_s = f_y \qquad [5.b]$$

region CD: $\epsilon_{sh} \leq \epsilon_s \leq \epsilon_{su}$

$$f_s = f_y \left[\frac{m\ (\epsilon_s - \epsilon_{sh}) + 2}{60(\epsilon_s - \epsilon_{sh}) + 2} + \frac{(\epsilon_s - \epsilon_{sh})(60 - m)}{2\ (30\ r + 1)^2} \right] \quad [5.c]$$

where

$$m = \frac{(f_{su}/f_y)(30r+1)^2 - 60\ r - 1}{15\ r^2} \quad [5.d]$$

and

$$r = \epsilon_{su} - \epsilon_{sh} \quad [5.e]$$

Prestressed Reinforcement

The typical stress-strain curves proposed by the PCI for 7-wire stress-relieved and low-relaxation strands are used in this analysis [24]. The curves are shown in Figure 7 and are defined as follows:

$\epsilon_p \leq 0.008$

$$f_p = 28{,}000\ \epsilon_p\ ,\ \text{ksi} \quad [6.a]$$

$\epsilon_p > 0.008$

$$\text{250 ksi strand} \quad f_p = 248 - \frac{0.058}{\epsilon_p - 0.006} < 0.98\ f_{pu} (\text{ksi}) \quad [6.b]$$

$$\text{270 ksi strand} \quad f_p = 268 - \frac{0.075}{\epsilon_p - 0.0065} < 0.98\ f_{pu} (\text{ksi}) \quad [6.c]$$

ANALYTICAL ANALYSIS

1- Theoretical Moment-Curvature Determination

The analysis is performed assuming two stages of behavior, namely; elastic uncracked stage and cracked stage. Figure 8 displays a fiber concrete partially prestressed section and figure 9 shows a typical moment-curvature curve. Basic elastic mechanics of prestressed section are used to obtain the two points defining the linear uncracked stage. Actual material properties are used for analysis of the cracked section response.

Elastic Uncracked Section:

Using properties of the uncracked section, points 1 and 3 on the moment-curvature curve are obtained as follows:

point 1: (zero moment)

$$f_t = -\frac{\Sigma\,(A_p)_i(f_{pe})_i}{A_c} + \frac{\Sigma(A_p)_i(f_{pe})_i\{(d_p)_i - c_t\}c_t}{I_g} \qquad [7.a]$$

$$f_b = -\frac{\Sigma\,(A_p)_i(f_{pe})_i}{A_c} - \frac{\Sigma(A_p)_i(f_{pe})_i\{(d_p)_i - c_t\}c_b}{I_g} \qquad [7.b]$$

$$\phi = \frac{f_b - f_t}{h\,E_c} \qquad [7.c]$$

point 3: (Cracking moment)

$$M_{cr.} = \frac{I_g}{c_b}\left[f_{cr} + \frac{\Sigma\,(A_p)_i(f_{pe})_i}{A_c} + \frac{\Sigma(A_p)_i(f_{pe})_i\{(d_p)_i - c_t\}c_b}{I_g}\right] \qquad [8.a]$$

$$f_b = f_{cr} \qquad [8.b]$$

$$f_t = -\frac{\Sigma (A_p)_i (f_{pe})_i}{A_c} + \frac{\Sigma (A_p)_i (f_{pe})_i \{(d_p)_i - c_t\} c_t}{I_g} - \frac{M_{cr} . c_t}{I_g} \quad [8.c]$$

$$\phi = \frac{f_b - f_t}{h E_c} \quad [8.d]$$

Cracked Section:

With the above mentioned constitutive models, a theoretical moment-curvature curve for the cracked section can be derived. The analysis deals with "average"curvatures with higher values occurring at a crack being averaged with the lower values between cracks [18]. For a given concrete strain in the extreme compression fiber ϵ_c and neutral axis depth c, the non prestressed steel strain ϵ_{s1}, ϵ_{s2}, ..., and the prestressed steel strain ϵ_{p1},ϵ_{p2}, ..., can be determined from similar triangles of the strain diagram (Figure 8). For example:

$$\epsilon_{s1} = \frac{c - d_1}{c} \epsilon_c \quad [9]$$

The stresses f_{s1},f_{s2},... corresponding to strains ϵ_{s1},ϵ_{s2},... and the prestressed stresses f_{p1}, f_{p2}, corresponding to strains ϵ_{p1},ϵ_{p2},..., may be obtained from the stress-strain curves shown in Figures 6 and 7, respectively. The strains ϵ_{p1}, ϵ_{p2}, are the summation of two values:

$$(\epsilon_p)_i = \epsilon_c \left[\frac{(d_p)_i - c}{c} \right] + \frac{(f_{pe})_i}{E_p} \quad [10]$$

Then, the reinforced forces S_{s1},S_{s2}, ..., and S_{p1}, S_{p2}, ...may be found from the steel stresses and the areas of steel. For example:

$$S_{s1} = f_{s1} * A_{s1} \quad [11]$$

The distribution of concrete stress over the compressed and tensioned parts of the section may be obtained from the stress-strain curves shown in Figures 3 and 5, respectively. For

any given concrete strain ϵ_c, the resultant concrete compression and tension forces C_C and C_T are calculated by numerically integrating the stresses over their respective areas.
The force equilibrium equation can be written as:

$$S_{s1}+S_{s2}+\ldots+S_{p1}+S_{p2}+\ldots.+C_T+C_C=0 \qquad [12]$$

The moment equation is:

$$M=\Sigma(A_s)_i(f_s)_i\{c-(d_s)_i\}+\Sigma(A_p)_i(f_p)_i\{c-(d_p)_i\}+C_T\lambda_T+C_C\lambda_C \qquad [13]$$

$$\text{the curvature},\ \phi=\frac{\epsilon_c}{c} \qquad [14]$$

The complete moment-curvature relationship may be determined by incrementing the concrete strain at the extreme compression fiber, ϵ_c. For each value the correct neutral axis depth, c is found by adjusting c value until the internal forces calculated satisfy Eq.[12]

2- Calculation of Deformations from Curvatures

The deformation of a member may be calculated by integrating the curvature along the member [5-14-18]. Figure 10 shows the changing form of the curvature distribution along the span at various load levels. To obtain the deflection at B, we sum the moment about A of area under the diagram between A and B. This calculation would reflect the large contribution to deflection which results from large curvatures developing in the middle portion of the span at the ultimate and post ultimate stages.

The flow charts for calculating the moment-curvature and load-deflection curves for fiber reinforced partially prestressed beams with flexure are illustrated in Figure 11.

3- Validation of Computer Algorithm

This program provides a complete moment-curvature and load-deflection analysis for Rectangular, T, I, and Box (by inverting it to equivalent I section) partially prestressed steel fiber reinforced section. It is available in BASIC language and runs on IBM compatible computers. The input consists of geometric dimensions, materials properties, amount and location of prestressed and non-prestressed reinforcements, and the amount of effective prestress. The data is provided using an easy graphic-interactive mode. Typical input data is shown in Figure 12.

The analytical results of the computer analysis were compared to published data. Three different cases are included to prove the validity of the program, namely;

a- Plain prestressed concrete beams (no fibers) [18].
b- Fiber reinforced conventional beams (no-prestressed reinforcement) [5].
c- Partially prestressed fiber concrete beams [13].

Figure 13,14,and 15 for cases a,b,and c, respectively indicate that the theoretical values agree well with experimental data.

CONCLUSION

Using the linear and non-linear stress-strain relationships of materials and the strain compatibility concept, this paper presents a computer algorithm that predicts the complete moment-curvature and load-deflection curves for partially prestressed steel fiber concrete beams. The program can also analyze beams reinforced with non-prestressed reinforcement only or prestressed reinforcement only with or without fibers. The analytical predictions of the proposed algorithm agree well with published experimental data. With the advent of microprocessors, the algorithm may be easily used to study both the strength and deformation characteristics of steel fiber concrete beams.

REFERENCES

1- Lankard,D.R., "Steel Fiber Reinforced Refractory Concrete", SP-57 Refractory Concrete , American Concrete Institute, Detroit, 1978, pp 241-263.

2-Johnston,C.D., "Steel Fiber Reinforced Concrete Pavements Trials", Concrete International, Dec.1984, Vol.6, No.12, pp 39-43.

3- Ramakrishnan, V., Balaguru,P., Kostaneski,L., and Johnston,D., "Field Performance of Fiber Reinforced Concrete Highway Pavements", Proceedings of the First Materials Engineering Congress, Denver, Colorado, August 1990, pp 903-912.

4- Batson,G., Terry,T.,and Change, M.S., "Fiber Reinforced Concrete Beams Subjected to Combined Bending and Torsion", ACI SP-81, Fiber Reinforced Concrete, 1984, pp. 51-68.

5- Craig,R. "Flexural Behavior and Design of Reinforced Fiber Concrete Members", ACI SP-105, Fiber Reinforced Concrete Properties and Applications, 1987, pp 517-563.

6- Henager,C.H., and Doherty,T.J., "Analysis of Reinforced Fibrous Concrete Beams", Journal of the Structural Division, ASCE, Vol. 102, No.ST1, Jan 1976, pp. 177-188.

7- Swamy,R.N., and Al-Ta'an, S.A., "Deformation and Ultimate Strength in Flexure of Reinforced Concrete Beams Made with Steel Fiber Concrete", Proceedings of ACI. Sept- Oct. , 1981, No.5, V.78, pp. 395-405.

8-Jindal, R.L. "Shear and Moment Capacities of Steel Fiber Reinforced Concrete Beams", ACI SP-81, Fiber Reinforced Concrete, 1984, pp.1-16.

9- Batson ,G., Jenkins,E., and Spatney,R., "Steel Fibers as Shear Reinforcement in Beams", ACI Journal, Proceedings, V.69, No.10, Oct.1972, pp.640-644.

10- Williamson,G.R., and Knab,L.I.,"Full Scale Fiber Concrete Beam Tests", Fiber Reinforced Cement and Concrete (RILEM Symposium, London), Construction Press, Lancaster, 1975, pp.209-214.

11-Sharma, A.K. "Shear Strength of Steel Fiber Reinforced Concrete Beams", ACI Journal, Proceedings, V.83, No.4, July-August 1986, pp.624-628.

12- Narayanan,R. and Darwish , I.Y.S., "USe of Steel Fibers as Shear reinforcement", ACI Structural Journal, V.84, No.3, May-June 1987, pp.216-227.

13- Balaguru,P. and Ezeldin,A.S., "Behavior of Partially Prestressed Beams Made with High Strength Fiber Reinforced Concrete", ACI SP-105, Fiber Reinforced Concrete Properties and Applications, 1987, pp.419-436.

14- Liqiu,G., and Guofan,Z.,"Analysis of the Complete Moment-Curvature Curve of Concrete Beam Reinforced with Steel Bars and Steel Fibres", Proceedings of the First International Congress by RILEM on "Combining Materials: Design ,Production, and Properties", Edited by Maso,J.C., Vol. 2, Sept. 1987, pp 706-713.

15- Lim,T.Y., Paramasivam,P., and Lee,S.L., "Bending Behavior of Steel-Fiber Concrete Beams", ACI Structural Journal, Vol.84, No.6, Nov-Dec. 1987, pp 524-536.

16- Naaman,A.E., "Prestressed Concrete Analysis and Design", McGraw-Hill, Inc., 1982, 670 pp.

17- Lin,T.Y., and Burns, N.H., "Design of Prestressed Concrete Structures", John Wiley & Sons, New York, 1981, 646 pp.

18- Burns,N.H., "Moment Curvature Relationships for Partially Prestressed Beams", Proceedings, PCI Journal, Feb. 1964, pp. 52-64.

19- Building Code Requirements for Reinforced Concrete (ACI 318-89) and Commentary -ACI 318R-89, American Concrete Institute, Detroit, Michigan, 1989, 353 pp.

20- Carreira,D.J., and Chu,K.M., "Stress-Strain Relationship for Plain Concrete in Compression", ACI Journal, Proceedings, Vol.82, No.6, Nov-Dec. 1985, pp 345-350.

21- Ezeldin, A.S., and Balaguru,P.N., "Normal and High-Strength Fiber Reinforced Concrete Under Compression", Journal of Materials in Civil Engineering, Proceeding of the American Society of Civil Engineers, Vol.4, No.4, In Press.

22-ACI Committee 544, Design Considerations for Steel Fiber Reinforced Concrete, ACI 544.4R. , ACI Structural Journal, V.85, No.5., Sept.-Oct. 1988, pp.563-580.

23- Park,R., and Paulay,T., "Reinforced Concrete Structures", John Wiley & Sons, Inc., New York, 1975, 769 pp.

24- PCI Design Handbook, Precast and Prestressed Concrete, Third Edition, Third Edition, Prestressed Concrete Institute, Chicago, Illinois,1985.

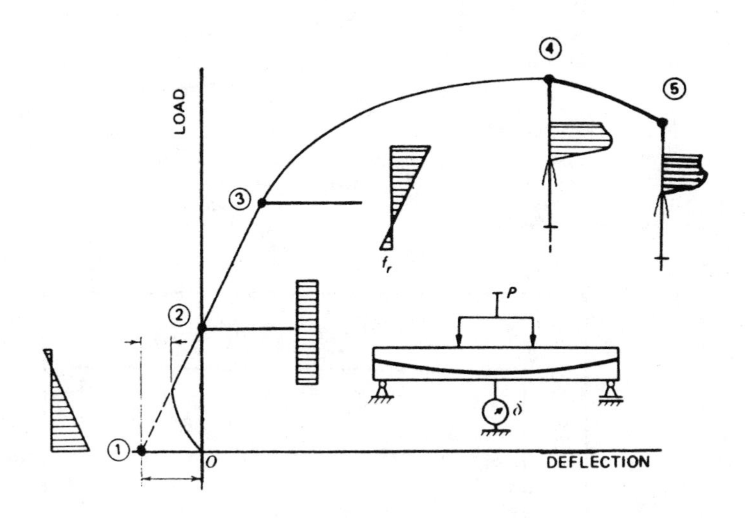

Fig. 1—Typical load-deflection curves of partially prestressed beams

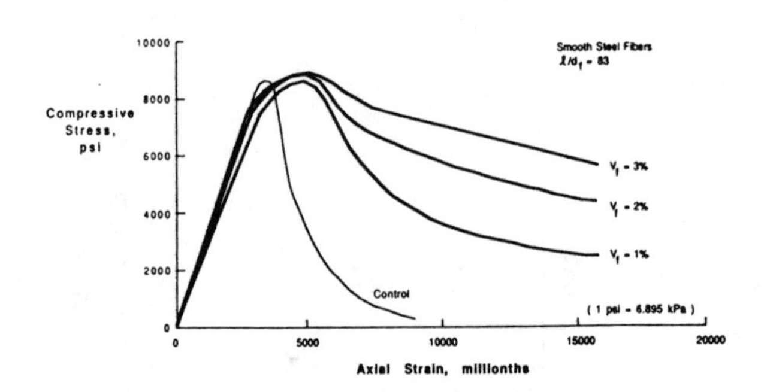

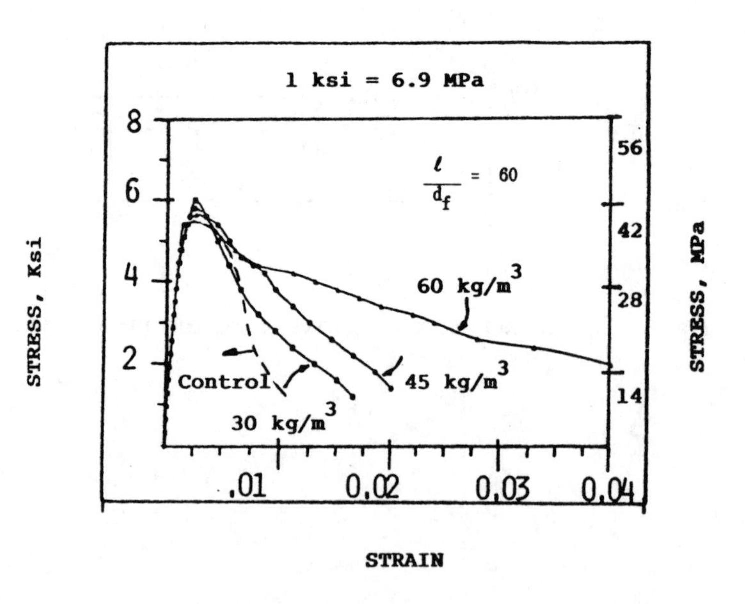

Fig. 2—Typical experimentally obtained compression stress-strain curves for plain and steel fiber concrete [21-22]

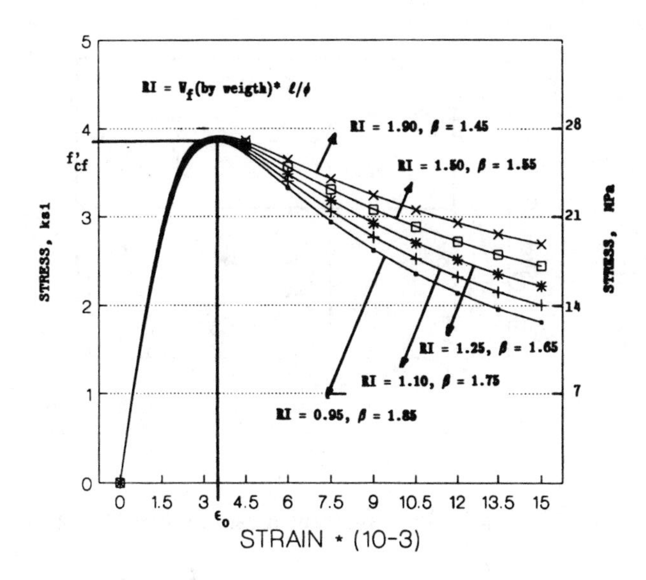

Fig. 3—Idealized stress-strain compression curve [21]

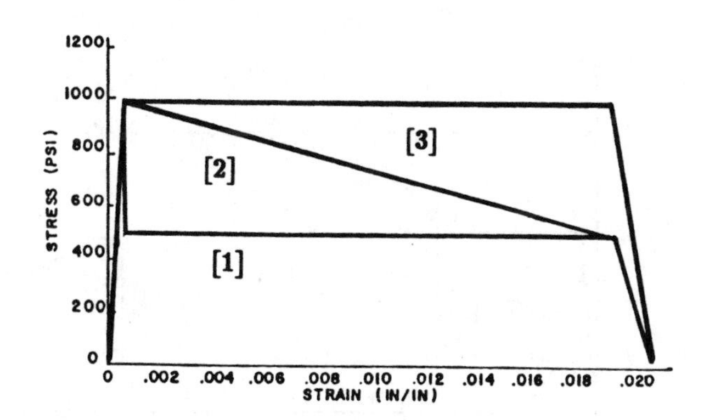

Curve 1: Moderate Fiber Content

Curve 2: High Fiber Content

Curve 3: Very High Fiber Content

Fig. 4—Idealized tension stress-strain curves for steel fiber concrete [5]

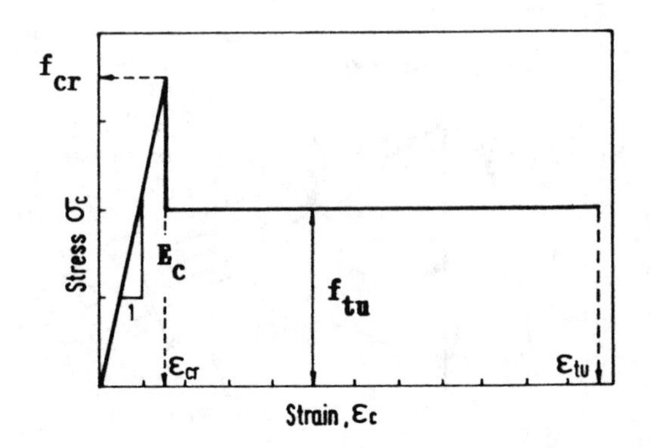

Fig. 5—Idealized stress-strain tension curve [15-22]

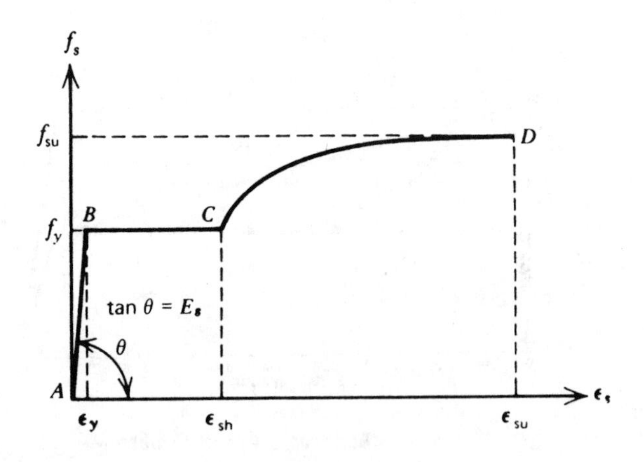

Fig. 6—Idealized stress-strain curve for non-prestressed reinforcement [23]

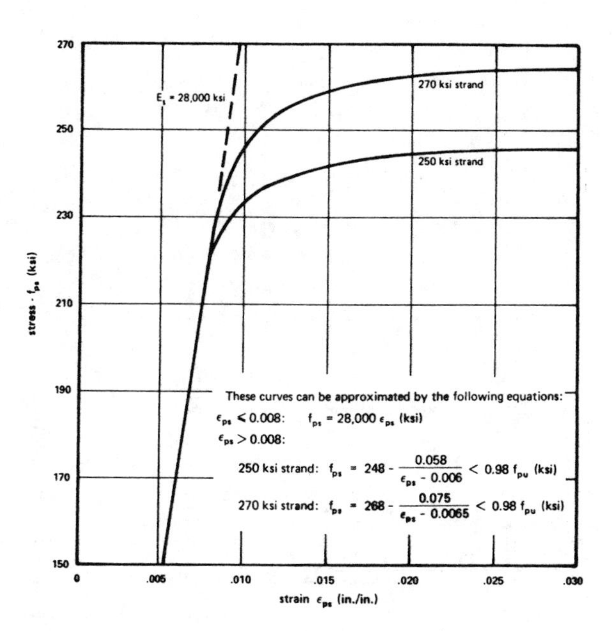

Fig. 7—idealized stress-strain curve for prestressed reinforcement [24]

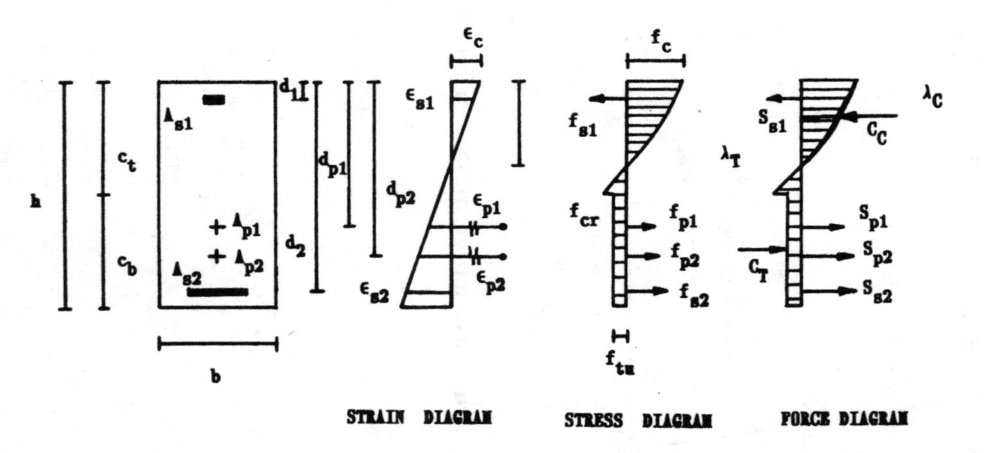

Fig. 8—Bending behavior of partially prestressed section

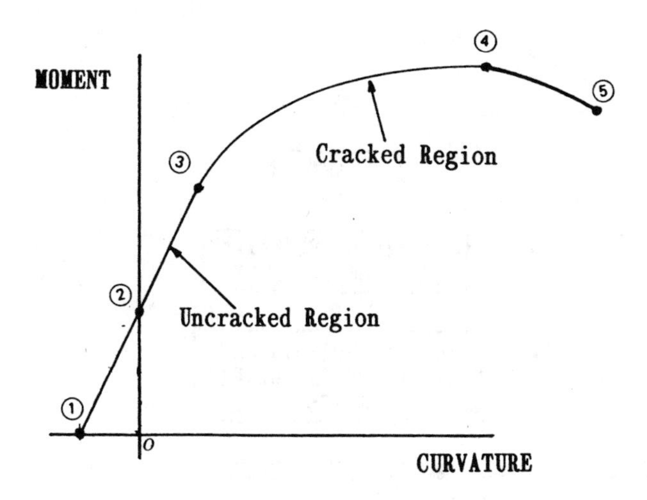

Fig. 9—Typical moment-curvature curve for partially prestressed section

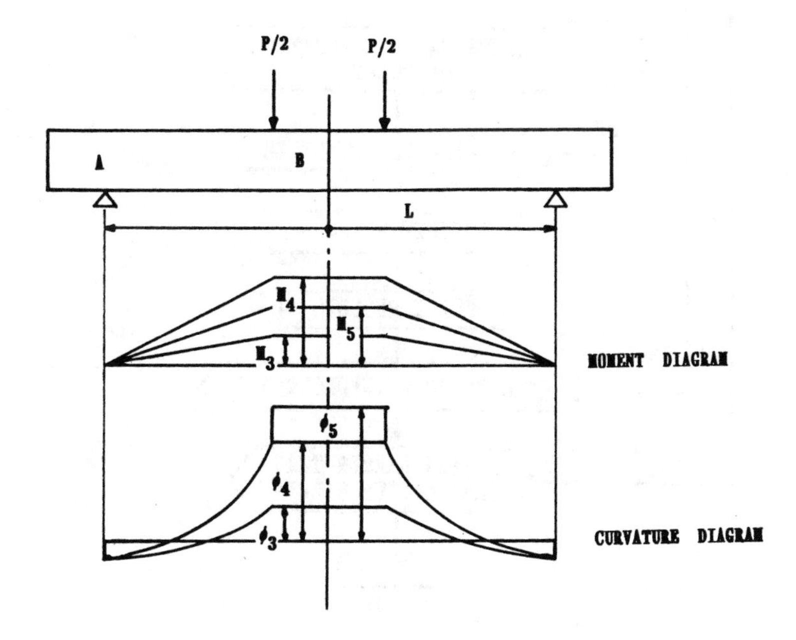

Fig. 10—Curvature distribution

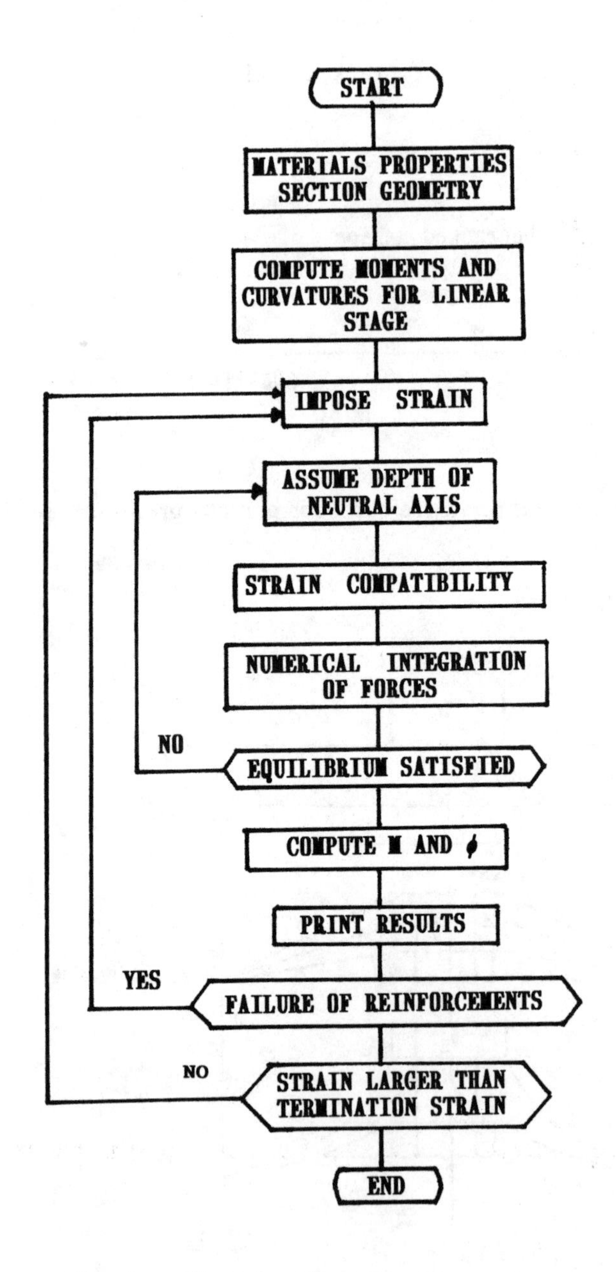

Fig. 11a—Flow chart for moment-curvature curve

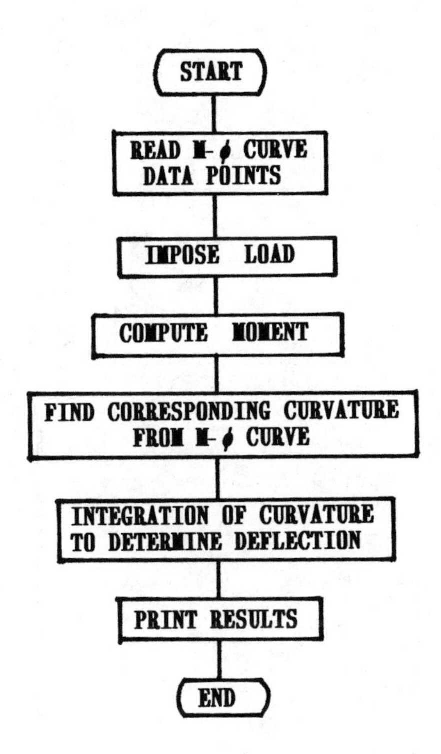

Fig. 11b—Flow chart for load-deflection curve

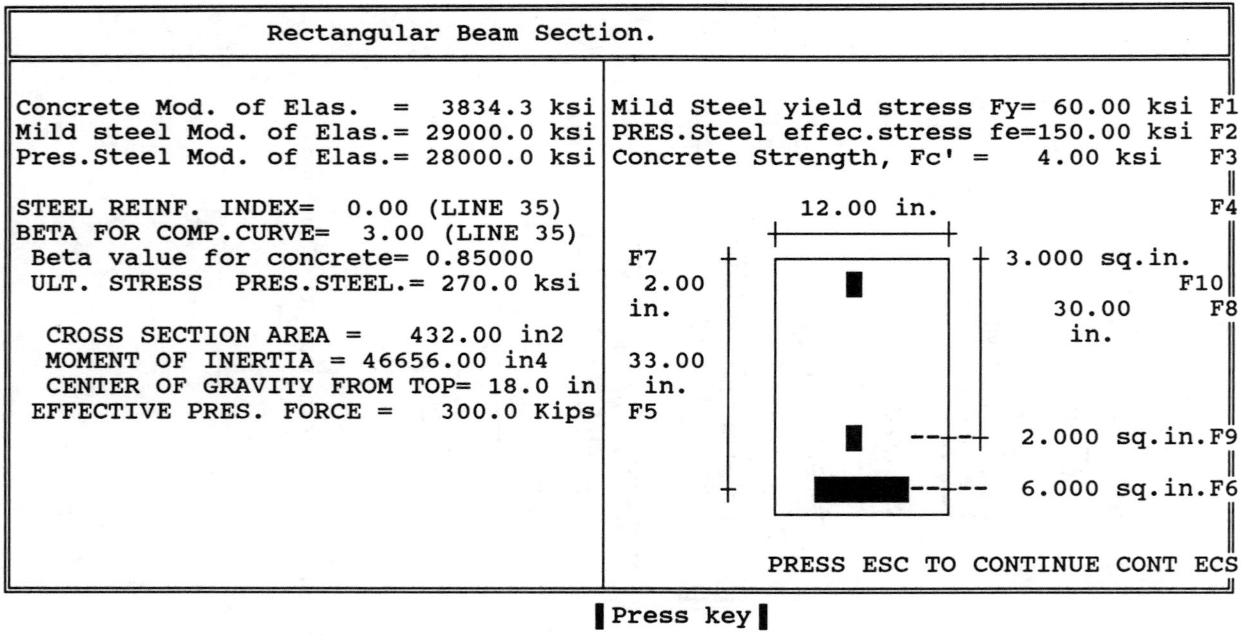

```
                Rectangular Beam Section.

Concrete Mod. of Elas.   =  3834.3 ksi  Mild Steel yield stress Fy= 60.00 ksi F1
Mild steel Mod. of Elas.= 29000.0 ksi   PRES.Steel effec.stress fe=150.00 ksi F2
Pres.Steel Mod. of Elas.= 28000.0 ksi   Concrete Strength, Fc' =   4.00 ksi   F3

STEEL REINF. INDEX=  0.00 (LINE 35)             12.00 in.                     F4
BETA FOR COMP.CURVE=  3.00 (LINE 35)
 Beta value for concrete= 0.85000       F7                      3.000 sq.in.
 ULT. STRESS  PRES.STEEL.= 270.0 ksi     2.00                                F10
                                        in.                        30.00     F8
  CROSS SECTION AREA =   432.00 in2                                 in.
  MOMENT OF INERTIA = 46656.00 in4      33.00
  CENTER OF GRAVITY FROM TOP= 18.0 in    in.
 EFFECTIVE PRES. FORCE =   300.0 Kips   F5
                                                                2.000 sq.in.F9

                                                                6.000 sq.in.F6

                                                PRESS ESC TO CONTINUE CONT ECS

                                 Press key
```

Fig. 12—Typical data input

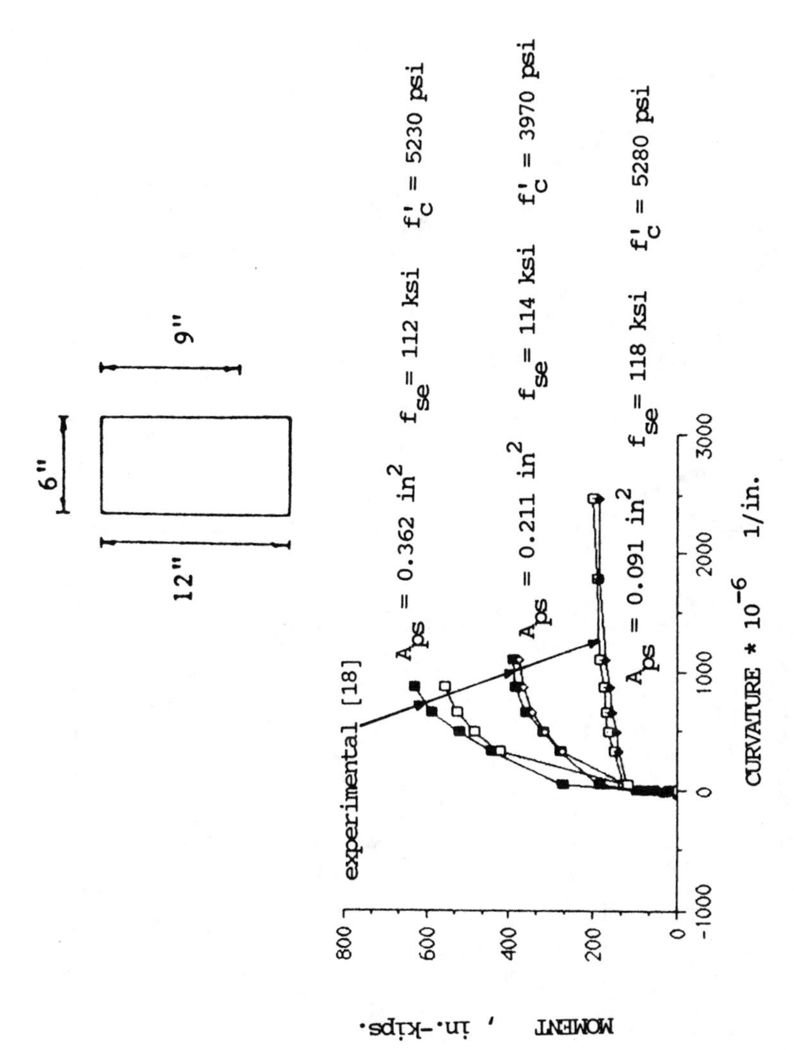

Fig. 13—Results comparison for prestressed concrete beams [18]

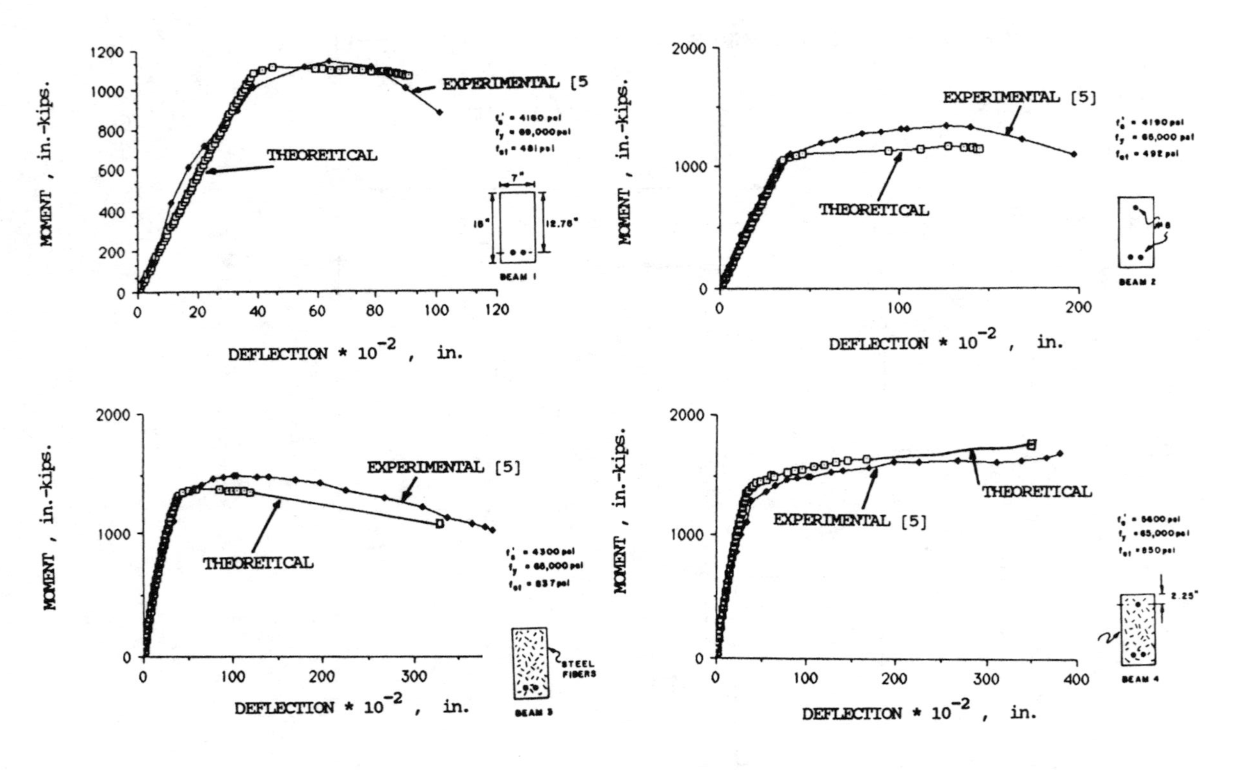

Fig. 14—Results comparison for conventional fiber concrete beams [5]

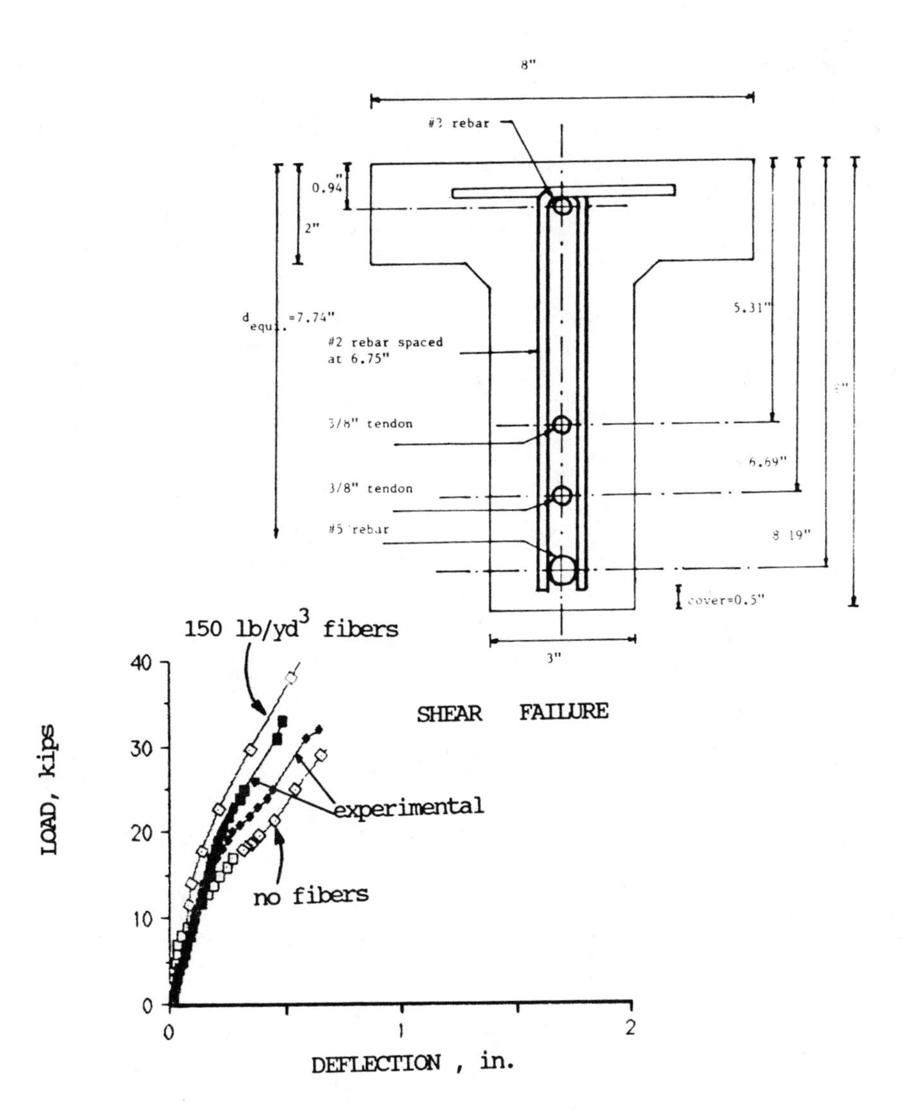

Fig. 15—Results comparison for partially prestressed fiber concrete beams [13]

Dynamic Tension Fatigue Performance of Fibrous Concrete Composites

by N.L. Lovata and P.B. Morrill

ABSTRACT

This research was specifically designed to test concrete in direct tension. Concrete prism specimens measured 4" X 4" X 16"in length. The specimens were first tested under monotonic loading conditions to determine ultimate stress-strain relationships. Samples were also tested under low frequency high cyclic loading conditions to simulate concrete fatigue.

Fibrous concrete containing steel, polypropylene and composite fiber reinforcement made up the test groups. A closed loop hydraulic test machine was used to develop a testing procedure to measure the monotonic and cyclic tension responses of fiber reinforced concrete. This procedure proved successful in determining the stress-strain relationship and cyclic behavior of the fiber reinforced concrete.

The concrete evaluation included monitoring concrete in the plastic state. Concrete temperature, slump, air content, mix design and mixing time were carefully controlled. The long term concrete curing period lasted 150 days. The testing of cured samples included mechanical testing, statistical treatment evaluation and (scanning electron microscope analysis). The fiber reinforced concrete and composite fiber specimens provided substantial performance improvement when compared to the plain concrete specimens.

Keywords: Composite materials; fatigue (materials); fiber reinforced concretes; load tests; mix proportioning; slump; stress-strain relationships; temperature; tension; tests

INTRODUCTION

This research project examined the effects of monotonic and cyclic tension loading on fiber reinforced concrete. A closed loop dynamic test machine tested the concrete specimens under strain control. Initially, twenty four of the virgin specimens were tested in a direct monotonic tension test (pre-test). To simulate cyclic fatigue, the remaining specimens were exposed to 1,000 cycles of tension loading. Each cycled sample was then monotonically tension tested (post-test). These data sets were statistically analyzed by comparison and experimental conclusions were drawn for the fatigue effects on fiber reinforced concrete.

PROBLEM OF THE STUDY

The problem of this study was to develop a technique to test concrete in direct tension. This procedure was designed to evaluate concrete in direct monotonic tension to the point of ultimate failure. Monotonic testing also has the capability of performing cyclic testing and measuring the fatigue effects on the material properties of the fiber reinforced concrete.

LIMITATIONS OF STUDY

1. This study was limited to the use of one concrete design mix which used only commercially available Type I Portland cement as a bonding agent.
2. This study was limited to the use of two commercially available liquid add-mixtures to the mix design, a superplasticizer and air entrainment additive.
3. This study was limited to one commercially available 1" collated fibrillated polypropylene fiber and one commercially available 1" ribbed steel fiber.
4. The concrete specimens used in this study were limited to a 4" x 4" x 16" prisms with a 4" un-reinforced concrete cube in the center of the specimen.

METHODOLOGY

Newly developed evaluation procedures were used in this research project. These procedures were all based on a direct axial tension test method. This tension test method is capable of accurately performing cyclic testing.

The first step of this research project begin by performing a direct monotonic test on noncycled specimens, to determine the stress strain relationship for each of the concrete treatment groups. This technique quantified the material properties for the none fatigued (virgin specimens) concrete treatment groups. This is the pre-test portion of the concrete research.

Step two of the research project performed a cyclic fatigue test on the remaining concrete specimens. This cyclic fatigue test was designed to simulate field loading conditions.

The third and final step of the project (post-testing), involved the monotonic direct tension test on the specimens exposed to cyclic fatigue. This post-test procedure was identical to the pre-test and determined if any changes occurred in the stress-strain relationship after the fibrous concrete was exposed to cyclic loading fatigue.

Determination of Sampling Size

The sample size was determined using standard ASTM guidelines for casting and testing concrete specimens. ASTM requires a minimum of five samples cast from each batch and a minimum of testing three of these samples. This investigation included a control group and three treatment groups. Nine sample prisms were cast and replicated for a total of 18 specimens per treatment group. A total of 72 specimens were cast and tested in this investigation. This procedure exceeds the ASTM specification requirements. The purpose of the replication procedure was to increase the reliability of the test results and improve the statistical analysis.

Material Selection

Concrete consists of four main ingredients, cement, water, fine aggregate and course aggregate. The cement used was a type I Portland cement meeting ASTM C-150 standards and was obtained from a local material supplier. All cement used in the experiment was intermixed during casting to eliminate any variance between bags of cement. The water used was tap water from the Madison municipal water supply. Both the fine and the coarse aggregate were obtained from a local quarry.

TABLE 1 — FINE AGGREGATE-SIEVE ANALYSIS

Sieve Number	Percent of Material Passing (by weight)	Cumulative Percent of Material Retained (by weight)
# 4	0.0	100.0
# 8	12.1	87.9
# 16	34.9	65.1
# 30	50.6	49.4
# 50	75.7	24.3
# 100	91.6	8.4
# 200	96.4	3.6

Finesses Modulus (FM) = 2.66

All materials used in this project were stored indoors, until use, to protect them from the natural elements.

Samples of the fine and coarse aggregates were tested to determine that they met specifications for the aggregate quality, size variation and sieve analysis. Table 1 shows the sieve analysis data for fine aggregate and Table 2 contains the sieve analysis for the 3/4" coarse aggregate.

TABLE 2 — COARSE AGGREGATE-SIEVE ANALYSIS

Sieve Number	Percent of Material Passing (by weight)	Cumulative Percent of Material Retained (by weight)
1.0 in.	0.00	100.0
0.75 in.	2.67	80.8
0.5 in.	11.27	19.2
0.375 in.	13.47	3.4
# 4	13.80	1.0
# 8	13.82	0.9
# 50	13.83	0.8
# 200	13.86	0.6

Coarse Aggregates-Fractional Components
% Gravel = 99.0
% Sand = 0.4
% Fines = 0.6

A water reducing admixture and an air entrainment admixture were used to modify the basic concrete mix. The water reducing agent or superplasticizer was used to reduced the amount of water added to the mix to increase concrete flowablity during placement. During the mix procedure this additive substantially increased the workability of the plain concrete and also the treatment groups with high volume fractions of fibers.

Air entrainment additives are widely used in concrete exposed to repeated freeze thaw cycles. Therefore this admixture was included to imitate actual field conditions. It maintained all eight of the batch mixes air contents within the required 3% to 8% range. This product satisfied the requirements of ASTM C-260 for air-entrainment admixtures.

The fibers selected for this project were a 1" ribbed carbon steel fiber and a 1" collated fibrillated polypropylene fiber.

The steel fibers are made by Ribtec Corporation. They are carbon steel, 1" in length, 1/8" wide and have a corrugated shaped design. ACI Committee 544 recommends the addition of steel fibers for normal weight concrete to range from 50 lb/yd^3 up to 200 lb/yd^3. In this investigation steel fibers were added at 100 lb/yd^3.

The polypropylene fibers (PPF) are produced by Forta Corporation. These fibers are made from collated fibrillated polypropylene and cut into 1" lengths. By manufacturers' design these polypropylene fiber bundles are added to the concrete mix, they separate and disperse into a three dimensional secondary reinforcement of the concrete matrix.

Collated fibrillated polypropylene will not react with the chemical admixtures used in this experiment. The typical recommended quantities vary from the common use of a 1.6 pound bag for a wire mesh substitution up to the three bag (4.8 pound) range for high-volume application. The PPF were used at three bag(4.8 lbs/yd^3) to determine the fatigue properties for high-volume fraction applications.

These fiber quantity were determined during an extensive direct tension monotonic pilot study. The quantity of fibers at 1" and 2" lengths were varied to determine the optimum fiber quantities and fiber lengths which had the maximum increase in monotonic tension strength. It was determined that the 1" long corrugated steel fiber produced optimum strength improvement at a 100 lbs/yd^3. The 1" polypropylene fiber reinforced concrete was strongest when added at 4.8 lbs/yd^3.

Table 3 shows the concrete mix design proportions for one cubic yard of concrete.

TABLE 3 — CONCRETE DESIGN MIX

Material	Quantity	Unit
Fine Aggregate	1431	Lbs./Cyd.
Course Aggregate	1431	Lbs./Cyd.
Cement	615	Lbs./Cyd.
Water	246	Lbs./Cyd.
Steel Fibers	100	Lbs./Cyd.
Polypropylene Fibers	4.8	Lbs./Cyd.
Air-Entrainment Admixture	5.7	Fl.oz./Cyd.
Superplasticizer Admixture	92.5	Fl.oz./Cyd.

Water Cement Ratio: W/C = .40

Sample Description

The specimens tested in this experiment were 4" x 4" x 16" concrete prisms. Each sample has a cross sectional area of 16 in^2. The steel reinforcing rods, 3/8" in diameter(# 3 reinforcing steel), were 6 3/4" long and threaded with 5/16"-20 threads on one end.

Specially constructed steel forms had 4 threaded rods mounted in them which produced a square reinforcing pattern which extended 6" into the specimen from each end. This arrangement produced a 4"x 4"x 4" unreinforced cube in the center of the specimen. This cube was the test area and contained only the secondary fiber reinforcing introduced into the concrete mix.

To investigate the effects the fibers have on the concrete matrix, four treatment groups were cast. Each treatment group varied by the type of fibers they contained. One group contained no fibers and was designated as the control group (PC). The other three treatment groups contained short steel fibers only (SS), polypropylene fibers only (PP) and a composite of steel and polypropylene fibers (SP). These 4 groups were replicated to increase the reliability and to detect any statistical variance within each batch. Table 4 illustrates the batch designation codes, fiber types and fiber quantities added to each batch.

TABLE 4 — PRISM SPECIMEN DESIGNATION & FIBER CONTENT

Batch Number	Designation Code Group	Pounds of Steel Fibers	Pounds of P.P. Fibers
1	PC - 1.1 Control	—	—
2	PC - 2.1 Replicate	—	—
3	SS - 1.1 Short Steel	100 Lbs./Cyd.	—
4	SS - 2.1 Replicate	100 Lbs./Cyd.	—
5	PP - 1.1 Short P.P.F.	—	3 Bag 4.8 Lb./Cyd.
6	PP - 2.1 Replicate	—	3 Bag 4.8 Lb./Cyd.
7	SP - 1.1 Composite	100 Lbs./Cyd.	3 Bag 4.8 Lb./Cyd.
8	SP - 2.1 Replicate	100 Lbs./Cyd.	3 Bag 4.8 Lb./Cyd.

Note:

PC = Plain concrete - No Fibers Added
SS = 1" Short Steel Fibers Added
PP = 1" Polypropylene Fibers Added
SP = 1" Steel and 1" Polypropylene Added

Concrete Mix Procedure

The mixing procedure followed ACI committee 544 recommendations for fiber reinforced concrete. Prior to casting a series of plastic tests were completed which included water/cement ratio, concrete temperature, ambient temperature, air content and slump testing which included the K-test. These tests were completed to insure consistency and quality control.

The fresh concrete was placed in two lifts into 4"x 4"x 16" steel forms. Between each lift the concrete was consolidated thoroughly using mechanical vibration. The forms were covered with plastic sheets to hold in moisture and allowed to cure for 24 hours. The samples were stripped from the steel forms and placed in a 100% humidity room, where they remained, until testing began after 150 days of moisture curing.

During the long term curing time monotonic cyclic testing (pre-test)was completed. After 150 days of curing the variation in strength from day to day became statistically insignificant.

Closed-Loop Hydraulic Test Machine

An MTS 810 closed-loop servo-controlled hydraulic test machine was used exclusively for this research project. This machine is specifically designed to perform high speed cyclic tests. It has high performance servo-controlled hydraulic rams that are controlled by a built in dedicated computer known as the microconsole. Figure 1 is a diagram of a concrete specimen in the machine jaws.

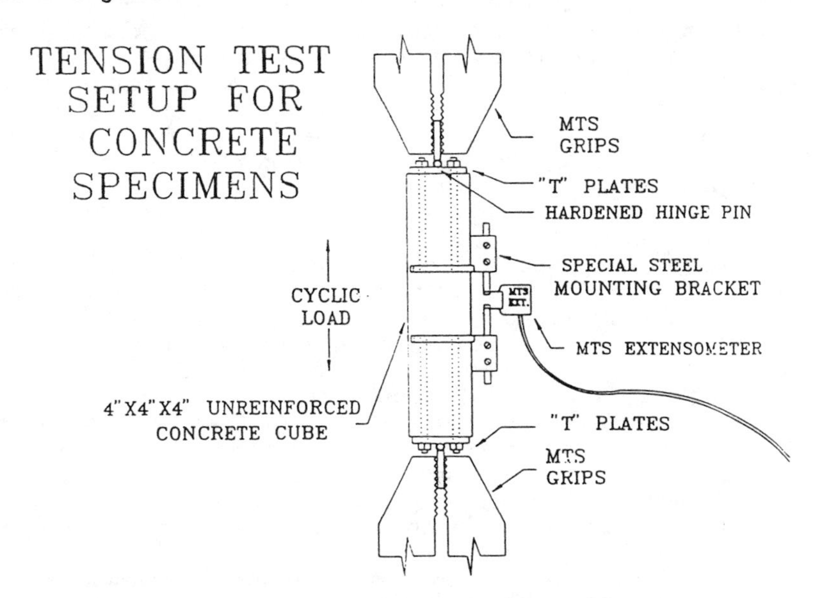

Fig. 1—Diagram of specimen in test machine

The machine is capable of controlling or monitoring in three different modes, load using a load cell, strain using an extensometer and deflection using a linear voltage displacement transformer (LVDT) which is built into the ram. It is typical to control the strain and monitor the load when performing cyclic fatigue tests. This is due to the response of the machine if cyclic testing was done in load control. Under load control the machine cycles between two preset load values. As internal deformation accumulates in the specimen microcracks begin to form and a decrease in cross sectional area occurs. The hydraulics controls however are set to maintain the same load and it responds by applying more force to a smaller area. This situation can easily become unstable resulting in a runaway condition, where the sample fractures within a few cycles. This phenomena can be instantaneous when working at high cyclic frequencies.

Strain control is preferred for fatigue testing. Under strain control, the strain range is set, and the load is monitored. It is possible to accurately maintain a specific deflection range, even as the material starts to yield, without resulting in a runaway condition. The load can be monitored during cycling and it is possible to actually witness the specimen experiencing strain hardening or strain softening.

Extensometer Calibration

A 0.005" range extensometer model #632.13C-20 with a 1.0" gage length was used in this test. The calibration apparatus functions much like a large micrometer. It is specifically designed to accurately measure the distance the extensometer moves for each volt of output. Due to the brittle nature of concrete, preliminary tests revealed the need for the very sensitive strain range of 0.005" to perform this concrete test procedure.

Test Procedure

After 150 days of curing time all specimens were removing from the curing room and prepared for testing. A specially designed "T" hinged plate was mounted to the protruding threaded reinforcing rods on each end of the specimen. Nuts attached to the threaded reinforcing rods were torqued to 20 inch pounds to insure consistency.

Working with the machine set in load control at the 20 kip range, the specimen was mounted in the machines knurled hydraulic grips. To avoid introducing any bending moment into the specimen during testing care was used to properly align each test sample vertically in the test machine.

Two "U" shaped extensometer mounting devices were attached to the sample using quick setting epoxy cement and heavy duty rubber bands.

Both extensometer mounting apparatus were positioned 4" apart and directly lined up with the un-reinforced 4" concrete test cube within the specimen. The extensometer was positioned on to this mounting bracket and held in place using rubber bands.

Monotonic Testing Procedure

Testing began by performing direct tension tests to determine ultimate stress and strain on virgin, non-cycled specimens. A total of 24 samples were initially tested under load control. These consisted of 6 randomly selected specimens from each of the 4 treatment groups.

Load control was set using the 20 kip load range cartridge and the 0.05% strain range cartridge. The load control set point was set at 0 volts and the span was set at 10 volts. The function generator was set to produce a ramp wave with a frequency of 0.01 Hz. This setup produced a constant linear increasing load up to 20 kips, capable of fracturing all the specimens in direct tension.

The microconsole on the MTS machine graphically and digitally recorded the ultimate stress-strain relationship for each specimen.

This procedure was repeated to test the remaining specimens after they were exposed to the cyclic fatigue in the final phase of the experiment.

Cyclic Testing Procedure

The cyclic test was performed under strain control. The MTS microconsole control setup procedure for each of the 4 treatment groups varied slightly. This was due to the large variations in strength, ductility and creep properties of each treatment group. Table 5 shows the mean strain range, load range, percent of ultimate virgin strength, set point and span for each of the treatment groups.

TABLE 5 — CYCLIC TEST MACHINE MICROCONSOLE SETTINGS

Treatment Groups	Deflection Range (in)	Load Range (lbs)	Percent of Ultimate Load	Set Point (volt)	Span (volt)
Control Group	0.00024 - 0.00014	4,437 - 2,812	42.6% - 27.0%	0.22	0.11
Polyp. Fibers	0.00063 - 0.00026	7,725 - 2,346	68.8% - 20.9%	0.47	0.43
Steel Fibers	0.00037 - 0.00018	5,662 - 2,898	50.6% - 25.9%	0.31	0.19
Composite Fibers	0.00040 - 0.00019	6,974 - 3,218	58.6% - 27.0%	0.35	0.23

By performing pilot tests on 3 to 4 specimens from each treatment group the allowable cycle range in tension was determined, these pilot calibrations made it possible to induce 1,000 cycles into each specimen. The function generator was set to produce a sin wave at a frequency of 0.5 Hz for the cyclic testing. The strain error detector was set to shut down the test machine at a .0025" change in distance.

Each specimen was cycled at the above prescribed parameters for 1,000 cycles. This was chosen as an appropriate maximum cycle limit because a number of pilot test samples fractured around this value. Testing time was also limited and it was necessary to chose a reasonable cutoff due to logistical problems.

During the cycling procedure a series of hysteresis loops recorded the behavior of each specimen. These were recorded at cycles 1-10, 20, 50, 100, 200, 500, 1,000 as is common for fatigue analysis.
This is due to the cumulative damage associated with cyclic fatigue and its logarithmic behavior.

Once the specimen was exposed to 1,000 cycles, the specimen was then direct tension tested to failure. This procedure was exactly the same as described earlier for the virgin specimens.

Results and Discussion

The results of this investigation demonstrated that it is possible to test concrete specimens under direct tension. This technique requires extremely sensitive and accurate measuring equipment. The process is expensive and requires extensive sample preparation time, machine setup and a sophisticated closed-loop test machine. With these problems resolved the goal of developing a direct tension test for concrete was proven possible.

Initially, there was some concern that the path of the fracture plane on the specimen could occur outside the extensometer gage length. However, this new mounting procedure used here resulted in only 10.5% (6 out of 57) of the specimens fracturing along the end plane of the reinforcing rods. Only one specimen fractured within the reinforcing rod lengths.

Examination of the aggregates along the fracture plane revealed there was excellent aggregate fracture with little aggregate pullout. The polypropylene fibers overwhelming failed by tearing apart. The steel fibers experienced both fiber pullout and actual fiber fracture. A majority of the steel fibers that pullout showed visible signs of elongation. The course aggregate fracture, polypropylene fiber tear and the steel fiber failure, confirmed a consistently strong reliable concrete mix design. This revealed excellent fiber bonding at the concrete matrix interface.

Statistical Testing

The ultimate loads and deflections were converted into stress and strain values for each specimen. The raw data was loaded into Statistical Analytical Systems (SAS), an inferential statistical analysis program. The program calculated the statistical significant test results. Three series of analysis of variance (ANOVA) hypothesis comparisons were computed for both stress and strain data.

These were (1) the virgin specimens control group versus treatment groups, (2) the cycled specimens control group versus treatment groups and (3) the virgin specimens versus the cycled specimens. The statistical analysis also determined the Least Significant Difference (LSD) within each hypothesis.

The hysteresis loop plots from the cyclic tests were compared to determine if it could be concluded that strain hardening or strain softening occurred in the fatigued concrete.

The results showed that a statistical significance existed in all three analysis in both stress and strain. The 0.05 P-value results and statistical data is summarized in the table below.

TABLE 6 — ANOVA STATISTICAL RESULTS

SAS Statistical ANOVA Group Comparisons	Stress Resulting P-value	Stat Sign. P<.05	Strain Resulting P-value	Stat Sign P<.05
Virgin Specimens 24 Samples	0.0424	*	0.0201	*
Cycled Specimens 33 Samples	0.0016	*	0.0171	*
Interaction Test 57 Samples	0.0073	*	0.1140	

* - ANOVA analysis showed significant difference at P< 0.05

The analysis of variance indicated that indeed a statistically significant difference did exist between the means of the treatment groups at a P-value less then 0.05. The data was then analyzed to determine the least significant difference (LSD) between each of the treatment groups.

Virgin Specimen Monotonic Tension Test Results

The mean test results of the direct tension test procedure for stress and strain are listed in Table 7.

These values are the means of three samples from a treatment group batch and three samples from the corresponding replicate batch.

This resulted in a total of six specimens for each treatment group. The group means are followed by the samples standard deviation values.

TABLE 7 — MONOTONIC TEST RESULTS — VIRGIN SAMPLES

Treatment Groups	Ultimate Stress(psi)	Standard Deviation	Ultimate Strain(in/in)	Standard Deviation
Control Group-PC	650.9	30.9	0.000179	0.000053
Polyp. Fibers-PP	701.5	26.1	0.000258	0.000043
Steel Fibers-SS	699.0	14.5	0.000218	0.000043
Composite Fibers-SP	744.1	53.8	0.000249	0.000078

The table above indicates that plain concrete achieved the lowest ultimate stress and strain values. This is what would be expected in a tension test where fiber reinforcing should introduce added strength and ductility to the otherwise weak concrete matrix. It is also shown that the ultimate strength of the plain polypropylene and plain steel fiber treatment groups were nearly equal (701.5 psi for PPF vs. 699.0 psi for steel). This is approximately a 7.5% increase above the plain concrete specimens. It should be noted, the strain for the PPF was much greater then the steel fibers, suggesting increased ductility or perhaps increased creep occurring in the polypropylene fiber reinforced concrete.

The composite fiber reinforced concrete showed a substantial increase in strength, 744.1 psi, over either fibers alone. This is an increase of 14.3% above the plain concrete. This suggests a possible cumulative strength effect taking place when combining the two fibers. In contrast the strain for the composite showed a decrease from the high strain present in the PPF, possibly due to the steel fibers introducing some stiffening effects.

Figure 2 graphically presents the above results for the virgin specimens. This figure shows the stress-strain relationship for all four treatment groups together. Note that all the fiber reinforced concrete treatment groups out perform the plain concrete control group in both stress and strain.

Once the specimens begin to be cyclically worked, it was found that the different fibers present in the concrete behaved in different ways. The plain steel and composite fiber treatment groups experienced strain hardening during cyclic loading in many of the specimens.

Figure 2 graphically presents the above results for the virgin specimens. This figure shows the stress-strain relationship for all four treatment groups together. Note that all the fiber reinforced concrete treatment groups out perform the plain concrete control group in both stress and strain.

Once the specimens begin to be cyclically worked, it was found that the different fibers present in the concrete behaved in different ways. The plain steel and composite fiber treatment groups experienced strain hardening during cyclic loading in many of the specimens. The specimens containing only the steel fibers actual sustained increasing loads at constant strain rates. This caused the hysteresis loop to raise up the stress-strain plot.

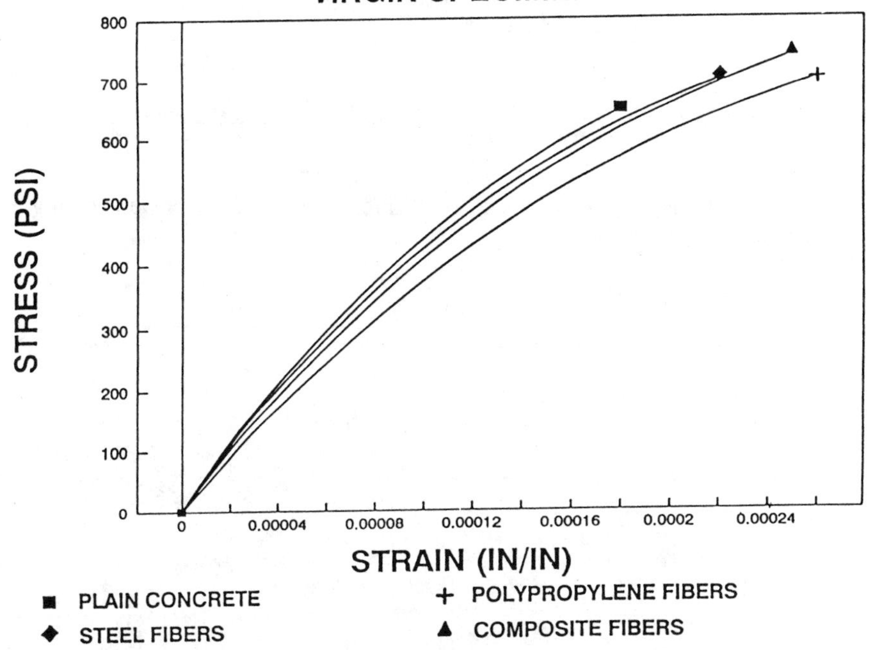

Fig. 2—Stress-strain graph of virgin treatment groups cyclic test results

An example of this behavior showing the strength increasing cyclically for an actual steel reinforced specimen can be seen in Figure 3.

The plain polypropylene fiber reinforced concrete displayed very different behavior, then the strain hardening of the steel fibers.

The graphic evidence produced by steel FRC was a narrower hysteresis loop and more pronounced when compared to the polypropylene graph.

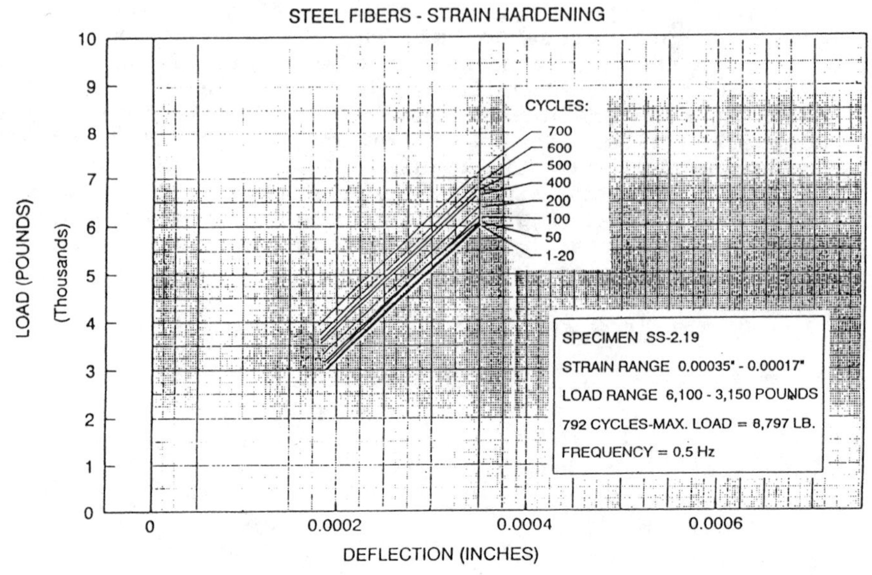

Fig. 3—Hysteresis loops of steel fiber reinforced concrete showing strain hardening

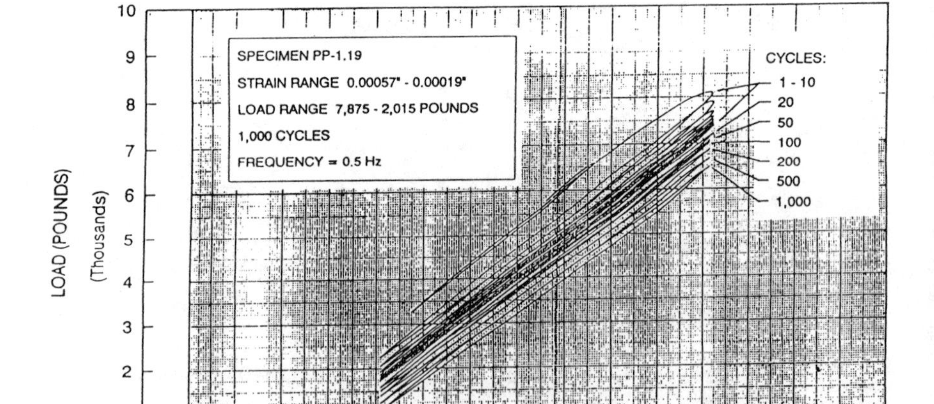

Fig. 4—Hysteresis loops of polypropylene fiber reinforced specimen showing strain softening

The polypropylene fibers increased the ductility of the concrete. It was possible to cycle these specimens at much greater load ranges without breaking the specimens then was possible with any of the other treatment groups. The PPF concrete showed signs of strain softening and an increase in stress relaxation as the hysteresis loops maintained decreasing loads at a constant strain range. This phenomenon is illustrated in figure 4 of the hysteresis loops for a polypropylene fiber reinforced specimen.

Upon completion of exposing the specimens to 1,000 cycles, the fatigued specimens were monotonically tension tested to determine their ultimate stress and ultimate strain. This was the post-test process. Table 8 summarizes the ultimate stress and strain test results for the cycled specimens.

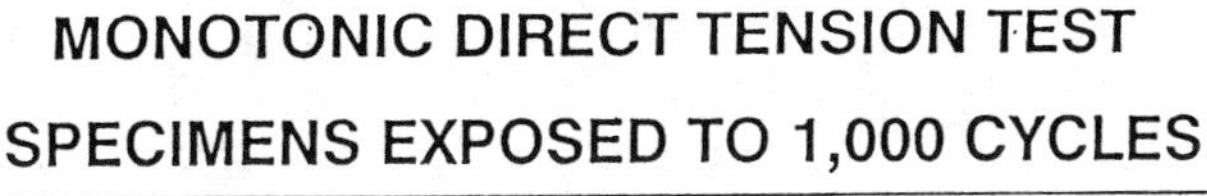

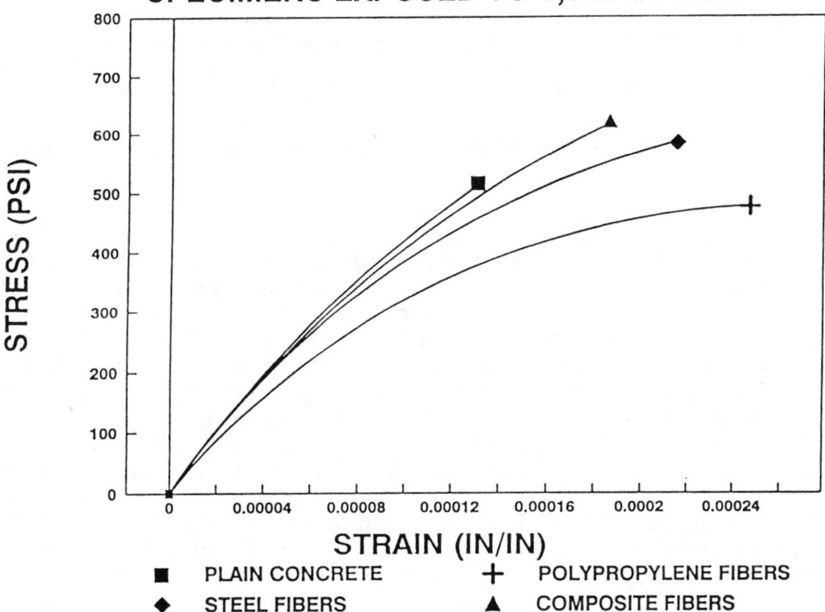

Fig. 5—Post-test stress-strain graph of tension cycled treatment groups

Composite fibers in the concrete matrix behaved after cyclic testing as projected. As a fatigued material it absorbed the most strain but not stress.

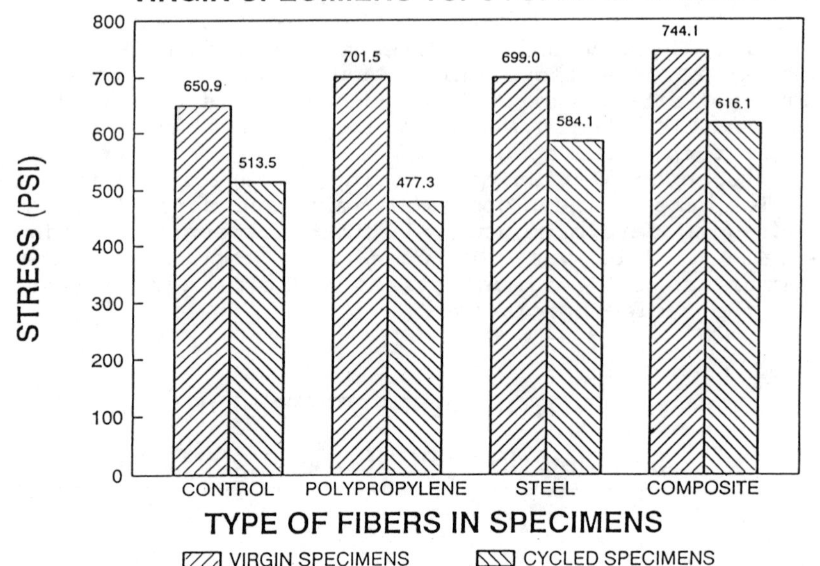

Fig. 6—Stress loss comparison chart

The summary percentages shown above in figure 6 and again in the bar chart in figure 7 reveal informative conclusions about the specimens behavior as fatigue occurs. The steel and composite fibers experienced about equal drops in ultimate stress, but the composite fibers have a significant drop in ultimate strain. This may be a result of introducing the polypropylene fibers and their high creep properties into the composite.

An important point to note, is that both treatment groups containing steel fibers did however lose strength at a slower rate then the plain concrete or the polypropylene fibers. This suggests that steel fibers add fatigue resistance to concrete when exposed to cyclic tension loading.

The plain polypropylene fibers show a dramatic decrease in stress(-32%) with no corresponding significant drop in strain. This supports the experimental observation that the polypropylene fibers sustain a large amount of stress relaxation as they under go cyclic loading.

It is interesting and important to note that the composite of steel and polypropylene fibers are still the strongest treatment groups. Yet after cyclic loading the polypropylene FRC alone is weaker then the cycle loaded plain concrete.

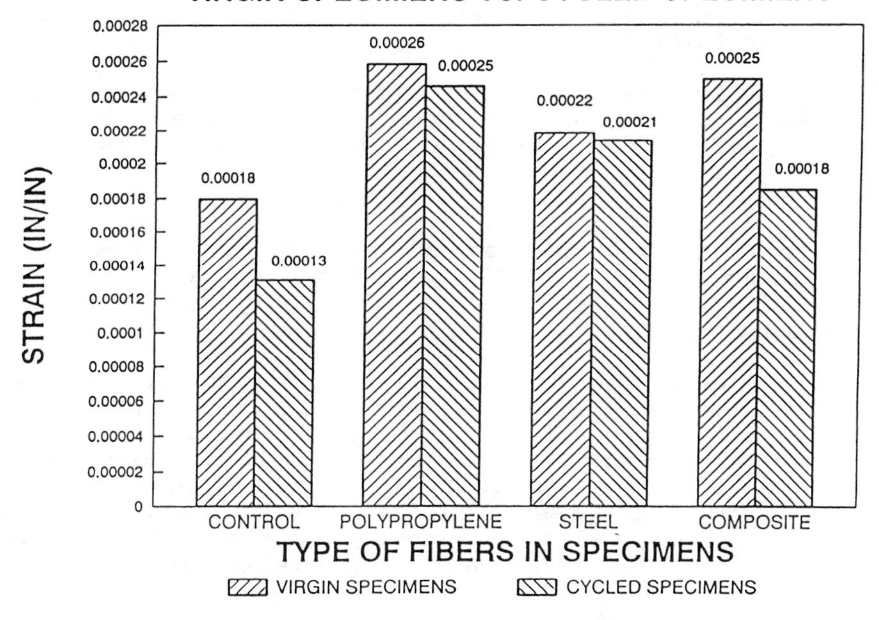

Fig. 7—Strain loss comparison chart

There appears to be a definite beneficial effect of combining the elasticity of the polypropylene fibers with the stiffening effects of steel fibers into the brittle plain concrete matrix, in figure. This fiber composite concrete is of superior tensile strength, inhibits creep and has increased resistance to cyclic fatigue, thus improving many of the traditional tensile material property problems that have plagued plain concrete

SUMMARY AND CONCLUSIONS

1. The overall results from this experiment demonstrate that it was possible to produce a direct tension test using both monotonic and cyclic procedures. The test results proved to be statistically acceptable.

2. Virgin fiber reinforced concrete tested under direct monotonic tension showed an increase above plain concrete. The plain steel fibers and plain polypropylene fibers performed equally well at 7.5% above the plain concrete control groups strength. The composite of steel and polypropylene fibers performed 7.2% above the two fibers alone and tested 14.8% above the plain concrete control group.

3. Under cyclic loading, polypropylene fiber reinforced concrete experienced strain softening. Under similar conditions, steel fiber reinforced concrete and the composite of steel and polypropylene fibers experienced strain hardening.

4. Polypropylene FRC specimens subjected to 1,000 cycles, then tested under monotonic direct tension showed a significant drop (-32%) in ultimate stress with little change in strain.

5. Steel FRC specimens subjected to 1,000 cycles under monotonic direct tension, showed less change from virgin specimens (17%) then the polypropylene FRC, suggesting steel fibers added tensile fatigue resistance and toughness to the concrete matrix.

6. A composite of steel and polypropylene fibers after experiencing 1,000 cycles were found to show superior material characteristics above each fiber added alone to the concrete mix. Suggesting a combined effect occurs when steel and polypropylene fibers are added together in concrete. This resulting composite concrete's tensile material properties are stronger, more ductile and show an substantial increase in the resistant to cyclic fatigue.

Acknowledgment

1. Department of Agricultural Engineering

2. Department of Civil and Environmental Engineering

3. University of Wisconsin Graduate School Grant

4. Rib Tech Fiber Corporation

5. Forta Corporation

6. Master Builders Corporation

References

ACI. 1989. Design Handbook 318-89. American Concrete Institute Press. Detroit, MI.

ACI Committee 544. 1985. State-of-the-art report on fiber reinforced concrete. In Craig, J.R. (ed.) Design with Fiber Reinforced Concrete. ACI Publication SCM-10(85) 1985 Fall Convention Chicago, Illinois. American Concrete Institute Press. Detroit, MI. pp.411-448.

ASTM. 1990. Standard specifications of sampling and testing concrete. American Society for Testing and Materials. Vol. 7.02. Philadelphia, PA.

Hannant, D.J. 1978. Fibre Cements and Fibre Concretes. John Wiley and Sons Inc., New York, NY.

Henager, C.H. 1980. Steel fibrous concrete - a review of testing procedures. Fibrous Concrete, Concrete International 1980. The Construction Press Ltd., Lancaster, England. pp. 16-28.

Johnston, C.D. 1970. Strength and deformation of concrete in uniaxial tension and compression. Magazine of Concrete Research, 22(70): 5-16.

Johnston, C.D., and Gray, R.J. 1978. Uniaxial tensile testing of steel fibre reinforced cementatious composites. In Swamy, R.N. (ed.) Testing and Test Methods of Fibre Cement Composites. RILEM Symposium 1978, The Construction Press Ltd., Lancaster, England. pp. 451-462.

Keer, J.G. 1981. Behavior of cracked fibre composites under limited cyclic loading. International Journal of Cement Composites, 3(3):179-183.

Kormeling, H.A., Reinhardt, H.W., and Shah, S.P. 1980. Static and fatigue properties of concrete beams reinforced with continuous bars and with fibers. ACI Journal, 77(1): 36-43.

Lovata, N.L. 1989. An analysis of post-peak loading conditions in fibrous concrete composites. In Swamy, R.N. and Barr, B. (eds.) Fibre Reinforced Cements and Concretes: Recent Developments. Elsevier Applied Science Publishers Ltd., Essex, England. pp. 171-184.

Lovata, N.L. 1990. Concrete composites, a new construction material. Journal of the American Institute of Constructors. Columbus, Ohio. 14(2): 7-10.

Ramakrishnan, V., Gollapudi, S., and Zellers, R. 1987a. Performance characteristics and fatigue strength of polypropylene fiber reinforced concrete. In Shah, S.P., and Batson, G.B. (eds.) Fiber Reinforced Properties and Applications. ACI SP-105. International Symposium, American Concrete Institute Press, Detroit, MI. pp. 159-178.

Ramakrishnan, V., Oberling, G., and Tatnall, P. 1987b. Flexural fatigue strength of steel fiber reinforced concrete. In Shah, S.P. and Batson G.B. (eds.) Fiber Reinforced Properties and Applications. ACI SP-105. International Symposium, American Concrete Institute Press, Detroit, MI. pp. 225-246.

Rangan, B.V., and Shah, S.P. 1971. Fiber reinforced concrete properties. ACI Journal, February Proceedings 68(2):126-135.

Sandor, Bela I. 1972. Fundamentals of Cyclic Stress and Strain. The University of Wisconsin Press, Madison, WI.

SAS Institute Inc. 1987. SAS/STAT Guide for Personal Computers, Ver. 6 Edition. SAS Institute Inc. Cary, NC.

Sparks, P.R., and Menzies, J.B. 1973. The effect of rate of loading upon the static and fatigue strength of concrete in compression. Magazine of Concrete Research, 25(6): 73-80.

CONVERSION FACTORS——INCH-POUND TO SI (METRIC)*

To convert from	to	multiply by
Length		
inch	millimeter (mm)	25.4E†
foot	meter (m)	0.3048E
yard	meter (m)	0.9144E
mile (statute)	kilometer (km)	1.609
Area		
square inch	square millimeter (mm^2)	645.1
square foot	square meter (m^2)	0.0929
square yard	square meter (m^2)	0.8361
Volume (capacity)		
ounce	milliliters (mL)	29.57
gallon	cubic meter (m^3)‡	0.003785
cubic inch	cubic millimeter (mm^3)	16390
cubic foot	cubic meter (m^3)	0.02832
cubic yard	cubic meter (m^3)‡	0.7646
Force		
kilogram-force	newton (N)	9.807
kip-force	kilo newton (kN)	4.448
pound-force	newton (N)	4.448
Pressure or stress (force per area)		
kilogram-force/square meter	pascal (Pa)	9.807
kip-force/square inch (ksi)	megapascal (MPa)	6.895
newton/square meter (N/m^2)	pascal (Pa)	1.000E
pound-force/square foot	pascal (Pa)	47.88
pound-force/square inch (psi)	kilopascal (kPa)	6.895
Bending moment or torque		
inch-pound-force	newton-meter (N•m)	0.1130
foot-pound-force	newton-meter (N•m)	1.356
meter-kilogram-force	newton-meter (N•m)	9.807

To convert from	to	multiply by
Mass		
ounce-mass (avoirdupois)	gram (g)	28.34
pound-mass (avoirdupois)	kilogram (kg)	0.4536
ton (metric)	megagram (mg)	1.000E
ton (short, 2000 lbm)	kilogram (kg)	907.2
Mass per volume		
pound-mass/cubic foot	kilogram/cubic meter (kg/m^3)	16.02
pound-mass/cubic yard	kilogram/cubic meter (kg/m^3)	0.5933
pound-mass/gallon	kilogram/cubic meter (kg/m^3)	119.8
Temperature§		
degrees Fahrenheit (F)	degrees Celsius (C)	$t_C = (t_F - 32)/1.8$
degrees Celsius (C)	degrees Fahrenheit (F)	$t_F = 1.8t_C + 32$

* This selected list gives practical conversion factors of units found in concrete technology. The reference sources for information on SI units and more exact conversion factors are ASTM E 380 and E 621. Symbols of metric units are given in parenthesis.

† E Indicates that the factor given is exact.

‡ One liter (cubic decimeter) equals 0.001 m^3 or 1000 cm^3.

§ These equations convert one temperature reading to another and include the necessary scale corrections. To convert a difference in temperature from Fahrenheit degrees to Celsius degrees, divide by 1.8 only, i.e., a change from 70 to 88 F represents a change of 18 F or 18/1.8 = 10 C deg.

INDEX